FMO16108NC

PREVENTIVE MAINTENANCE

A practical step-by-step guide to reducing equipment operating costs and downtime and improving operating safety

FUNDAMENTALS OF MACHINE OPERATION

PUBLISHER
DEERE & COMPANY
JOHN DEERE PUBLISHING
one John Deere Place
Moline, IL 61265
http://www.johndeere.com/publications

Fundamentals of Service (FOS) is a series of manuals created by Deere & Company. Each book in the series is conceived, researched, outlined, edited, and published by Deere & Company, John Deere Publishing. Authors are selected to provide a basic technical manuscript that could be edited and rewritten by staff editors.

HOW TO USE THE MANUAL: This manual can be used by anyone — experienced mechanics, shop trainees, vocational students, and lay readers.

Persons not familiar with the topics discussed in this book should begin with Chapter 1 and then study the chapters in sequence. The experienced person can find what is needed on the "Contents" page.

Each guide was written by Deere & Company, John Deere Publishing staff in cooperation with the technical writers, illustrators, and editors at Almon, Inc. — a full-service technical publications company headquartered in Waukesha, Wisconsin (www.almoninc.com).

FOR MORE INFORMATION: This book is one of many books published on agricultural and related subjects. To download the latest catalog or for order information, please visit: http://www.johndeere.com/publications

ACKNOWLEDGEMENTS:

Original Author:
Louis Hathaway

Contributing Authors and Editors:
Frank Buckingham
Keith R. Carlson
Robert H. Gunter
Thomas A. Hoerner
Ralph J. Moens

John Deere gratefully acknowledges help from the following people and groups:
Pat Farrell, DeWitt, Iowa
Everette Hainline, Cedar Falls, Iowa
Fred Hileman, Waterloo, Iowa

ACDelco; Aeroquip Group of Eaton Corp.; American Association for Vocational Instructional materials; American Society of Agricultural Engineers, Champion Spark Plug Co., Dana Corp.; DelcoRemy Division of General Motors; Federal-Mogul Corp.; Bridgestone Firestone North American Tire, LLC; The Goodyear Tire & Rubber Company; BFGoodrich Tires.; Link-Belt Construction Equipment Company; Motorola Automotive Electronics and Communication Systems; SPX Corporation/OTC; Prestolite Wire Corp.; Rexnord Industries; Rubber Manufacturers Assn.; Shell Oil Co.; BP America Inc.; Sun Electric Corp.; Sundstrand Corp.; Texaco Inc.; Union Carbide Corp.

We have a long-range interest in Vocational Education

CONTENTS

3   ENGINE FUEL SYSTEMS

8 HYDRAULIC SYSTEMS

9 OTHER COMPONENTS

12 *SAFETY*

13   ANSWERS TO TEST YOURSELF QUESTIONS

Definitions Of Terms And Symbols

Abbreviations

Fastener Torque Values

O-Ring Seal Service Recommendations

Answer To Test Yourself Questions

Index

6 ENGINE ELECTRICAL SYSTEMS

7 POWER TRAINS

4

ENGINE LUBRICATION SYSTEMS

5

ENGINE COOLING SYSTEMS

Introduction

1

JDPX5061

Fig. 1 — Preventive Maintenance Keeps Machines Going when Jobs Are the Toughest

IMPORTANCE OF PREVENTIVE MAINTENANCE

Do you know the leading cause of premature failure in agricultural machines today? Putting things off until tomorrow! Yes, how many times have you heard, I'll grease it tomorrow. Tomorrow comes and work is waiting — no time to grease it now.

Putting it off becomes a bad habit that leads to machine breakdown or high operating costs. You can make preventive maintenance a good habit. Just do one thing: Always perform maintenance either at the end of the day or early in the morning before you go to the field.

By knowing the fundamentals of good preventive maintenance, you can perform it efficiently and correctly. Then you will be assured of getting the most out of your equipment. And you will be pleased with your efforts and savings.

JDPX5089

Fig. 2 — Damaged Bearing Caused by Lack of Lubrication

Preventive maintenance can do three things:

- Reduce failures
- Save on operating costs
- Help prevent injuries

Let's look at each of these.

REDUCE FAILURES

When the work load is heaviest, your equipment needs preventive maintenance the most. You can't afford to have your machine down when the crop has to be planted in the spring or harvested in the fall. You won't, of course, prevent the possibility of failure, but you will reduce it to a minimum.

SAVE ON OPERATING COSTS

Believe it or not, the few dollars it costs to perform preventive maintenance will pay for themselves many times over. For example, an engine tune-up can save you a possible 15 percent in fuel consumption and increase maximum power by more than 10 percent. On a 100-horsepower (75 kW) tractor, this could mean 4 or 5 gallons (15 to 19 liters) of fuel saved each day, plus a bonus of 10 extra horsepower (7.5 kW) to work with. These savings can be measured in dollars and cents. And maintenance of other components will save you even more in repairs during the life of your equipment. All these things mean more profit for you.

Preventive maintenance also provides a cumulative effect in terms of energy conservation. A properly maintained engine burns less fuel per hour and a well-cared-for machine can do more work per hour; so fewer operating hours are required to complete needed tasks. These reductions in fuel consumption save dollars and conserve energy.

HELP PREVENT INJURIES

If your machine is not performing well, you tend to take chances to make up the time lost by poor performance. In your haste you may try to correct a malfunction without stopping or turning off the machine. Good preventive maintenance should include the checking of safety systems, including guards and shields and the replacement of any damaged safety signs. Complete preventive maintenance means a safer machine to operate and less chance of injury to you and others.

KEEPING RECORDS

A good way to be sure that all maintenance is performed on schedule is to keep records. A simple form like the one shown in (Fig. 3) is easy to use. You can make up your own form or you may find one available from your local implement or petroleum supply dealer. Such forms are also provided in some operator's manuals.

Follow the recommendations in your operator's manual for specific service intervals. Enter the various jobs to be performed under the "hours of operation" headings. Then check off the intervals of service after they are performed. It only takes a few minutes each day.

Keep this record in a handy place, such as near the service center of the farm.

Many machines have an hour meter which operates whenever the engine is running and shows the total hours of operation. Record the hour meter reading and watch this meter to tell when services are required.

JDPX5090

Fig. 3 — Preventive Maintenance Schedule

JDPX5091

Fig. 4 — Use Records Instead of Your Memory — It Will Pay

Hour
Meter

JDPX5092

Fig. 5 — Recording Hour Meter Readings Tells when Periodic Services Are Needed

RECOMMENDED SERVICE INTERVALS

The American Society of Agricultural Engineers (ASAE) recommends service on machines at regular hourly intervals. These periods are commonly after 5, 10, 50, 100, 250, 500, and 1000 hours of operation. See the chart in Fig. 6 for typical service on a tractor.

The hourly intervals represent days of operation as shown below:

- 5 Hours (Twice Daily)
- 10 Hours (Daily)
- 50 Hours (Weekly)
- 250 Hours (Monthly)
- 500 Hours (Bimonthly)
- 1000 Hours (Seasonally)

However, most farm machines are operated only 250 to 500 hours a year, so the yearly or twice-yearly services can often be combined with the other intervals and completed at the same time.

Keep in mind that the suggested intervals of service shown in this book are the average intervals between different machines and manufacturers. Since recommended intervals of service vary widely between machines, refer to your operator's manual for specific instructions. Here we are primarily concerned with the fundamentals of preventive maintenance, and this book is not intended as a maintenance manual for specific machines.

The intervals of service are cumulative. For example: you should perform 10-hour maintenance every ten hours, including at the 50-, 100-, 250-, 500-, and 1000-hour intervals.

JDPX5093

Fig. 6 — Typical ASAE Service Intervals for a Tractor

PROPER OPERATION TO PREVENT ABUSE

While agricultural machines are designed tough for special types of work, they were not intended to be "hot rods." They must be handled with respect. Besides causing premature wear and damage, abuse can endanger your personal safety. Although in use for only a few hours, the tire in (Fig. 7) shows severe, premature wear caused by the operator spinning the tires. Ignoring the recommended inflation pressure is another form of tire abuse.

JDPX5094

Fig. 7 — Improper Operation Causes Premature Wear (Spinning Wear on Tire)

TIPS FOR GOOD MACHINE OPERATION

DO:

1. Follow suggestions in your operator's manual.

2. Perform daily (5- and 10-hour) maintenance before using machine.

3. Check the machine for damage and potential failures before starting it.

4. Run the engine until it is warm before putting it under load.

5. Let a hot engine run a few minutes without load so that it cools before shutting it off.

6. Keep bolts and nuts tight.

7. Watch the instrument panel (Fig. 8).

8. Keep the machine properly serviced.

9. See a serviceman for major repairs.

10. Operate at safe speeds.

JDPX5096

Fig. 8 — Watch Your Instrument Panel for Trouble Signs

DO NOT:

1. Jump on the machine, start it, and take off with a cold engine.

2. Start the engine and turn it off before it has warmed up.

3. Jam the transmission into gear.

4. Snap or pop the clutch.

5. Spin the tires.

6. Overload the capacity of the machine.

7. Let the engine idle for long periods of time.

8. Store a machine without properly preparing it for storage.

9. Neglect to perform periodic maintenance on schedule.

10. Remove safety shields or disable safety systems.

SAFETY RULES

IMPORTANT: Be sure to read "Safety" on page 12-1, before performing any work on your machine.

Use safe procedures when performing machine maintenance. First, stop the engine (Fig. 9). Don't attempt to service your equipment when it is running, except when instructed to do so.

JDPX5097

Fig. 9 — Turn Off Engine Before Servicing Machine

Always think about what you are going to do before you do it. This is the most basic rule of safety. For example, don't remove the radiator cap until you have determined whether or not the coolant is still under pressure. Wait until it cools and the pressure drops — then remove the cap slowly.

Carefully read all safety messages in this manual and on your machine safety signs. Keep safety signs in good condition. Replace missing or damaged safety signs.

Learn how to operate the machine and how to use controls properly. Do not let anyone operate without instruction.

Keep your machine in proper working condition. Unauthorized modifications to the machine may impair the function and/or safety and affect machine life.

STUDY YOUR OPERATOR'S MANUAL

Read your operator's manual carefully before attempting to operate or service your machine (Fig. 10). Follow the safety rules and you may avoid injury to yourself or others. Safe operation also reduces accidents that could damage equipment and require costly repairs or replacement. Where they apply, safety suggestions are included in this book.

WATCH YOUR INSTRUMENT PANEL

When you drive a machine, glance at the instrument panel from time to time (Fig. 8). The gauges and lights will tell you the condition of various engine systems and will signal you when they need maintenance. Don't delay! If a gauge gives you a warning, maintenance or repair is probably overdue and should be performed at once.

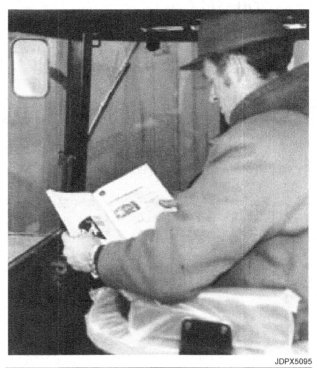

JDPX5095

Fig. 10 — Study Your Operator's Manual

COVERAGE IN THIS BOOK

This book will cover not only tractors, but all engine-powered machines, such as self-propelled combines, windrowers, hay cubers, and forage harvesters.

Typical preventive maintenance is included for each system on a typical machine. Chapters will cover engine intake and exhaust systems, lubricating, cooling, and electrical systems, as well as power trains, hydraulics, and other components such as cab air conditioning and accessories.

Although diesel engines presently outnumber gasoline engines in sales of new equipment, thousands of gasoline engines are still used regularly on combines, tractors, and other machines. Preventive maintenance is equally important on old as well as new equipment. Therefore, significant coverage is provided here for both engine types.

This book is not intended for making you, the reader, into a mechanic. Rather it is designed to give you a better understanding of the importance of preventive maintenance and the steps of performing maintenance jobs on farm machines. It is your responsibility to follow through and actually perform these steps and those in your operator's manual. Only then will you get the full benefits of this book.

TEST YOURSELF

QUESTIONS

1. What are the three things that preventive maintenance accomplishes?

2. What are the economic advantages of preventive maintenance?

3. Why should you refer to your operator's manual when performing maintenance?

4. What are the two most important things you must do before starting your machine each day?

5. What is the most basic rule of safety?

Engine Intake and Exhaust Systems

2

INTRODUCTION

An engine must "breathe" to create energy just as you do (Fig. 1). The intake and exhaust systems are the breathing apparatus of an engine. They carry the fuel-air mixture into the engine and remove the exhaust gases after combustion (Fig. 2).

INTAKE SYSTEM

The intake system supplies the engine with clean air of the proper quantity and temperature for good combustion.

The intake system has six basic parts (Fig. 2 and Fig. 3):

- Air cleaners
- Turbocharger (if used)
- Air inlet
- Charge Air Cooler (Aftercooler)(if used)
- Intake manifold
- Intake valves

Fig. 2 — Intake and Exhaust Systems

Air cleaners filter dust and dirt from the air passing through them enroute to the carburetor. Precleaners prevent larger particles from reaching the air cleaner and lengthen service intervals.

Turbochargers (or superchargers) increase power by forcing more air or fuel-air mixture into the engine cylinders than the engine could draw in by itself.

The air inlet allows incoming air into the intake manifold. For spark-ignition engines the speed of the engine is controlled by the throttle plate in the air inlet which allows more or less air into the intake manifold, depending on the position of the throttle plate.

Fig. 1 — An Engine Must "Breathe"

Fig. 3 — Intake and Exhaust Systems of a Typical Engine

A charge air cooler (aftercooler) is used on some turbocharged engines to cool the intake air before it enters the intake manifold. As the air is compressed by the turbocharger, it is heated and expands. The compressed, heated air from the turbocharger outlet is routed to the charge air cooler (aftercooler) before entering the intake manifold.

Intake manifolds transport the fuel-air mixture (pure air in diesel engines) to the engine cylinders.

Intake valves admit the air or fuel-air mixture to the engine cylinders for burning. They are normally opened and closed by linkage from the engine camshaft.

EXHAUST SYSTEM

The exhaust system collects the exhaust gases after combustion and carries them away. This is really three jobs: removing heat, muffling engine sounds, and carrying away burned and unburned gases.

The exhaust system has four basic parts (Fig. 2 and Fig. 3):

- Exhaust valves
- Exhaust manifold
- Turbocharger
- Muffler

Exhaust valves open to release the burnt gases from the cylinder after combustion. The valves are normally opened and closed by the camshaft.

The exhaust manifold collects the exhaust gases and conducts them away from the cylinders.

The turbocharger is also part of the exhaust system. The turbocharger is mounted to the exhaust manifold. Exhaust gasses from the engine are used to drive the turbocharger.

The muffler reduces the sound of the engine during the exhaust period.

A more detailed explanation of the intake and exhaust systems follows.

FINAL TIER 4 EXHAUST SYSTEM

To control nitrogen oxide (NOx) emissions, selective catalytic reduction (SCR) is being utilized. Diesel exhaust fluid (DEF), which is a reducing agent, is injected into the exhaust stream to create a catalyzed chemical reaction to reduce NOx levels.

When the ECU determines the need for DEF injection, DEF is drawn from the DEF tank through the DEF tank header and into the DEF dosing unit. The DEF dosing unit will pressurize and pump DEF into the DEF injector pressure line and up to the DEF injector. DEF is then injected into the exhaust stream in the decomposition tube mixer to create a catalyzed chemical reaction to reduce nitrogen oxide (NOx) levels. Upon entering the SCR, the exhaust gases nitrogen oxide (NOx) content is transformed into nitrogen (N) gas and water. After the exhaust gases exit the SCR, another catalyst reaction takes place in the AOC. This reaction transforms any ammonia residue into nitrogen (N) gas. There are two aftertreatment nitrogen oxide (NOx) sensors constantly monitoring the nitrogen oxide (NOx) output. The ECU uses this information to assess the nitrogen oxide (NOx) conversion efficiency of the system.

When the key switch is turned to the off position, the DEF dosing unit drains the system to prevent damage in cold weather conditions. At a predetermined temperature, the ECU will turn on the DEF dosing unit internal heater to defrost all of the components to ensure that DEF will flow through the system during priming and normal operation. A temperature sensor is located in the DEF dosing unit by which the ECU is able to monitor the temperature of the DEF dosing unit and the DEF in the system. (See Fig. 4).

ASH BUILDUP

Ash is non-combustible residue from normal oil consumption. Regeneration will not burn off the ash buildup in the diesel particulate filter (DPF) which can cause an exhaust flow restriction. The use of recommended fluids will extend the life of the aftertreatment system and extend the maintenance intervals of the DPF. When the exhaust filter requires service, the ECU will alert the operator by means of a diagnostic trouble code (DTC).

JDPX5100

Fig. 4 — Modern Aftertreatment Exhaust System

A — Inlet Air
B — Fixed Turbocharger
C — Wastegate Turbocharger
D — Compressed Air from Wastegate Turbocharger
E — EGR Cooler
F — Charge Air Cooler
G — EGR Valve
H — Diesel Oxidation Catalyst (DOC)
I — Diesel Particulate Filter (DPF)
J — Aftertreatment Temperature Sensor
K — Aftertreatment NOx Sensor
L — DPF Differential Pressure Sensor

M — DEF Injector
N — Decomposition Tube Mixer
O — Selective Catalytic Reduction (SCR)
P — Ammonia Oxidation Catalyst (AOC)
Q — Exhaust Gas Outlet
R — DEF Injector and DEF Tank Coolant Lines
S — DEF Injector Pressure Line
T — DEF Dosing Unit
U — DEF Tank Header
V — DEF Tank
W — Radiator

EXHAUST FILTER

The exhaust filter contains the diesel oxidation catalyst (DOC) and the diesel particulate filter (DPF). Exhaust gas flows through the filter radial inlet, DOC, and DPF, and exits through an axial or radial outlet, depending on the application.

With the engine under load, Nitric Oxide (NO) oxidizes in the DOC into nitrogen dioxide, which is an agent that allows particulates to oxidize more easily in the DPF. During active regeneration, additional fuel is dosed into the exhaust and oxidized in the DOC. The ECU monitors the DOC outlet temperature to determine the temperature increase across the DOC.

The DPF traps particulate matter, or soot. Exhaust gas passes through channels in the ceramic filter core. Every other channel is obstructed at the outlet. Exhaust gas moves through porous channel walls until it exits through an open outlet. While the exhaust gas circulates within the filter, particulates get trapped on the channel walls. The channel walls are coated with precious metals that help oxidize particulates into less harmful emissions.

Regeneration increases exhaust temperatures and burns and oxidizes trapped particulate matter from the DPF. (See Fig. 5).

JDPX5114

Fig. 5 — Exhaust Filter

    A — Exhaust Gas from Engine
    B — Exhaust Filter Temperature Measurement
    C — DPF Differential Pressure Sensor Port
    D — Diesel Oxidation Catalyst (DOC)
    E — Diesel Particulate Filter (DPF)
    F — Exhaust Gas Outlet

EXHAUST REGENERATION
Passive Regeneration

The diesel particulate filter (DPF) is regenerated during normal engine operation under moderate to heavy load when the exhaust temperatures are high. No fuel dosing occurs during these ideal conditions, and no operator input is required.

Active Regeneration

Certain applications do not generate sustained high exhaust gas temperatures and require regeneration controlled by the ECU. Regeneration occurs when the elevated exhaust temperatures are required. The exhaust throttle actuator is commanded to close and exhaust gas temperatures increase. When DOC (H) temperatures exceed 300°C (572°F), regeneration will take place. The ECU initiates fuel injection into the exhaust gas via in cylinder dosing. The additional fuel reacts with the DOC to generate heat. The exhaust filter cleaning indicator light comes on when the exhaust gas temperature in the DPF is in the 500°C - 650°C (932°F - 1202°F) range. The ECU monitors sensor inputs to determine when regeneration is no longer needed. (See Fig. 6)

JDPX5115

Fig. 6 — Exhaust Regeneration

    A — Inlet Air
    B — Fixed Turbocharger
    C — Wastegate Turbocharger
    D — Compressed Air from Wastegate Turbocharger
    E — EGR Cooler
    F — Charge Air Cooler
    G — EGR Valve
    H — DOC
    I — DPF (if equipped)
    J — DOC Temperature
    K — SCR Inlet Temperature
    L — DPF Differential Pressure
    M — Exhaust Gas Outlet

AIR CLEANERS AND AIR DUCTS

The average engine mixes 9,000 to 10,000 gallons (liters) of air (by volume) with every gallon (liter) of fuel it consumes. Turbocharged engines use even more air. This amount of air can contain enough dirt to wear out the engine prematurely if the air is unfiltered, or if the air intake system leaks.

An air cleaner must have the capacity to hold material taken out of the air so that the engine can operate for a reasonable period before cleaning and servicing are necessary.

Multiple air cleaner installations are sometimes used where engines are operated under extremely dusty conditions or where two small air cleaners must be used in place of a single large cleaner.

JDPX5101

Fig. 7 — Good Air Cleaner Maintenance Keeps Engines Going when Conditions Are Toughest

HOW DIRTY AIR CAN DAMAGE ENGINES

Consider these facts:

In some dusty environments, an engine can be ruined:

1. If an air hose comes off for only a few hours.
2. If a mere pinhole leak in a hose is left for a full season.

Keep this in mind when you think of air-cleaning systems.

Agricultural engines operate in some very tough conditions (Fig. 7) and this makes air cleaner service doubly important.

TYPES OF AIR CLEANERS

The major types of air cleaners are:

- Precleaners
- Dry element air cleaners
- Oil bath air cleaners

Let's examine these more closely.

PRECLEANERS

Precleaners (Fig. 8) are usually installed at the end of a pipe extended upward into the air from the air cleaner inlet. This places them in an area relatively free of dust.

JDPX5102

Fig. 8 — Precleaner and Prescreener

Precleaners remove larger particles of dirt or other foreign matter from the air before it enters the main air cleaner. This relieves much of the load on the air cleaner and allows longer intervals between servicing.

Most precleaners have a prescreener (Fig. 8) which prevents lint, chaff, and leaves from entering the air intake. However, the prescreener can become plugged quickly under some conditions, thus preventing air from entering the air cleaner.

DRY-ELEMENT AIR CLEANERS

Two major types of dry-element cleaners are used at the present time (Fig. 9).

Dry-element air cleaners are built for two-stage cleaning:

1. Precleaning
2. Filtering

Dry-Element Air Cleaner with Unloading Valve

Dry-Element Air Cleaner with Dust Cup

JDPX5397, 5398

Fig. 9 — Dry-Element Air Cleaners — Two Types

The first stage (precleaning) directs the air into the cleaner at high speed so that it sets up centrifugal rotation (cyclone action) around the filter element.

The cleaner shown in (Fig. 9, top) directs the air into the precleaner so it strikes one side of the metal shield. This starts the centrifugal action, which continues until it reaches the far end of the cleaner housing. At this point, the dirt is collected into a dust cap, or dust unloader, at the bottom of the housing.

The cleaner shown in (Fig. 9, bottom) conducts the air past tilted fins which start the centrifugal (cyclone) action. When the air reaches the end of the cleaner housing, the dirt passes through a slot in the top of the cleaner and enters the dust cup.

In both types, this precleaning action removes from 80 to 90 percent of the dirt particles and greatly reduces the load on the filter.

The partially cleaned air then passes through the holes in the metal jacket surrounding the pleated paper filter. Filtering is done as the air passes through the paper filter. It filters out almost all of the remaining small particles. This is the second stage of cleaning.

Some heavy-duty cleaners use a spiral rotor device for precleaning the air as shown in (Fig. 3). Others have a small safety element built into the unit in case the main element fouls.

If the air cleaner has a dust cup (Fig. 9, bottom) it should be emptied daily. If an automatic dust unloader is used in place of a cup (Fig. 9, top), it is usually recommended that it be checked at least once daily to make certain it doesn't become clogged. The dust unloader is a rubber duck bill device that is held closed by engine suction while the engine is running. When the engine stops, the flaps open so dirt can drop out. Check the flaps regularly to see that they close during operation so precleaner will work properly to give longer filter life.

Some dry-element cleaners are equipped with a vacuum gauge or restriction indicator to show when the filter needs cleaning. The indicator is attached to the intake manifold of the tractor. As the dirt accumulation builds up on the filter, air flow is restricted. This increases the suction in the intake manifold and causes the indicator to show red. To maintain engine operating efficiency, it is important that the filter be serviced at once.

ASPIRATED AIR CLEANERS

JDPX5062

Fig. 10 — Aspirated Air Cleaners

Some dry-element cleaners are equipped with an aspirator tube (Fig. 10). In photo shown, an exhaust check valve and hose are connected between the dust separator and the engine exhaust pipe. A vacuum is created as the engine exhaust rushes out of the exhaust pipe. This vacuum will open the exhaust check valve and draw the larger debris from the dust separator into the exhaust gas stream, preventing it from going to the filter canister. The exhaust check valve will be closed if the exhaust gas velocity is low. This prevents exhaust soot from contaminating the air filters. In other aspirated air cleaners, such as used on some tractors, the aspirator tube is routed to the radiator shroud and uses air drawn past the cooling package instead of the engine exhaust to aid in the removal of debris.

OIL BATH AIR CLEANERS

Oil bath air cleaners (Fig. 11) draw air down a center tube where it strikes the surface of oil in a partly filled cup. The impact causes a mixture of air and oil spray to be carried up into the element of baffles and wire mesh. The separating element breaks up the dust-laden air, and fine dust particles are trapped by the oil film. The particles are then washed down as the oil later drains back into the cup. Clean air continues through the element and on to the engine.

The washing down of the oil keeps the filter element fairly clean.

Dirty Air In

Filtering Element

Oil Spray Drawn Up, Cleans Particles from Air

Oil Bath

Clean Air To Engine

LEVEL

Oil Cup

JDPX5399

Fig. 11 — Oil Bath Air Cleaner

The major services are (1) to keep the oil cup filled to the proper level with the correct weight of oil, and (2) to replace the oil when it gets dirty or thickens, reducing its ability to clean particles from the air.

However, at least once each year, the air cleaner should be disassembled and the filter element cleaned in solvent.

NOTE: Today's detergent oils may hold the dirt in suspension. For this reason the need for oil cup service cannot be determined by the layer of dirt which has settled into the bottom of the cup. Instead, see if the oil has thickened due to dirt.

Some air cleaners are fitted with an oil trap. This trap catches the oil which otherwise would be thrown out of the cleaner when the engine backfires.

IMPORTANCE OF SERVICE

Air cleaner efficiency depends upon your performing proper maintenance and service.

Oil bath cleaners must be properly maintained or the oil cup will become filled with sludge, preventing the screens and elements from cleaning the air properly. This will restrict air flow to the engine (the same effect as choking the engine) and may allow dirty air to enter. Restricted air flow through the air cleaner will eventually cause incomplete combustion, increased carbon formation, and crankcase oil dilution.

Clean air and unrestricted air flow help conserve fuel and enable the engine to produce more power per unit of fuel burned.

Leaks in the connecting pipes, loose hose connections, or damaged gaskets which allow dust-laden air to enter the engine defeat the purpose of the air cleaner. Always check for dust paths in the air intake and around the ends of the filters. *Remember: Dirty air going directly into an engine cylinder is abrasive and will cause premature wear of moving parts.*

AIR CLEANER SERVICES

"How do I know when to service my engine's air cleaner?" Check the operator's manual.

No hard and fast rule can be given for servicing an air cleaner, since this depends upon the type of cleaner, condition of air, and type of application.

Normal service intervals are designated by the manufacturer, but frequent inspection can tell whether or not this is adequate for the conditions under which the engine is operating.

A cleaner operating in severe dust conditions will require more frequent service than one operating in clean air.

Refer to your operator's manual for service information.

MATERIALS NEEDED

For oil bath air cleaners:

- Wrenches for removing air cleaner housing (if required).
- Cleaning cloths.
- Container to catch waste oil.
- Bucket of cleaning solvent (not gasoline).
- Clean oil of the same viscosity used in the crankcase.

For dry-element air cleaners:

- Goggles or glasses for eye protection.
- Wrenches for removing air cleaner (if required).
- Compressed air source (not over 30 psi, 205 kPa, of pressure).
- Bucket of warm water with a nonsudsing detergent.
- Water source (not over 40 psi, 275 kPa, of pressure).

SERVICING PRECLEANERS

Every 10 hours, check the precleaner bowl. If dirt has built up to the line, remove the bowl (Fig. 12) and empty it.

If the unit has a prescreener (Fig. 8), check it daily. Blow or brush off any chaff or other foreign matter.

If the precleaner unit is allowed to clog, a greater load is placed on the main air cleaner.

SERVICING OIL BATH AIR CLEANERS

Every 10 hours of operation, check the oil cup for correct oil level and for dirt accumulation.

NOTE: Under extremely dirty conditions, check the oil cup twice daily.

Service the air cleaner as follows:

1. Loosen oil cup and remove from filter (Fig. 12).

   Don't try to remove cup with engine running. This allows unfiltered air to enter directly.

2. Check depth of sediment deposit in outer chamber.

   If sediment in the outer compartment is about 1/2 inch (12 mm) deep, proceed with the remaining steps. (Some manufacturers recommend cleaning when 1/4 inch (6 mm) of dirt has accumulated. Check your operator's manual for recommendations.)

JDPX5103

Fig. 12 — Emptying Precleaner Dust Bowl

If the oil has thickened, even though the dirt depth may not be as high as 1/2 inch (12 mm), change the oil. Thickened oil acts as a choke on your engine, causing it to use more fuel. Fuel consumption may increase as much as a gallon (4 liters) or more per hour.

There is also a possibility of drawing dirt-laden oil into the carburetor, then into the engine, where it acts as a grinding compound, causing extremely fast wear.

With today's high-detergent oils, dirt may never settle to the bottom of the cup, so watch for thick oil as your signal that the oil needs to be changed.

If there is water in the cup, you will probably find the air intake cap has been removed, allowing rain to enter. Proceed with cleaning the cup and be sure to replace air intake cap. Water interferes with effective air cleaning action.

3. If cup needs cleaning, dispose of dirty oil properly. Scrape and then wash inner and outer cups with clean diesel fuel (Fig. 14).

 CAUTION: Don't use gasoline or other highly flammable liquids such as naptha or benzene, which could explode or catch fire and burn.

Remove all caked dirt from bottom of cup.

Also clean dirt from tray (if used). (See Fig. 14).

Fig. 13 — Removing Oil Cup from Air Cleaner

Clean Oil Cup in Diesel Fuel   **Remove Dirt from Tray (If Used)**

JDPX5105

Fig. 14 — Cleaning Oil Cup and Tray

Fill Cup Only To Level Mark With Oil

JDPX5106

Fig. 15 — Fill Oil Cup to Level Mark

4. Check air intake pipe (air stack) for dirt accumulation.

This will not need cleaning often, but it is good practice to check it each time the oil cup is serviced.

If dirty, swab it out with your cleaning material. The more dirt you allow to accumulate in the stack, the more it acts as a choke to air flow and increases fuel consumption.

5. Refill cup with oil to "oil level" mark (Fig. 15). Most operator's manuals recommend the same weight as used in the engine crankcase.

If you use an oil that is too heavy, the washing action is lessened. It also acts as a choke on the engine and increases fuel consumption.

Oil that is too light will pull into the engine. This lowers the oil Level in the cup until the cleaner is not efficient. With diesel engines, the oil is used as fuel, causing the engine to run wild. When this happens, you have no control of engine speed.

Don't use old crankcase oil. It may contain unburned fuel which evaporates quickly and lowers the oil level in the cup. It also contains dirt which limits washing action.

An additive oil can be used, but it is of no particular benefit for this purpose.

Don't overfill the oil cup. On spark-ignition engines it increases fuel consumption and cause loss of power. On diesel engines, the oil may be drawn into the engine and used as fuel, causing the engine to run wild.

6. Replace oil cup (and screen tray, if used) and tighten clamp.

7. Check air duct between cleaner and carburetor (or intake manifold on diesel engines) for holes or loose clamp connections.

Air entering the engine here bypasses the air cleaner. Dirt particles pass directly to the engine, causing rapid wear.

8. Check air inlet screen, or precleaner, and remove trash if necessary.

OIL BATH CLEANING

At least once each year, completely disassemble and clean the air cleaner system. This is vital for long engine life.

Over long periods, dirt collects in the air cleaner center tube and in the lower part of the filter element. Dirt chokes off the air supply to the engine. Cleaning the system at least once each year pays off in reduced fuel consumption and more engine horsepower.

Swab out the center tube with a cloth soaked with diesel fuel. If the filter element is dirty, wash it in diesel fuel or solvent. Drain all parts and wipe dry. Then reassemble the air cleaner.

When assembling, be sure all hoses and gaskets are in good condition and that all connections are tight.

SERVICING DRY-ELEMENT AIR CLEANERS

If the dry-element air cleaner has a dust cup, empty it daily. If an automatic dust unloading valve (Fig. 20) is used in place of a dust cup, check it daily for clogging.

Service the dry-element air cleaner element every 50 hours or at the following times:

1. Units with restriction indicator: Clean element whenever indicator glows or signals a restriction. (Some indicators may stick, so watch conditions and hours of operation carefully.)

2. Units without indicator: Clean element at recommended intervals-more often during dusty or unusual operation.

NOTE: Avoid too-frequent cleaning of dry-element air cleaners as cleaning always presents the danger of damaging the filter element.

Fig. 16 — Dry-Element Air Cleaner

When the engine smokes too much or loses power, there may be a restriction in the dry-element air cleaner.

Dusty Element: Remove filter element and tap element gently on heel of hand to remove dust. Rotate element while tapping it. **Never tap element on hard surface** such as wheel of machine, as this may dent it and create an opening for dirty air.

 CAUTION: Wear goggles or glasses to protect eyes from dust and dirt when using compressed air.

If tapping does not remove the dust, use a compressed air cleaning gun (pressure not to exceed 30 psi, 205 kPa) to clean the element (Fig. 17). Blowing from inside to outside, direct clean, dry air up and down the pleats.

Patting the Element

Blowing Out The Element

JDPX5108

Fig. 17 — Cleaning the Dry Element

IMPORTANT: Be careful not to rupture the element. Do not try to clean off outside of air cleaner with an air hose as it may clog it.

To clean with water: First blow out dirt with compressed air as described above. Then attach garden hose to cleaning gun and flush remainder of dirt from inside to outside of element. Be sure to allow element to dry before installing it. (It is a good idea to have two elements on hand in case one is damaged. Also, the completely dry element can then be installed each time.)

Oily or Sooty Elements: Blow out the dust with compressed air or flush with clean water. Soak and gently agitate element in a solution of lukewarm water and commercial filter element cleaner or an equivalent nonsudsing detergent (Fig. 18).

Rinse element thoroughly with clean water from hose (Fig. 18) having maximum pressure of 40 psi (275 kPa) or less. Shake excess water from element and allow it to air dry (requires 24 hours or longer). Protect from freezing.

IMPORTANT: Never wash a dry element in fuel oil, gasoline, or solvent. Never use compressed air to dry the element.

After cleaning the element, inspect it for damage by placing a light inside it. Discard any element that shows the slightest damage.

Inspect filter element gasket for damage. Replace element if gasket is damaged or missing.

IMPORTANT: Replace the filter element:
 • If damaged.
 • After a recommended service period (such as one year or six washings).
 • When attempts to clean it fail.

Washing the Element   **Rinsing the Element**

JDPX5109

Fig. 18 — Washing and Rinsing the Dry Element

Thoroughly clean inside of cleaner body with a clean, damp cloth. Install element in cleaner body, gasket and fin end first. Be sure gasket is in place.

Draw cover tight on cleaner. Reset restriction indicator (if used).

SERVICING SECONDARY ELEMENT

Secondary Element   Primary Element

JDPX5400

Fig. 19 — Primary and Secondary Elements

Some large engines have a secondary element in case the primary element ruptures and fails (Fig. 19). Normally these elements are not cleaned, only replaced once each season. However, check the condition of the secondary element during service. If it is very dirty, the primary element has probably failed and both elements must be replaced to maintain efficient engine operation.

SERVICING DUST UNLOADING VALVE (IF USED)

Every 10 hours, inspect rubber dust unloading valve (if used) (Fig. 20). Squeeze the rubber end of the valve to make sure it is still open and free of clogging. Be sure valve closes when engine is running. This prevents dirt from being sucked into the engine through the valve. Clean the valve if necessary. Replace if cracked or worn.

JDPX5401

Fig. 20 — Dry-Element Air Cleaner Dust Unloading Valve

CHECKING AIR CLEANER CONNECTIONS

Every 500 hours of operation, make a general check of all connections from the air cleaner to the engine (Fig. 21). Remove the hood or cowl if necessary. Tighten any clamps on hoses or tubes to prevent dirty air from entering engine through loose connections.

Air Cleaner Connections

JDPX5402

Fig. 21 — Checking Air Cleaner Connections

Also inspect all intake hoses (pipes) for cracks or other damage. Replace as necessary. If equipped with an aspirator tube, inspect tube for damage and restrictions.

This concludes our air cleaner service story. Remember that dry air cleaners are as effective as oil bath types, but they do require careful handling and more inspection for breaks or holes that could allow dirty air to harm the engine.

INTAKE MANIFOLD

On gasoline engines, the fuel-air mixture is carried from the carburetor to the engine intake valves by the manifold (Fig. 22).

Diesel engine intake manifolds are similar to spark-ignition engine manifolds, except that they do not require heat (to vaporize fuel) and are usually located on the side of the engine opposite the exhaust manifold.

LP-gas fuel vaporizes at normal temperatures, so a mixing valve and converter are used instead of a carburetor.

Even though heat transfer from the exhaust manifold is not required to vaporize fuel, a similar intake system (following the carburetor) can be used for LP-gas as for gasoline systems.

(Fig. 22) illustrates a typical gasoline engine manifold. Heat is supplied either by having the exhaust manifold touch the intake manifold at various spots or by having exhaust passages built into the intake manifold.

JDPX5111

Fig. 22 — Typical Intake Manifold (Spark-Ignition Engines)

TURBOCHARGERS

The power delivered by an internal combustion engine is determined by the amount of fuel and air which can be compressed into each cylinder. The more the fuel-air mixture, the more power the engine develops.

The turbocharger is a type of air pump and gives the engine a higher overall compression pressure than it would normally have (Fig. 23).

Turbocharged Engine   **Naturally Aspirated Engine**

JDPX5112

Fig. 23 — Turbocharger Compress More Air into Engine for Greater Combustion and Power

It does this by taking intake air, compressing it, and forcing it into the engine cylinders (Fig. 24).

JDPX5403

Fig. 24 — A Turbocharger

Pumping air into an engine also aids in getting exhaust gases out. This, too, results in more efficient combustion.

Some engines are designed and built for turbocharging. If an engine is not equipped with a turbocharger, it may be damaged if one is added. Be sure to check with your dealer before you try to turbocharge an engine yourself.

SERVICING TURBOCHARGERS

IMPORTANT: **Turbochargers operate at speeds of 40,000 to 130,000 rpm or more. This means they must have adequate lubrication at all times and air must be clean to avoid excessive wear.**

The major causes of turbocharger failures are:

- Lack of lube oil (quick starts and hot shutdowns)
- Oil contamination
- Ingestion of foreign objects
- Restricted oil drainage
- Low oil level
- Operation on excessive side slopes
- Abnormally high exhaust temperatures

IMPORTANT: **Clean air is vital to a turbocharger as dirty air can pit the rotary vanes and alter their balance.**

Periodically make the following inspections:

1. Inspect the mounting and connections of the turbocharger to be certain they are secure and there is no leakage of oil or air.

2. Inspect turbocharger oil supply line to make sure it is not kinked or bent.

3. Inspect turbocharger oil drain tube and engine breather tube for damage or restriction.

4. Check the engine crankcase vent to be sure there is no restriction to air flow.

5. Operate the engine at approximate rated output and listen for unusual turbocharger noise. If a shrill whine (other than normal) is heard, stop the engine immediately. The whine means that the bearings are about to fail. Have the turbocharger removed for inspection.

Do not confuse the normal whine heard during "run down" as the engine stops with a bearing failure during operation.

Other unusual turbocharger noises could mean improper clearance between the turbine wheel and housing. In these cases, a serviceman should remove the turbocharger for inspection.

6. Check the turbocharger for unusual vibration while engine is operating at rated output. If necessary, have the turbocharger removed for inspection.

7. Check engine under load conditions. Excessive exhaust smoke indicates an incorrect fuel-air mixture. This could be due to engine overload or turbocharger malfunction.

INTAKE AND EXHAUST VALVES

The valves let fuel and air in and exhaust gases out of each engine cylinder during the combustion cycle.

OPERATION OF VALVES

You, as a machine operator, should understand how the intake and exhaust valves work.

The engine must take in fuel-air and expel spent gases at precise intervals. The valves do this job by opening and closing the intake and exhaust ports to the cylinder.

JDPX5404

Fig. 25 — Valve Operation in a Four-Stroke Cycle Engine

The sequence of valve operation for a typical four-stroke cycle engine is shown in (Fig. 25). Each cylinder has two valves, intake and exhaust. Many engines are equipped with four valves per cylinder, two intake and two exhaust.

1. During the intake stroke, the intake valve opens as shown, allowing the fuel-air mixture to enter the combustion chamber.

2. During compression and power strokes, both valves are closed to seal in the combustible mixture.

3. During the exhaust stroke, the exhaust valve opens, allowing gases to be exhausted.

4. At the end of the exhaust stroke, the intake valve opens, beginning another cycle.

The camshaft (Fig. 26) is turned by the engine crankshaft. A lobe (cam) on the camshaft causes the cam follower and push rod to push the valve open. The spring closes the valve when the cam allows the push rod and cam follower to return to the low side of the cam. Cam movements are designed to open or close the valves at the right moment.

Fig. 26 — Typical Valve Operating Mechanism

JDPX5405

IMPORTANCE OF VALVE CLEARANCE

If proper valve maintenance is not performed, the engine will not work efficiently and may be damaged.

When valves are properly adjusted, there is normally a small clearance between the valve stem and the end of the rocker arm (This clearance is sometimes referred to as "valve clearance," "valve lash," or "tappet clearance.")

Valve clearance allows for the heat expansion of valve operating parts. Without clearance, the heated parts would cause the valves to stay partly open during operation and the engine would lose compression and power (Fig. 27).

This valve clearance is small, varying from approximately 0.006 inch to 0.030 inch (0.15 to 0.75 mm). The engine manufacturer recommends a definite clearance for each engine model. The valve clearance may vary, depending on the engine model and whether the engine should be hot or cold during adjustment (some engines run hotter than others).

Fig. 27 — Importance of Valve Clearance

JDPX5406

Too little valve clearance throws the valves out of time. This causes valves to open too early and close too late. Also, valve stems may lengthen from heating and prevent valves from seating completely (Fig. 27). Hot combustion gases rushing past the valves cause overheating because the valves seat so briefly or so poorly that normal heat transfer into the cooling system does not have time to take place. This causes burned valves (Fig. 28).

Fig. 28 — Burned from Too Little Valve Clearance

JDPX5407

Too much valve clearance causes a lag in valve timing which throws the engine-out of balance. The fuel-air mixture is late entering the cylinder during the intake stroke. The exhaust valve closes early and prevents waste gases from being completely removed.

The valves themselves also become damaged. When valve clearance is properly adjusted, the camshaft slows the speed of valve movement as it closes. But with too much clearance, the valves close with great impact, cracking or breaking the valve (Fig. 29) and scuffing the cam and follower.

Starting Point
of Break

Impact Break

JDPX5408

Fig. 29 — Broken Valve from Too Much Valve Clearance

SUMMARY: WHY PROPER VALVE ADJUSTMENT IS IMPORTANT

• The engine will use fuel more efficiently.

• The engine will start more easily.

• Maximum power will be achieved.

• Valves will give longer service.

• Overheating of the engine is less likely to occur.

TOOLS AND MATERIALS NEEDED

To make valve clearance adjustments, the following are needed (Fig. 30):

• Set of box-end wrenches (inch or metric, as required)

• Set of open-end wrenches (inch or metric, as required)

• Spark plug wrench (inch or metric, as required)

• Feeler gauge (inch or metric, as required)

• Torque wrench and socket set (inch or metric, as required)

• Screwdriver

• Clean cloths

• Bucket of cleaning solvent (not gasoline)

• Container for nuts and cap screws

• New gasket to replace old valve cover gasket

PREPARING FOR VALVE TAPPET ADJUSTMENTS

Check valve tappet adjustments every 2000 hours of operation, or at intervals indicated in your operator's manual. Before adjustments can be made, you must determine how you are going to make them. Some manufacturers recommend that valve adjustments be made by an authorized dealer or trained mechanic. Read your operator's manual, or obtain a technical service manual for your engine for step-by-step procedures. Many agricultural engines are enclosed under fuel tanks and engine shrouds. Often these parts must be removed before the valve cover or rocker arm cover can be removed to obtain access to the valves (Fig. 31).

NOTE: If you are adjusting valves for the first time, have someone help you, or practice on an older engine or a small engine until you become proficient.

Open-End
Wrench

Box-End
Wrench

Torque
Wrench

Feeler
Gauge

Spark Plug
Socket

Screwdriver

JDPX5409

Fig. 30 — Tools Needed for Adjusting Valve Tappet Clearances

Let's assume that you must remove parts which interfere with removal of the valve cover.

1. Remove parts as necessary (Fig. 31).

2. Clean dirt from the valve cover and from around the spark plugs.

3. Remove the nuts or cap screws which hold the cover in place.

4. Carefully remove the valve cover (Fig. 32). Strike the cover on one side and then on the other with the palm of your hand. Don't worry about damaging the gasket because you should replace it with a new one each time the cover is removed.

 CAUTION: If these precautions are not followed, the engine could start during valve adjustment and cause serious injury to you.

Fig. 31 — Parts That May Need to be Removed before Valve Cover is Removed

Fig. 32 — Removing Engine Valve Cover

5. To prevent accidental starting of the engine during valve adjustment, disconnect the battery negative (–) terminals.

ADJUSTING VALVE TAPPET CLEARANCE

Since most manufacturers recommend that the valve clearance adjustment be made when the engine is stopped, we will cover procedures for adjusting valves with the engine cold. Refer to your operator's manual for recommendations.

Unless your operator's manual gives a shortcut, you must rotate the engine crankshaft each time a different pair of valves is to be adjusted. We will show adjustment of valves using this method, which works for all engines.

CAUTION: To prevent accidental starting of engine while performing valve adjustments, always disconnect NEGATIVE (–) battery terminal.

IMPORTANT: Valve clearance MUST BE checked and adjusted with engine COLD.

Fig. 33 — Rocker Arm Cover and Wiring Harness

1. Disconnect main wiring harness from right side of intake manifold (Fig. 33).

2. Remove rocker arm cover with vent tube.

IMPORTANT: Visually inspect contact surfaces of valve tips and rocker arm wear pads. Check all parts for excessive wear, breakage, or cracks. Replace parts that show visible damage.

Rocker arms that exhibit excessive valve clearance should be inspected more thoroughly to identify damaged parts.

NOTE: Use a flexible socket extension when rotating engine to avoid interference with fuel filter assembly (Fig. 34).

3. Remove plastic plug from cylinder block bores and install flywheel turning tool and timing pin (Fig. 34).

Fig. 34 — Flywheel Turning Tool

4. Rotate engine with the flywheel turning tool until timing pin engages timing hole in flywheel.

5. If the rocker arms for No. 1 (front) cylinder are loose, the engine is at No. 1 TDC-compression.

6. If the rocker arms for No. 6 (rear) cylinder are loose, the engine is at No. 6 TDC-compression. Rotate the engine one full revolution (360 degrees) to No. 1 TDC-Compression.

Feeler Gauge Access

Rocker Arm Foot

JDPX5414

Fig. 35 — Valve Clearance-Setting Procedure

NOTE: *To assist in adjusting valve clearance, push the rocker arm foot forward for easier feeler gauge access (Fig. 35).*

IMPORTANT: **If engine has been overhauled where the roller camshaft followers have been removed and/or replaced, BE CERTAIN to apply a firm downward pressure over the rocker arm adjusting screw, using a push rod to seat roller follower on camshaft. Loose valve clearance settings can result if this step is not completed. If the valve clearance is being checked or reset, this step is not necessary.**

7. With engine lock-pinned at TDC of No. 1 piston's compression stroke, use a bent feeler gauge to check valve clearance on No. 1, 3, and 5 exhaust valves and No. 1, 2, and 4 intake valves (Fig. 36 and Fig. 37). If out of specification, loosen lock nut on rocker arm adjusting screw. Turn adjusting screw until feeler gauge slips with a slight drag. Hold the adjusting screw from turning with screwdriver and tighten lock nut to specifications.

Recheck clearance again after tightening lock nut.

Readjust clearance as necessary.

8. Rotate flywheel 360° until No. 6 piston is at TDC of its compression stroke. Rocker arms for No. 6 piston should be loose.

9. Check and adjust valve clearance to the same specifications on No. 2, 4, and 6 exhaust and No. 3, 5, and 6 intake valves (Fig. 38).

IMPORTANT: **When reinstalling rocker arm cover, DO NOT reuse gasket. Install cover using a new gasket.**

10. Install rocker arm cover gasket.

JDPX5415

Fig. 36 — Checking Valve Clearance with Feeler Gauge

← Front of Engine

| 1-E | 1-I | | 2-I | 3-E | | 4-I | 5-E |

JDPX5416

Fig. 37 — Valve Checking Sequence — No. 1 TDC

← Front of Engine

| 2-E | | 3-I | 4-E | | 5-I | 6-E | 6-I |

JDPX5417

Fig. 38 — Valve Checking Sequence — No. 6 TDC

REASSEMBLY AFTER VALVE ADJUSTMENTS

1. Clean and install spark plugs (see "Servicing Spark Plugs" on page 6-18).

2. Before installing valve cover, start engine to check lubrication of rocker arms. You may have to install some of the parts you removed if they are required to run the engine. Be certain an ample supply of oil is being delivered to all rocker arms. If your operator's manual recommends that you check the valve clearances again with the engine thoroughly heated, do this now. A different set of clearances must be used because, as the engine heats, the valve stems lengthen and less clearance is needed.

3. Position new gasket on the cylinder head.

4. Install valve cover. Be certain that the gasket fits properly under the edges of the valve cover or oil will leak by and increase oil consumption.

5. Install all remaining parts.

EXHAUST MANIFOLDS AND MUFFLERS

EXHAUST MANIFOLDS

Exhaust manifolds receive burned gases from each cylinder and carry them away from the engine (Fig. 39). Some heat from the exhaust manifold on gasoline engines is used to maintain the intake manifold at the proper temperature.

The exhaust ports in the engine and the passages in the exhaust manifold are large to allow free flow and expansion of the hot escaping gases. This is important because it permits better removal of gases or scavenging of the engine cylinders.

NOTE: *Usually the No. 1 cylinder is next to the radiator on vertical engines, or next to the flywheel on horizontal engines.*

If any burned gases are left in the cylinders following the exhaust stroke, the amount of fuel-air mixture which can be taken in on the next intake stroke is limited. This reduces engine power and increases fuel consumption.

MUFFLERS

There are two common types of mufflers:

• Straight-through

• Reverse-flow

Let's look at these types.

Straight-through mufflers (Fig. 40) consist of a perforated inner pipe enclosed by an outer pipe roughly three times larger in diameter. The space between the pipes is sometimes filled with a sound-absorbing and heat-resistant material.

JDPX5419

Fig. 39 — Exhaust Manifold

Straight-Through Muffler

Reverse-Flow Muffler

JDPX5418

Fig. 40 — Two Types of Mufflers

Reverse-flow mufflers (Fig. 40) are hollow chambers using short pieces of pipe and baffles to force the exhaust gases to travel a back-and-forth path before being discharged.

The muffler acts as an expansion chamber, reducing the noise of the spent gases. It also serves as a spark arrester, to reduce fire hazards when operating near combustible material.

MUFFLER SERVICE

Exhaust systems are designed to provide the least amount of restriction. Excessive restrictions cause back-pressure, resulting in incomplete cylinder scavenging. This, in turn, causes loss of power and increased fuel consumption.

It has been estimated that each 2 psi (14 kPa) of back-pressure causes a loss of about four engine horsepower.

⚠ CAUTION: One of the products of combustion is carbon monoxide. This is a deadly, odorless, poisonous gas. To avoid inhalation of gas, ventilate the area any time the engine is operating.

The complete exhaust system must also be free of leaks. When they do occur, repair them immediately. This is particularly true when the engine is in a machine equipped with a cab or other enclosure.

JDPX5420

Fig. 41 — Spark-Arresting Muffler

CLEANING SPARK-ARRESTING MUFFLERS

Spark-arresting mufflers should be cleaned every 50 hours of operation.

1. Park the machine in an area where the possibility of fire is not a hazard.

2. Remove pipe plug from muffler (Fig. 41) to provide an outlet for loosened particles and start the engine. Run the engine from slow to fast idle two or three times to blow out deposits.

3. Stop engine and replace plug.

WEATHER CAPS FOR MUFFLERS

Some engines have a hinged cap on the muffler or exhaust pipe which closes when the engine stops to protect against rain and weather. Rain water can rust the engine valves or damage the turbocharger. Check frequently to see that the cap opens fully when the engine starts and closes tightly when it shuts off. A cap that doesn't open can cause excessive heat that can burn the hood.

EXHAUST SYSTEM SERVICE

1. Inspect exhaust system for leaks or restrictions. Check manifold for cracks. Repair or replace as necessary.

2. Check that turbocharger-to-exhaust gas recirculator (EGR), cooler, etc., clamps are securely tightened and do not leak.

3. Check exhaust stack for evidence of oil leakage past valve stem seals. Oil in exhaust stack may be caused by excessive valve stem-to-guide clearance or excessive light load engine idling.

EGR SYSTEM

JPDX5421

Fig. 42 — EGR System

Many modern diesel engines are equipped with an EGR (exhaust recirculation system). EGR is used to improve engine performance and aid in controlling emissions. In the EGR system shown, a portion of the engine exhaust is routed from the exhaust manifold, through an EGR cooler, to an EGR valve. The EGR valve allows a metered amount of exhaust air back into the intake manifold to mix with fresh incoming air. The EGR valve is controlled by the engine control unit (ECU), which monitors inputs from several sensors such as manifold air pressure, exhaust pressure, and others to determine the proper amount of exhaust air that needs to pass through the EGR valve and into the intake manifold.

FINAL TIER 4 EXHAUST EMISSIONS

In accordance with federal emissions regulations, FT4 engines must achieve NOx reduction of 80 percent while maintaining the same percentage of particulate matter (PM) reduction as IT4 engines. This requirement is obtained by recirculating exhaust gas using a wastegate turbocharger and an EGR cooler. However, lower combustion temperatures cause PM levels to rise. Therefore, a diesel particulate filter (DPF) is used (application specific) to control the PM levels. The addition of the selective catalytic reduction (SCR) system further reduces NOx and at the same time extends the maintenance interval of the diesel particulate filter.

CRANKCASE VENTILATION

During normal operation, unburned fuel vapor and water vapor are created in the engine. If allowed to condense, these vapors become contaminating liquids that drain into the crankcase. The purpose of the ventilation system is to circulate fresh air through the engine to carry away these harmful vapors.

As with all ventilating systems, there must be the following:

• An air inlet

• An air and vapor outlet

• A means of circulating air between the two

The most common types of crankcase ventilation are oil filler caps, vent tubes, manifold vent, and circulating pump systems.

OIL FILLER CAP VENT

The oil filler cap is probably the most common inlet. A small air cleaner built into the cap filters the air as it is drawn into the system. Some systems use the main air cleaner as the inlet.

CRANKCASE VENT TUBES

Fig. 43 — Crankcase Vent Tube

The use of a vent tube is one means of circulating the air through the system (Fig. 43). As the machine moves, the air moving past the tube opening creates a lower pressure than that at the breather. Air in the engine naturally flows to this low-pressure area, and the tube becomes an outlet for the system. Some vent tubes use a wire mesh screen to filter oil particles out of the vapor.

INTAKE MANIFOLD VENT

On some engines, the intake manifold circulates the air and is also the vent outlet. In this type of ventilation system a tube connects the crankcase to the intake manifold. The intake vacuum draws the air through the engine, into the manifold, then into the cylinders, and out the exhaust system. A ventilation valve is used to regulate the flow of air into the manifold.

VENT SYSTEM WITH CIRCULATING PUMP

Another type of system uses a vane or impeller pump to circulate the air. The air is taken from the main air cleaner and pumped through the engine. The outlet can be either a vent tube or the intake manifold.

AIR EMISSION CONTROLS

Future developments will probably mean that more agricultural engines will have pollution control devices that route crankcase vapors back to the carburetor or manifold for burning. This will reduce the emission of raw vapors into the atmosphere.

SERVICING THE VENTILATION SYSTEM

Every 50 hours, service the ventilation system. Begin with the inlet. If the oil filler cap is the inlet, clean it with a solvent. If the main air cleaner is the inlet, service it regularly as recommended by the engine manufacturer.

If the system uses a ventilating valve, service it regularly. Some manufacturers recommend cleaning the valve with solvent, while others recommend replacing the valve rather than cleaning it.

If a vent tube is used in the system (Fig. 43), periodically remove and clean it with a solvent. If a filter is used with the vent tube, be sure to clean it, too.

Keeping the engine clean and free of caked-on dirt and oil also helps in crankcase ventilation and general engine cooling.

Fig. 45 — Testing Manifold Depression with a Vacuum Gauge (Spark-Ignition Engine)

TESTING AIR INTAKE SYSTEM

When the air flow into the engine is restricted, there is more vacuum or suction in the cylinders. This can cause oil to be drawn in around the valve stems and pistons and so increase oil consumption.

Complete air cleaner service will usually correct the air flow restriction to the engine. However, if a restriction is still suspected, use the tests which follow.

INTAKE VACUUM TEST (DIESEL ENGINES, NON-TURBOCHARGED)

Test as follows:

1. Warm up the engine.

2. Connect the gauge to the intake manifold (Fig. 44).

3. Set engine speed at fast idle and note the reading on the gauge. Too high a reading means that there is a restriction in the air intake system. Check the engine technical manual for correct specifications.

4. If a restriction is shown by this test, have a serviceman inspect the engine.

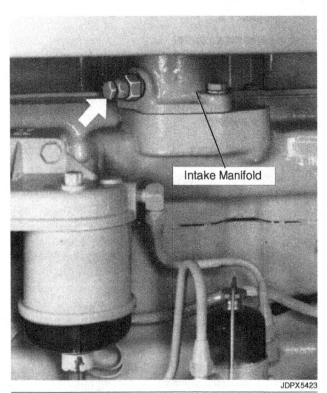

Fig. 44 — Manometer or Gauge Connection Point (Diesel Engine)

MANIFOLD DEPRESSION TEST (SPARK-IGNITION ENGINES)

Use a vacuum gauge calibrated in inches of mercury to perform this test.

Connect the vacuum gauge to the intake manifold (Fig. 45).

Warm up the engine and operate it at idle speed.

Note the reading on the vacuum gauge. Check the engine technical manual for exact specifications.

Interpret the gauge reading as given below.

JUDGING TEST RESULTS

- If the reading is steady and low, loss of power in all cylinders is indicated. Possible causes are late ignition, bad valve timing or loss of compression at valves or piston rings. A leaky carburetor gasket will also cause a low reading.

- If the needle fluctuates steadily, a partial or complete loss of power in one or more cylinders is indicated. This can be due to an ignition defect, or loss of compression due to stuck piston rings or a leaky cylinder head gasket.

- Intermittent needle fluctuation indicates occasional loss of power due to an ignition defect or a sticking valve.

- Slow needle fluctuation is usually caused by improper carburetor idle mixture adjustment.

- A gradual drop in the gauge reading at idle engine speed indicates back-pressure in the exhaust system due to a restriction.

Be very careful in analyzing abnormal readings since the gauge readings can indicate more than one thing. An air cleaner restriction is the most common cause, but this should be corrected before making the above test. If a problem still exists, have a serviceman inspect the engine.

MEASURE INTAKE MANIFOLD PRESSURE (TURBO BOOST)

JDPX5425

Fig. 46 — Measuring Intake Manifold Pressure (Turbo Boost)

1. Remove plug from intake manifold and install the appropriate fitting (Fig. 46). Connect gauge and hose assembly to fitting. Be sure all connections are tight.

2. Before checking boost pressure, warm up engine to allow the lubricating oil to reach operating temperature.

IMPORTANT: **Engine speed and load should be stabilized before taking a gauge reading. Be sure the gauge works properly and familiarize yourself with the use of the gauge.**

Turbo boost pressure checks are only a guide to determine if there is an engine problem (valve leakage, faulty nozzle, etc.). Low-pressure readings are not a conclusive reason for increasing injection pump fuel delivery. Pump adjustment should be with the specifications as established by an authorized diesel repair station.

On some vehicles, it may be impossible to meet the turbo boost pressure due to the inability to reach full rated speed. In these cases, see the machine's operation and test manual for the appropriate test method and pressure.

3. Observe pressure reading on gauge. Boost pressure should be within ranges when engine is developing rated power at full load rated speed.

4. If boost pressure is too high, remove fuel injection pump and have it checked for high fuel delivery by an authorized diesel repair station.

If boost pressure is too low, check for the following:

- Restriction in air cleaner.
- Leak in air intake between turbocharger and cylinder head.
- Leak in exhaust manifold gasket.
- Restricted exhaust.
- Leak in fuel system piping.
- Restricted fuel filter elements.
- Incorrect injection pump timing.
- Low fuel injection pump delivery.
- Faulty fuel supply pump.
- Low cylinder compression pressure.
- Faulty fuel injection nozzles.
- Carbon build-up in turbocharger.
- Turbocharger compressor or turbine wheel rubbing housing.

TESTING ENGINE COMPRESSION

JDPX5426

Fig. 47 — Checking Engine Compression with a Pressure Gauge

Weak compression results in loss of horsepower and poor engine performance. This is even more true in diesel engines, which depend upon the heat of compression to ignite the fuel in the cylinders.

If you suspect a compression loss, check the engine compression as follows:

1. Warm up the engine to operating temperature and then shut off the engine.

2. Remove the spark plugs or injection nozzles.

3. Connect a pressure gauge to the cylinder port (Fig. 47).

4. On spark-ignition engines, disable the ignition circuit. Refer to machine technical manual for recommended procedure to disable ignition.

5. On diesel engines, the air intake system has no throttle valve, so merely be sure that the engine speed control is in the "stop" position and/or the engine control unit (ECU) has been disconnected.

6. Turn the engine with the starter until the pressure gauge registers no further rise in pressure. It is a good practice to count the number of compression strokes (indicated by movement of the gauge needle) and check each cylinder with the same number of strokes. The engine must be at full cranking speed to get a good reading.

7. Check the pressure reading against the engine technical manual.

8. If the compression is very low, apply oil to the ring area of the piston through the openings. Do not use too much oil to avoid getting oil on the valves. Then check the compression again.

9. Judge the compression readings as given below.

JUDGING COMPRESSION READINGS

IMPORTANT: **All cylinder pressures should be about the same. Variations are usually limited to about 10 percent of the full reading.**

If compression is too low, the engine must be reconditioned before a tune-up can be effective.

If compression in one cylinder is higher than the others, the other cylinders need reconditioning.

Altitude affects compression pressures. Normally there is about a 4 percent loss for every 1000 feet (300 m) of altitude above sea level. Pressures given are normally for about 1000 feet (300 m) above sea level.

Cranking speed of the engine affects compression pressures. Therefore, be sure the batteries are in good condition and fully charged when making a compression test.

If it appears that engine service is needed, take the engine to a qualified serviceman for inspection.

TEST YOURSELF

QUESTIONS

1. Place an "I" by the parts of the intake system, an "E" by the parts of the exhaust system, an "N" by the parts that are not in either system, or a "B" by the parts of both systems.

   _____ muffler
   _____ gasoline
   _____ air cleaner
   _____ turbocharger
   _____ manifold
   _____ fuel injectors

2. The intake system supplies the engine with clean air of proper _____.

   a. Quantity

   b. Temperature

   c. Mixture

   d. All of these

3. Which of the following does not apply to dry element air cleaners?

   a. Clean off outside of element with an air hose.

   b. Tap element on a hard surface to remove surface dust.

   c. Wash element in any good detergent.

   d. Use compressed air to dry element.

   e. None of the above.

4. Match the following items:

   a. too little valve   1. cause cracking or
      clearance   breaking of the valve

   b. too much valve   2. cause the valve to burn
      clearance

5. (Fill in blank.) During the _____ stroke you can measure the valve clearance.

6. (T/F) The valve clearance for intake and exhaust valves would need to be checked in the operator's manual since they may be different.

7. (T/F) Air cleaners may contain oil.

8. What is the firing order for a 4-cylinder engine?

9. (Fill in blank.) If you identified the end of the compression stroke on an engine, you would say the cylinder is at

   _____.

10. (Fill in blanks.) What are two types of mufflers? _____ and _____.

11. (Fill in blank) What does the acronym DPF mean?

12. (Fill in blank) What does the acronym DOC mean?

13. If the DPF is regenerated during the normal engine operation, which regeneration is it?

   a. Passive

   b. Active

   c. Manual/Parked

   d. All of these

14. Diesel exhaust fluid (DEF) is a:

   a. Chemical

   b. Reducing agent

   c. Catalyst

   d. None of the above

Engine Fuel Systems

3

Introduction

Dirt and water are the major enemies of the engine fuel system.

However, today's engines need quality fuels, and these fuels will remain reasonably clean if handled properly.

In addition, good maintenance will help keep the fuel system free of dirt and water and will guarantee longer life and smoother operation.

How Engines Use Fuels

Gasoline, diesel and LP-gas engines require fuels with certain qualities. This is because of the difference in the way the fuel is ignited in each type.

If you're not familiar with the major types of engines and how they use fuels, study (Fig. 2 and Fig. 3). They show the operating principles of spark-ignition (gasoline) and diesel engines.

In the Four-stroke cycle engine (Fig. 2), there are four strokes of the piston, two up and two down, during each cycle. Then it starts over again on another cycle of the same four strokes. This cycle occurs during two revolutions of the crankshaft. Most engines today operate on the four-stroke cycle.

Gasoline and diesel engines ignite their fuel in different ways as shown in (Fig. 3).

JDPX5427

Fig. 1 — Modern Diesel Engines Require Ultra Low Sulfur Diesel (ULSD).

Intake

Fuel-Air Mixture Is Drawn into Cylinder from Intake Manifold through Open Intake Valve by Down-Stroke of Piston.

Compression

Mixture Is Compressed by Up-Stroke of Piston. Both Intake and Exhaust Valves Are Closed.

Power

Compressed Mixture Is Ignited by Spark Plug, and Expanding Gases Force Piston to Bottom of Cylinder. Valves Remain Closed.

Exhaust

Piston on Up-Stroke Forces Burned Gases from Cylinder through Open Exhaust Valve.

JDPX5428

Fig. 2 — How a Four-Stroke Cycle Gasoline Engine Works

1. Fuel and Air Are mixed in Intake Manifold
2. Mixture Enters Cylinder and Is Compressed
3. Spark Ignites the Mixture

1. Air Enters Cylinder
2. Air Is Compressed
3. Fuel Is Sprayed In
4. Fuel-Air Mixture Ignites From Heat of Compression

JDPX5429

Fig. 3 — Spark-Ignition (Gasoline) and Diesel Engines Compared

COMPRESSION RATIOS AND OCTANE RATINGS OF SPARK-IGNITION FUELS

Fuel	Engine Compression Ratio (Approx.)	Approx. Octane No.
Kerosene, No. 1 fuel oil*	4.0 to 1	0–30 (Motor Method)
Farm Tractor Fuel**	4.7 to 1	45–70 (Motor Method)
Gasoline (Low Grade)	5.0- 6.0 to 1	70–75 (Research Method)
Gasoline (Regular)	7.0- 8.5 to 1	88–94 (Research Method)
Gasoline (Premium)***	9.0-10.0 to 1	About 100 (Research Method)
LP-Gas: Butane	7.8 to 1	95–100 (Research Method)
Natural Gas	11.0 to 1	130
Propane	8.75 to 1	110–115 (Research Method)

*Well adapted to magneto ignition because of longer spark duration.

**Standard name used in place of a number of other terms such as: distillate or power fuel.

***Not normally used in farm and industrial machines.

Table 1 — Compression Rations

In gasoline engines, fuel and air are mixed outside the cylinders, in the intake manifold. The mixture is forced in due to the partial vacuum of the pistons' intake stroke.

In diesel engines, there is no premixing of air and fuel outside the cylinders. Air is drawn through the intake manifold and compressed in the cylinders. Fuel is then sprayed into the cylinder and mixed with air as the piston nears the top of its compression stroke.

Gasoline engines use an electric spark to ignite the fuel-air mixture, while diesel engines use the heat of the compressed air for ignition.

Compression and Fuels

Compression ratio is the total volume inside the engine cylinder when the piston is at the bottom of its stroke, compared to the volume when the piston is at the top-closest to the cylinder head (Fig. 4). Note that a common compression ratio for gasoline engines is 8:1, while a 16:1 ratio is common for diesels.

Each fuel has limits on how much it can be compressed and still burn properly. The fuel required for each type of engine is governed by the compression ratio of the engine. Fuel is formulated according to the design of the engine in which it is to be used.

Table 1 gives the compression ratios and octane ratings expected with modern fuels. The cetane number or ratings of diesel fuels are a measure of the fuel's ignition value and are a prime factor in fuel-engine performance.

8 to 1 Ratio   16 to 1 Ratio

Gasoline   **Diesel**

JDPX5430

Fig. 4 — Compression Ratios Compared for Gasoline and Diesel Engines

Selecting Fuels

The selection of fuel for your engine will affect the maintenance required and the performance you can expect. By choosing quality fuels you can be assured that you will get the proper octane or cetane rating plus beneficial additives and clean fuel.

Selecting Fuel for Gasoline Engines

Your assurance of getting a fuel with an adequate anti-knock quality is indicated by its bold type number rating. The operator's manual tells you what the minimum octane rating should be for your engine. Compare it with the octane rating of the fuel supplied by your dealer.

Fuels with the least tendency to knock have higher octane numbers. The names "premium," "regular," and "low grade" are rough comparative measures of octane ratings. Most farm and industrial machines use regular grade (88 to 94 octane). If your operator's manual recommends an octane number within the regular range, don't use low grade (70 to 75 octane) fuel. You can use premium grade gasoline, but there is usually no advantage because most machine engines are not designed (lack the compression ratio) to secure the benefits of the higher octane rating.

JDPX5431
Fig. 5 — Use Only a Good Grade of Gasoline

Heavy LP-Gas Tank Holds High Pressures

JDPX5432
Fig. 6 — LP-Gas Engines Have High-Pressure Fuel Tanks

Additives have become essential ingredients of modern gasolines. They are used to raise octane number and to combat surface ignition (anti-knock), spark plug fouling, gum formation, rust, carburetor icing, deposits in the intake system, and intake valve sticking.

Gasohol, a mixture of 90 percent unleaded gasoline and 10 percent ethanol (grain alcohol), is available in many areas as a substitute for gasoline. Gasohol burns cleaner and may provide better mileage in motor vehicles compared to straight gasoline. However, some engine manufacturers have not approved of the use of gasohol in certain engines. So, always be sure the fuel is compatible before using it in an engine or the warranty may be voided. Also, in engines used infrequently, water may combine with the alcohol and cause serious corrosion or damage to some engine components.

IMPORTANT: **Never use non-leaded gasolines unless your operator's manual specifies they can be used in your machine's engine. Non-leaded fuel can damage some agricultural engines.**

Selecting Fuel for LP-Gas Engines

LP-gas is short for "liquefied-petroleum gas." It is sometimes indicated as LPG.

Most LP-gas used in engines today is all propane or a mixture of mostly propane with some butane.

LP-gases must be stored and handled in high-pressure containers to keep them in liquid form (Fig. 6). Butane boils at approximately +33°F (1°C), while propane boils at –44°F (–42°C). When confined to a closed container, the pressure varies with the outside temperature. Butane develops pressure of 37 psi (255 kPa) at 100°F (38°C), while propane develops pressure of 195 psi (1350 kPa) at the same temperature.

An LP-gas engine is similar to a gasoline engine, but the LP-gas engine is designed with a higher compression ratio, about 7.8:1 to as high as 10:1. Also, LP-gases have a high-octane rating ranging from about 95 for butane to as high as 125 for propane.

There is very little that can be done about selecting LP-gas fuel except to deal with a reliable distributor. You are entirely dependent on him to supply fuels that are relatively free of sulfur compounds and other contaminants which may cause difficulties such as filter plugging, valve failures, etc. For cold weather operation, your dealer should give you a different blend (more propane) than for warm weather.

Selecting Fuel for Natural Gas Engines

Natural gas is a fossil fuel found in the earth's crust. It is a mixture of methane, ethane, propane, butane, and trace amounts of other inert gases. However, methane is by far the largest component—about 90 percent of the total volume of natural gas.

Methane has very good anti-knock characteristics, which means that it does not ignite readily. The octane level of natural gas is approximately 130. Because of this, the engine's compression ratio is typically higher for natural gas than for gasoline.

Natural gas burns more slowly than gasoline because natural gas ignites at a much higher temperature (1300°F, 704°C) than gasoline (1100°F, 593°C). For this reason, the ignition spark is often advanced farther for natural gas engines, and a higher spark voltage may be required.

Modern natural gas engines typically use a high-energy, coil-on-plug, inductive ignition system.

Natural gas is in a gaseous state at any temperature above –259°F (–126°C). At atmospheric pressure, the temperature of –259°F (–126°C) is the boiling point of natural gas, while water is gaseous (steam) at +212°F (+100°C). Because of this property, natural gas must be stored in a closed fuel tank to prevent vapor from escaping.

Natural gas is stored in one of the following forms:

- Compressed natural gas (CNG)
- Liquefied natural gas (LNG)

Compressed natural gas (CNG) is produced in CNG fueling facilities that compress the pipeline supply of natural gas to pressures of 3000 to 3600 psi. The compressed gas is stored in high-strength tanks.

Liquefied natural gas (LNG) is produced through a cryogenic (or freezing) process in which the gas is cooled to –259°F (–126°C) to form a liquid. The liquefied gas is then stored in high-strength, insulated tanks.

With the exception of the method of storage, compressed natural gas systems and liquefied natural gas systems have many things in common.

Selecting Fuel for Diesel Engines

You may have heard a saying, "Diesel engines will burn anything." It is true that they will burn a wide variety of fuels. In fact, powdered coal was the first fuel used for diesel engines.

From this you may gain the wrong impression that selecting fuel for your diesel engine is simply supplying anything it will burn. But diesel fuel selection is far more critical than this.

In all cases, the fuel shall meet the following properties:

Cetane number of 43 minimum. Cetane number greater than 47 is preferred, especially for temperatures below –20 °C (–4 °F) or elevations above 1,500 m (5,000 ft.).

Cold Filter Plugging Point (CFPP) should be at least 5 °C (9 °F) below the expected lowest temperature or Cloud Point below the expected lowest ambient temperature.

Fuel lubricity should pass a maximum scar diameter of 0.52 mm as measured by ASTM D6079 or ISO 12156-1. A maximum scar diameter of 0.45 mm is preferred.

Diesel fuel quality and sulfur content must comply with all existing emissions regulations for the area in which the engine operates. DO NOT use diesel fuel with sulfur content greater than 10,000 mg/kg (10,000 ppm).

Sulfur content for Interim Tier 4, Final Tier 4, Stage III B, and Stage IV Engines

- Use ONLY ultra low sulfur diesel (ULSD) fuel with a maximum of 15 mg/kg (15 ppm) sulfur content.

Sulfur Content for Tier 3 and Stage III A Engines

- Use of diesel fuel with sulfur content less than 1000 mg/kg (1,000 ppm) is RECOMMENDED.

- Use of diesel fuel with sulfur content 1,000—2,000 mg/kg (1,000—2,000 ppm) REDUCES the oil and filter change interval.

- BEFORE using diesel fuel with sulfur content greater than 2,000 mg/kg (2,000 ppm), contact your John Deere dealer.

Sulfur Content for Tier 2 and Stage II Engines

- Use of diesel fuel with sulfur content less than 2,000 mg/kg (2,000 ppm) is RECOMMENDED.

- Use of diesel fuel with sulfur content 2,000—5,000 mg/kg (2,000—5,000 ppm) REDUCES the oil and filter change interval.

- BEFORE using diesel fuel with sulfur content greater than 5,000 mg/kg (5,000 ppm), contact your John Deere dealer.

Sulfur Content for Other Engines

- Use of diesel fuel with sulfur content less than 5,000 mg/kg (5,000 ppm) is RECOMMENDED.

- Use of diesel fuel with sulfur content greater than 5,000 mg/kg (5,000 ppm) REDUCES the oil and filter change.

Consult your local fuel distributor for properties of the diesel fuel available in your area. In general, diesel fuels are blended to satisfy the low temperature requirements of the geographical area in which they are marketed.

Diesel fuels specified to EN 590 or ASTM D975 are recommended. Renewable diesel fuel produced by hydrotreating animal fats and vegetable oils is basically identical to petroleum diesel fuel. Renewable diesel that meets EN 590 or ASTM D975 is acceptable for use at all percentage mixture levels.

Knowing how a diesel engine works will help you to understand why certain grades of fuel must be used in them. The operating principles for a four-stroke cycle diesel engine as compared to a gasoline engine are shown in (Fig. 3).

JDPX5433

Fig. 7 — Precision Diesel Components Require Clean Fuel

Note that there is no spark plug to start the diesel fuel burning. Instead, the air is compressed until it is so hot that fuel injected into it will start burning spontaneously.

The compression ratios for diesel engines are much higher than for spark-ignition engines. This extra compression of the air provides enough heat (900° to 1,200°F, 480° to 650°C) so that the fuel is ignited by heat alone when sprayed into the cylinder. Note in (Fig. 4) that the compression ratio for a diesel engine is 16:1. This compares with the compression ratios of about 8:1 in gasoline engines.

The average compression ratio for diesel tractors is approximately 16.3:1. The ratios vary from as low as 14:1 to as high as 20:1.

Diesel Fuel Grades

The following are the two major grades of diesel fuels are:

• No. 1-D Diesel Fuel

• No. 2-D Diesel Fuel

Both fuels (or fuel oils) are used in high-speed diesel engines on the farm or ranch. Their differences are explained below.

Grade No. 1-D Fuel

Grade No. 1-D is a higher class of volatile fuel oils from kerosene to the intermediate distillates. These fuels are for use in high-speed engines with variable loads and speeds, and also for extremely cold weather and high-altitude operation.

Grade No. 2-D Fuel

Grade No. 2-D is the class of distillate gas oils of lower volatility. These fuels are for use in high-speed engines with relatively high loads and more uniform speeds, or in engines not requiring fuels having the higher volatility or other properties specified for Grade No. 1-D.

Remember that engine design and operation materially affect the grade of fuel best suited for an engine.

RECOMMENDED DIESEL FUEL GRADES FOR AGRICULTURAL MACHINES

The following is a typical recommendation from a diesel tractor operator's manual.

Type of Engine Service	Surrounding Air Temperature	Diesel Fuel Grade No.
Light load, low speed, considerable idling.	Above 80°F (25°C)	2-D
	Below 80°F (25°C)	1-D
Intermediate and heavy load, high speed, minimum of idling.	Above 40°F (5°C)	2-D
	Below 40°F (5°C)	1-D
At altitudes above 5,000 feet.	All	1-D

Table 2 — Recommended Diesel Fuel Grades for Agricultural Machines

Cetane Number

The method of determining the ignition quality of diesel fuel is similar to that used for determining the anti-knock quality of gasoline. However, for diesel fuels this is called cetane number instead of octane. These qualities are opposites as shown in (Fig. 8).

In general, high-cetane fuels permit an engine to be started at lower air temperatures, provide faster engine warm-up without misfiring, reduce varnish and carbon deposits, and help eliminate engine knock.

However, too-high cetane numbers may lead to incomplete combustion and exhaust smoke if the ignition delay period is too short to allow proper mixing of the fuel and air within the combustion space.

RECOMMENDED CETANES FOR DIESEL FUELS

Diesel fuels marketed in the United States range from 33 to 64 in cetane number. A typical high-speed engine on a farm tractor or combine calls for diesel fuel with a cetane of 43 minimum. Cetane number greater than 47 is preferred, especially for temperatures below –20 °C (–4 °F) or elevations above 1,500 m (5,000 ft.).

Fig. 8 — Octane and Cetane Numbers Are Opposite

Knock In Diesel Engines

In diesel engines, knock is due to the fuel igniting TOO SLOWLY. It should start to burn almost as soon as it is injected (Fig. 9, top). If there is much delay, a fuel build-up results, which burns with explosive force (Fig. 9, bottom) and causes knocking.

Proper Burning
(Fuel Charge Ignites Early and Burns Evenly to Overcome Knocking)

Poor Ignition
(Ignition of Fuel Charge Is Delayed, Followed by a Small Explosion)

JDPX5434

Fig. 9 — In Diesel Engines Knock Is Due to Fuel Igniting Too Slowly

By contrast, in spark-ignition engines, where the fuel-air charge is mixed and then compressed before ignition takes place, knock is caused by the fuel burning TOO RAPIDLY.

Good diesel fuel provides for early spontaneous burning. By contrast, good gasoline fuels avoid this spontaneous action.

The difference between octane numbers (gasoline) and cetane numbers (diesel fuel) is shown in (Fig. 8).

Diesel Fuel Compared with Furnace Fuel

The question is often asked, "Are diesel fuel and furnace fuel the same?" It is possible for your fuel supplier to have one fuel that he supplies for both diesel-engine use and heating purposes. Where there is one dominant use, such as home heating compared to limited diesel fuel use, the dealer may not be justified in stocking a separate diesel fuel. So he purchases fuel from his supplier to meet the specifications for both fuels. The refiner can meet this demand because the specifications for both fuels are broad enough that they overlap.

If a dealer is supplying large quantities of fuel for both heating and diesel engines, he will normally stock two fuels. In this case the furnace oils usually contain more of the heavy cracked distillates, which are quite satisfactory for furnaces, but are not suitable for diesel engines (especially with light intermittent loads) and do not generally meet standards.

FUEL AND COLD WEATHER STARTING

The higher the cetane number, the more easily your engine will start on diesel fuel. However, in very cold weather, some diesel engines need a starting aid, such as ether which has a cetane rating of 85 to 96 and is highly volatile (Fig. 10). Cylinder block heaters and manifold air heaters are other cold weather starting aids.

 CAUTION: Never use ether in a diesel engine equipped with glow plugs or a manifold air heater.

IMPORTANT: Spray ether into an engine ONLY while cranking with the starter. Ether is highly explosive and can damage the engine if too much is sprayed in before cranking.

Key Switch

Starting Aid Switch

JDPX5435

Fig. 10 — Starting a Diesel Engine in Cold Weather Using Ether Starting Fluid

Storing Fuels

The importance of proper fuel storage cannot be stressed too highly. Many engine difficulties can be traced to dirty fuel and fuel that has been in storage too long.

To keep the fuel system in its most efficient condition, keep all dirt, scale, water, and other foreign matter out of the fuel, and avoid storing fuel for a long period of time. Fill the fuel tank at the end of each day's operation to prevent water condensation and freezing during cold weather.

Keep all storage tanks as full as practicable to minimize condensation.

Ensure that all fuel tank caps and covers are installed properly to prevent moisture from entering. Monitor the water content of the fuel regularly.

When using biodiesel fuel, the fuel filter may require more frequent replacement due to premature plugging.

Check the engine oil level daily prior to starting engine. A rising oil level may indicate fuel dilution of the engine oil.

When fuel is stored for an extended period or if there is a slow turnover of fuel, add a fuel conditioner to stabilize the fuel and prevent water condensation. Contact your fuel supplier or John Deere dealer for recommendations.

Fuel should be stored in a convenient place outside of buildings.

Each state has its own laws regarding the handling, storage and use of fuels. It is important that you become acquainted with and obey fuel handling regulations for your own safety and for insurance purposes.

Proper storing and handling of fuels can affect your safety, how easily your machine starts, and how much maintenance your fuel system requires.

A complete discussion of the storage and safe handling of fuels is given in the John Deere Fundamentals of Service (FOS) manual in "Fuels, Lubricants, and Coolants."

Storing Diesel Exhaust Fluid (DEF)

CAUTION: Avoid contact with eyes. In case of contact, immediately flush eyes with large amounts of water for a minimum of 15 minutes. Reference the Materials Safety Data Sheet (MSDS) for additional information.

Do not ingest DEF. In the event DEF is ingested, contact a physician immediately. Reference the Materials Safety Data Sheet (MSDS) for additional information.

The following storage information is provided for reference and is to be used as a guideline only.

It is preferred to store DEF out of extreme ambient temperatures. DEF freezes at −11 °C (12 °F). Exposure to temperatures greater than 30 °C (86 °F) can degrade DEF over time.

Dedicated DEF storage containers must be sealed between uses to prevent evaporation and contamination. Containers made of polyethylene, polypropylene, or stainless steel are recommended to transport and store DEF.

The following conditions for storing DEF are ideal:

- Store at temperatures between –5 °C and 30 °C (23 °F and 86 °F).

- Store in dedicated containers sealed to avoid contamination and evaporation.

Under these conditions, DEF is expected to remain useable for a minimum of 18 months. Storing DEF at higher temperatures can reduce its useful life by approximately 6 months for every 5 °C (9 °F) temperature above 30 °C (86 °F).

If unsure how long or under what conditions DEF has been stored, test DEF. See Testing Diesel Exhaust Fluid (DEF).

Long-term storage in the DEF tank (over 12 months) is not recommended. If long-term storage is necessary, test DEF prior to operating engine. See Testing Diesel Exhaust Fluid (DEF)

It is recommended to purchase DEF in quantities that will be consumed within 12 months.

Sulfur in Fuel

Sulfur in fuel will combine with water and form harmful sulfuric acid in engines. Changing oil more often is the best way to remove the acid. Avoiding high sulfur fuel also helps to reduce the acid problem. In general, NEVER use diesel fuel with a sulfur content greater than one percent.

IMPORTANT: **Do not mix used diesel engine oil or any other type of lubricating oil with diesel fuel. Improper fuel additive usage may cause damage on fuel injection equipment of diesel engines.**

Supplemental Diesel Fuel Additives

Diesel fuel can be the source of performance or other operational problems for many reasons. Some causes include poor lubricity, contaminants, low cetane number, and a variety of properties that cause fuel system deposits. These and others are referenced in other sections of this Operator's Manual.

To optimize engine performance and reliability, closely follow recommendations on fuel quality, storage, and handling, which are found elsewhere in this Operator's Manual.

To further aid in maintaining performance and reliability of the engine's fuel system, John Deere has developed a family of fuel additive products for most global markets. The primary products include Fuel-Protect Diesel Fuel Conditioner (full feature conditioner in winter and summer formulas) and Fuel-Protect Keep Clean (fuel injector deposit removal and prevention). Availability of these and other products varies by market. See your local John Deere dealer for availability and additional information about fuel additives that might be right for your needs.

Refueling Machines

Proper refueling of your machine is more than just filling the tank with fuel. The time and method of refueling are important because of their influence on:

- Keeping out moisture

- Keeping out dirt

- Avoiding fire hazards

Most operator's manuals suggest that you fill the fuel tank at the end of the day or whenever you finish using the machine. This keeps moisture from accumulating in the tank.

Most water in fuel comes from moisture condensing inside the fuel tank. This is true of all fuels except LP-gas.

Here is why: As fuel is used, air is drawn in. Much of the time the air contains considerable moisture. The warmer the air, the more moisture it can hold. At the end of the day, the fuel tank is full of warm moist air, which, when cooled at night, deposits moisture on the sides of the tank. As it collects, it runs into and under whatever fuel is left in the tank. (No air enters an LP-gas tank.) This is shown in (Fig. 11).

Water doesn't do much damage to the tank. Most tanks have a protective coating that helps prevent rust. But in a spark-ignition engine, any moisture that gets past the sediment bowl in the feed line from the tank moves into the fuel pump (if the machine has one) and then into the rest of the fuel system. Any sulfur present in the fuel combines with water and attacks the metal parts. In cold weather, water that has collected in the sediment bowl or fuel line may freeze and cause starting trouble.

Diesel fuel and water mix rather readily, and the water is slow to settle out, much slower than with gasoline. Yet if water gets to the injection pump, it causes galling and sticking of the finely-machined pump parts. Next is an expensive repair job.

By filling the tank immediately after the machine is used, there is a period of several hours during the night that allows time for most of the water already in the fuel to collect at the bottom of the tank. This is why it is recommended that water be drained from the sediment bowl before starting the engine each day.

Dirt is another major contaminant. In spark-ignition engines it can build up in the fuel injectors, restricting flow, and can also alter the spray pattern, resulting in poor performance. Dirt build-up can also prevent injection nozzles from closing properly allowing fuel past the injector and into the cylinder. In diesel engines, it speeds the wear of the close-fitting plungers in the injector pump.

Warm Moist Air Replaces Gasoline Used from Fuel Tank

Wrong: Empty Tank

As Air Cools, Moisture Deposits on Side of Tank and Runs into Fuel

Right: Full Tank

If Tank Is Filled after Stopping Machine, There Is No Room for Moist Air

JDPX5437

Fig. 11 — Why Fuel Tanks Should Be Filled at the End of Each Day

Fire hazards exist when handling any kind of fuel. But with gasoline and LP-Gas the risk is somewhat greater. There are two reasons:

• Both fuels vaporize at temperatures around zero. Only a small amount mixed with air (6 percent or less of gasoline vapor) will explode if exposed to a spark or flame.

• Since the vapors are heavier than air, they settle to a low spot and remain there unless ventilated out.

Kerosene and fuel oil don't vaporize readily until the temperature reaches 110°F (45°C) or more. This makes them less of a hazard than gasoline, unless you spill them on a hot manifold or other hot surfaces. Then they vaporize readily. With so much vapor present, a spark or flame will readily ignite it.

Consequently, if your machine is hot and you haven't time to wait 4 or 5 minutes for it to cool, wait and refuel the next morning. The risk of water in your fuel tank becomes less important than the risk of fire or explosion from refueling a hot engine.

Refueling of machines is discussed as follows:

• Refueling with liquid fuels
• Refueling with LP-gas

We will now explain each one.

Fig. 12 — Fuel in Storage Containers

Refueling with Liquid Fuels

When filling a fuel tank with gasoline, kerosene, or diesel fuel:

1. Check against fire hazards.

   Shut off engine and turn off all electrical switches to lessen the danger of a spark.

   Allow engine to cool if extra hot. Be sure there are no open flames and that no one is smoking.

2. Check mouth of container or hose nozzle for dirt. Remove any dirt with a clean cloth.

   Be sure to use closed containers if you are hauling fuel to the field (Fig. 12). There is less chance of dirt and moisture entering the fuel tank if you fill your machine directly from an overhead supply tank or pump (Fig. 12).

   Use only authorized gasoline containers; these are red in color. Make sure your kerosene, distillate, or diesel fuel containers are colored green.

3. Remove dust and loose dirt from fuel tank cap and area around tank opening.

 CAUTION: Never smoke while filling a fuel tank.

4. Fill fuel tank almost full.

   Leave space in neck of opening for fuel to expand if heated. This helps avoid overflow and possibility of fire.

   Don't move fuel drums as the movement can agitate the fuel, causing water and dirt to mix with it.

   With diesel fuel, leave 3 or 4 inches of fuel in the bottom of the storage tank as a safeguard against moisture and dirt.

   If your fuel supply is low in the supply tank, you run a risk of drawing off both dirt and water into your fuel tank. Rather than take this risk, line a clean funnel with a chamois and filter the fuel through it. The chamois removes both dirt and water.

   Let fuel stand at least 10 hours after supply tank is filled before fueling machines to permit any dirt in the fuel to settle out.

5. Replace fuel tank cap tightly.

   Make it a practice to check the opening in the fuel tank cap occasionally. If it becomes clogged, a vacuum tends to develop in the fuel tank and fuel won't feed into the carburetor satisfactorily.

Refueling with LP-Gas

 CAUTION: Check to make sure engine is turned off and that no one is smoking or there are no open flames nearby. These precautions are extremely important. It is difficult to know when you have an LP-gas leak. The gas is invisible and the odor is not as easy to detect as with gasoline. In other respects, it has about the same hazards as when filling a gasoline tank.

Never attempt to fuel your machine inside a building or over a pit. There is too much danger of gas pocketing and providing conditions for an explosion.

As we discussed earlier, LP-gas is a petroleum gas, commonly made up of propane and butane (some is all propane). At ordinary temperatures it changes to a gas, and in order to keep it in liquid form it must be kept under pressure. For this reason, the method of filling the machine fuel tank is different than with other fuels.

Note in (Fig. 13) there are two hose lines extending from the storage tank to the machine fuel tank. One line delivers liquid fuel from the supply tank to the machine tank, while the second line allows vapor to flow from the machine tank back to the supply tank. In this way no air enters either tank and there is no loss of pressure due to escaping gas vapor.

 CAUTION: Don't ever attempt to fill the tank without a vapor-return hose line. While it is true that it can be done by allowing vapor to escape to open air, this practice violates all safety regulations. It is extremely dangerous, and fire or explosion is almost certain if continued over a period of time.

Fig. 13 — Refueling with LP-Gas

As long as the level of the liquid in the supply tank is above the level of the liquid in the machine tank, it will flow by gravity from the storage to the machine tank. If the storage tank is lower than the machine tank, a hand-operated or motor-operated pump is used to pump the liquid from the supply tank (Fig. 13).

IMPORTANT: A different set of valves is used for filling the fuel tank from those used when operating the machine. Check your operator's manual for details on fueling your type of machine. In general, the procedures are as follows.

1. Remove dust caps (covers) from machine fuel tank connections and hose ends.

    Valves inside the tank keep liquid and gas from escaping.

    The vapor return valve is built somewhat differently from the filler valve. It has one check valve and an excess-flow valve on the end. The excess-flow valve closes in case there is a rapid movement of gas from the tank, such as might happen if a hose should break.

2. Attach vapor-return hose to vapor-return connection on machine and open hand valve (Fig. 14).

    When this valve is opened, pressure is equalized between the storage tank and tractor tank. This is necessary for the liquid to flow into the tractor tank.

3. Attach liquid-fill hose to connection on machine tank and open valve (Fig. 14).

4. Operate pump if storage tank is below level of machine.

5. Watch fuel gauge to determine when tank is 75 percent full.

    This step is important in order to keep from overfilling the fuel tank.

    Your gauge may be of the float type. If so, it shows the percentage of liquid fill in your tank at all times.

Fig. 14 — Hand-Operated Valves on Hoses Which Connect to Machine Tank

Some gauges are of the tube type. To determine percentage of fill with this type of gauge, level of liquid is checked by rotating tube inside tank. It is connected to a dial handle on the gauge.

6. Check fuel overflow valve until liquid appears.

   Open this valve momentarily, then close until liquid appears. This shows when liquid has reached proper level in tank. Don't leave this valve open during the filling process. As discussed earlier, this is extremely dangerous and violates all codes and laws regarding proper and safe handling of LP-gas tanks.

 CAUTION: When the hoses are disconnected from the machine tank, a small amount of liquid fuel is lost. Continue to avoid smoking or lighting a match until the fuel has had time to vaporize and be ventilated away from the machine.

7. Close both line valves and disconnect from machine tank.

   The machine fuel tank is now around 80 to 85 percent full. This still leaves room for vapor at the top and provides for expansion of the fuel in case of heat.

8. Replace dust caps.

   A safety-relief valve is mounted on your tank to relieve pressure in case you overfill and the pressure gets too high for safety.

Refueling with Natural Gas Fuels

Refer to the machine operator's manual for specific procedures and safety instructions regarding filling a machine with compressed natural gas (CNG) or liquid natural gas (LNG).

Gasoline Fuel Systems

The gasoline fuel system supplies a combustible mixture of fuel and air to power the engine.

The gasoline fuel system (Fig. 15) has four basic parts:

- Fuel tank
- Fuel pump
- Fuel injectors
- Fuel pressure regulator

The fuel tank stores the gasoline for the engine.

The fuel pump moves fuel from tank to fuel injectors.

A fuel pump is needed only with force-feed supply systems. Older carburetor fuel systems often have the fuel tank mounted above the engine, using gravity to move fuel from the tank to the carburetor.

Fig. 15 — Gasoline Fuel Systems

The Fuel pressure regulator controls the fuel pressure in the fuel line and at the fuel injectors.

The fuel injectors produce a fine mist of fuel that is injected into the intake manifold where it is mixed with air.

Most systems also have a fuel sediment bowl and strainer below the tank outlet, or it may be part of the fuel pump.

Operation

How do these parts work together as a team?

Operation of the basic system is shown in (Fig. 15).

The fuel pump draws fuel from the tank and forces it through a line to the fuel pressure regulator, where the pressure is reduced to the proper pressure. The fuel continues to the fuel injectors where it is stopped.

Servicing Gasoline Sediment Bowl and Fuel Strainer

Most agricultural machines are equipped with a combination sediment bowl and fuel strainer.

NOTE: *In extremely trashy or dry conditions, some manufacturers recommend replacing glass sediment bowls with metal bowls to reduce the possibility of a bowl breaking and causing a fire.*

Most sediment bowls should be visually checked every 10 hours for dirt and water deposits. However, actual service intervals vary widely and some manuals say "periodically."

The tools and materials needed to clean these parts are:

- Container of cleaning solvent (not gasoline)
- New gaskets (where used)
- Clean, lint-free rags

To clean the sediment bowl and strainer, proceed as follows:

1. Shut off fuel supply line at fuel tank or sediment bowl (Fig. 16).

2. Remove sediment bowl gasket and strainer screen.

3. Wash screen in cleaning solvent. If screen is difficult to clean, remove varnish or gum deposits with a carburetor cleaning solvent.

4. Clean sediment bowl with cloth dampened in cleaning solvent. Wipe bowl dry and remove any lint remaining in bowl.

5. Drain sediment from bottom of fuel tank, or open fuel valve and observe fuel as you catch it in a container. This should remove dirt or water from the tank and fuel line. If the vent hole in the fuel tank cap is plugged, the flow will be slow. Clean the cap, if clogged, in solvent.

Fig. 17 — Servicing Gasoline Fuel Sediment Bowl and Strainer

Fig. 16 — Fuel Sediment Bowl and Strainer

6. Reassemble sediment bowl, strainer, or filter and gasket (Fig. 17) and tighten the jam nut. (On some systems you must let fuel run into the bowl before tightening it completely.)

7. Open the fuel valve. Start the engine and check for fuel leaks.

8. Reassemble the sediment bowl, strainer or filter, and gasket (Fig. 17).

9. Tighten the bowl against gasket. (On some systems you must let fuel run into bowl before tightening it airtight.)

10. Open the fuel valve. Start the engine and check for leaks.

LP-Gas Fuel Systems

LP-gas vaporizes very easily. In fact, it normally remains a liquid only when under pressure. Therefore, it must be kept in strong tanks.

LP-gas is vaporized before it reaches the carburetor, while gasoline remains a liquid until this point. This is the basic difference between the two systems.

Operation

In most LP-gas systems, the fuel is drawn from the tank as a pressurized liquid and then vaporized (Fig. 18).

Vapor is taken from the top of the tank only for starting the engine. This is done because in a cold engine there is not enough heat to convert liquid fuel to vapor. Once the engine is started and warmed up, it can be switched to liquid withdrawal again.

Fig. 18 — LP-Gas Fuel System

Parts of an LP-Gas Fuel System

The LP-gas fuel system (Fig. 18) has four basic parts:

- Pressurized fuel tank
- Fuel strainer
- Converter
- Carburetor

The pressurized fuel tank stores the liquid fuel under pressure. A space for vapor is left at the top of the tank.

The fuel strainer cleans the liquid fuel. It normally has a solenoid valve which permits flow only when the engine ignition is turned on.

The converter changes the liquid fuel to vapor by warming it and then lowering the pressure of the vapor.

The carburetor mixes the fuel vapor with air in the proper ratio for the engine.

Importance of Service

The LP-gas fuel system requires maintenance similar to the gasoline system. To achieve the maximum fuel economy and horsepower, you must perform periodic service to keep the system operating correctly.

As with gasoline fuel systems, if the carburetor is not adjusted correctly, fuel consumption can be excessive or power can be lost.

Clean fuel is not a major problem with LP-gas; however, don't neglect it. Small particles of dirt or gummy residues can lodge in the finely machined valve openings and damage the seats when valves are closed. This can cause dangerous gas leaks or plugging of the lines. Plugging can be detected by frosting of the filter or line at the point of stoppage.

Cleaning the LP-Gas Fuel Strainer

Clean the LP-gas strainer as recommended. Intervals vary from every 100 hours to yearly. However, if the strainer clogs, frost will form on the outside of the metal strainer.

The tools and materials needed to clean the filter are:

- Set of wrenches (inch or metric, as required)
- Container of solvent (not gasoline)
- New gaskets (where used)
- Clean, lint-free cloths
- Source of air pressure

To clean the strainer, proceed as follows:

1. Close liquid and vapor valves at fuel tank (Fig. 19).
2. Remove the drain plug from the strainer (Fig. 19).

 CAUTION: Never open vapor valve in the vicinity of a flame as a spark or explosion could result. Also, be sure there is plenty of ventilation.

3. Open the vapor valve at tank slowly. This should blow accumulation of moisture and sediment from the strainer bowl.

Fig. 19 — Cleaning LP-gas Fuel Strainer

4. Close the vapor valve and reinstall the plug.

This procedure will clean some of the contamination from the strainer bowl, but to clean the filter completely, it must be removed.

For complete cleaning of strainer:

1. Be sure that both the vapor and liquid supply valves are closed.

2. Loosen the drain plug in the bowl slowly so that any pressure build-up can be relieved.

3. Loosen the nut or bolt holding the filter bowl and remove bowl, gasket, and filter element.

4. Wash the filter in solvent if the filter is washable. Replace disposable filters with new ones.

5. If a disk-type filter is to be reinstalled, finish drying the filter by blowing air through one end. This forces out any particles from inside the filter element.

6. Clean sediment bowl with a cloth dampened with the cleaning solution. Wipe the bowl dry and be sure no lint remains in the bowl.

7. Install gasket, filter, and sediment bowl and tighten nuts or bolts to hold filter in place.

8. Open the fuel supply valves at tank and check for leaks. Brush on a soapy-water solution around connections. If bubbles are present, tighten connections. If tightening does not correct the problem, replace the necessary parts.

Adjusting the LP-Gas Carburetor

Refer to your operator's manual for specific instructions. Some manufacturers recommend that you take your machine to your local dealer for this service. However, many LP-gas carburetors can be adjusted as follows:

Fig. 20 — Adjusting Points on a Typical LP-Gas Carburetor

1. Warm up the engine fully.

2. Adjust the idle speed at the throttle stop screw (Fig. 20). Normally, adjust with the throttle disk closed and try to get the slowest engine idling speed without stalling or "roughening." See your operator's manual for recommended idle rpm.

3. Adjust the idle fuel mixture at the adjusting link (Fig. 20). With the engine at slow idle, turn the link until the engine begins to stall. Then turn the link the other way until the engine idles smoothly.

4. If necessary, readjust the idle speed (step 2).

5. Adjust the full-load fuel mixture per the specification. For safety, load the engine but keep the engine stationary (as with a dynamometer). With a tractor you can use the tractor to power a grinder or other PTO-driven unit. With self-propelled machines such as cotton pickers or combines, the harvesting mechanism can provide the engine with a load.

IMPORTANT: **Never let an LP-gas engine run with the fuel mixture too lean. LP-gas burns hotter than gasoline and will allow the engine to develop maximum horsepower. However, this lean burning will result in burned valves and pistons.**

Be sure the throttle is wide open. Turn the full-load fuel adjusting screw until the engine starts to lose power. Then back it out until the engine picks up speed and runs smoothly.

NOTE: *This adjustment has no effect unless the engine is at full throttle under load and the throttle disk is wide open.*

Servicing the LP-Gas Converter

JDPX5452

Fig. 21 — LP-Gas Converter

The converter (Fig. 21) is constructed so that it will seldom cause trouble, provided that clean fuel is used in the tank and clean, soft water in the cooling system.

If the converter frosts up when the engine is cold, it is probably due to a leaking high-pressure valve caused by dirt under the valve seat.

If frosting occurs when the engine is hot, it is probably due to poor coolant circulation through the heat exchanger or a restriction in the high-pressure valve.

To check the converter for leaks, turn on the ignition switch without starting the engine and open the vapor withdrawal valve.

Then remove the radiator cap and check the coolant for bubbles, which would mean that the converter has a leaking gasket.

For converter service, see your dealer.

Servicing LP-Gas Fuel Tank, Valves, and Gauges

Be sure that you are familiar with all rules and regulations before servicing LP-gas equipment.

Two rules are important here:

- Never service the fuel tank except to remove and install valves or gauges.
- Never service the valves or gauges except to remove and install them or to replace caps or dust covers. Your dealer should perform all major LP-gas service.

Replacing Parts

If a valve or gauge is damaged or worn and must be replaced, first empty all fuel from the tank to remove the pressure. If possible, do this outdoors by running the engine until all fuel is exhausted. If not possible, consult your local LP-gas distributor for the approved method in your locality for emptying the tank.

 CAUTION: Never use an open flame to test for gas leaks.

When replacing a valve, use a small amount of Permatex or similar sealer on the threads. Install the valve and tighten securely. Test for leaks by using soapy water.

For other information, see your machine dealer.

Natural Gas Fuel Systems

Parts of Natural Gas Fuel System

The major parts of a natural gas fuel system are (Fig. 22):

- Fuel tanks
- Fuel pressure regulator
- Fuel metering valve
- Fuel-air mixer
- Throttle assembly

Fuel tanks store natural gas in either a compressed or liquefied state.

The fuel pressure regulator reduces the fuel pressure to the pressure required by the specific engine. Natural gas fuel systems vary in the types and number of regulators used. There are three basic systems:

- Two-Regulator System — uses a high-pressure (first stage) regulator and a low-pressure (second stage) regulator. This system controls the gas flow and pressure to the fuel-air mixer (carburetor) and is typically used with an air valve type fuel-air mixer.

Fig. 22 — Natural Gas Fuel System

- Single Regulator System — uses one regulator with three stages. This system also controls the gas flow and pressure to the fuel-air mixer. This system is typically used with a venturi type fuel-air mixer.

- Fuel Injection System — uses a single regulator that drops the fuel pressure to between 80 psi and 150 psi.

Fuel flows to a metering valve body that electronically controls the amount of fuel delivered to the engine.

The fuel metering valve is used with natural gas fuel injection systems.

The fuel-air mixer is located upstream of the throttle body. The fuel-air mixer combines the natural gas with air to form the fuel-air mixture for combustion. The two basic types of fuelair mixers are the air valve mixer and the venturi mixer.

Air valve mixers use a spring-loaded diaphragm (air valve) to meter the correct amount of fuel to the engine. The diaphragm is positioned over the top of the mixer throat so that air passing around it creates a pressure differential between the top and bottom of the diaphragm. The pressure differential causes the air valve to move off its seat, opening the gas metering valve to allow the gas to mix with the air.

The system meters fuel in direct and constant proportion to the amount of airflow. Thus, the greater the airflow, the more fuel is delivered.

Venturi mixers use the "venturi principle." The venturi shape of the mixer causes the airflow to speed up, creating a low-pressure area in the mixer.

Small holes or slots below the venturi allow fuel to pass into the air stream and mix with the air. These mixers combine with the regulator to deliver fuel to the engine on demand.

The throttle assembly controls the volume of airflow through the fuel-air mixer. The amount of natural gas introduced into the airflow will be proportional to the amount of air flowing through the mixer. Thus, varying the airflow to the engine controls the power output of a natural gas engine.

Types of Natural Gas Fuel Delivery Systems

Two basic types of natural gas fuel delivery systems are in common use today. They are:

- Fuel-air mixer system carburetor
- Electronic fuel injection system

The carburetor fuel-air mixer system uses either an air valve mixer or a venturi mixer combined with the pressure regulator to deliver fuel to the engine on demand.

The carburetor fuel-air mixer systems meter fuel in direct and constant proportion to the amount of air flowing through the mixer.

The electronic fuel injection system (Fig. 23) uses an electronic engine control unit (ECU) to optimize the engine airflow, natural gas fuel delivery, and ignition spark timing.

The ECU monitors engine performance and, based on monitored operating conditions, controls electrically-pulsed fuel injectors to precisely meter natural gas to the engine.

Electronic Fuel Injection System

JDPX5606

Fig. 23 — Natural Gas Electronic Fuel Injection System

A — Fuel Pressure Regulator
B — Regulator Fuel Inlet
C — Fuel Filter
D — Pressure Relief Valve
E — Coolant Outlet
F — Coolant Inlet
G — Gas Temperature Sensor
H — Fuel Metering Block
I — Fuel Injectors
J — Common Outlet Port
K — Gas Pressure Sensor
L — Fuel Lockoff Solenoid
M —Metering Block Fuel Inlet
N — Fuel-Air Mixer
O — Turbocharger

To better understand how a natural gas fuel injection system operates, let's trace the fuel flow through a typical system.

In operation, compressed natural gas flows from the individual fuel tanks into a common high-pressure fuel line. A pressure gauge and 1/4-turn shutoff valve is plumbed into the common fuel line. The pressure gauge measures the common fuel line pressure. The 1/4-turn shutoff valve shuts off the fuel flow to the common fuel line.

Fuel flows through the common fuel line into a high pressure lockoff and a coalescing filter.

The high-pressure fuel lockoff device is a valve that shuts off the fuel flow to the engine when the engine is not running, even if the ignition switch is in the ON position. The lockoff device opens when the ignition switch is in the ON position and the engine is either being started or is running.

The fuel flows through the coalescing filter to the fuel pressure regulator (Fig. 23). The pressure regulator reduces the high-pressure gas to the proper working pressure, approximately 130 psi, for the fuel system.

As the pressure drops, the gas expands and increases in volume. The rapid expansion of the gas through the regulator causes the gas to act as a refrigerant, absorbing heat and possibly causing icing of the regulator. To prevent icing, engine coolant is circulated through the pressure regulator. The heat from the engine coolant is transferred to the regulator.

A regulator pressure relief valve protects against overpressure problems. The pressure relief valve is connected to the vehicle vent line.

From the pressure regulator, fuel flows to the fuel metering valve. The fuel metering valve contains a low-pressure lockoff solenoid that is activated by the ignition switch and the electrically-pulsed injectors that deliver a precise amount of fuel to the engine.

The lockoff solenoid controls a normally closed valve that opens when the solenoid is energized. The lockoff solenoid will be closed any time the ignition is OFF or is ON but hasn't been in the START position for a specific period of time.

An electronic engine control unit (ECU) controls the "on" time (pulse width) of each pair of injectors to deliver the correct amount of fuel to the engine.

Natural gas pressure and temperature are measured at the metering valve. The ECU uses these measurements to adjust the injector pulse width to compensate for variations in the natural gas density.

A common outlet port from the fuel metering valve delivers fuel to the fuel-air mixer. The fuel-air mixer combines the fuel with air to form the fuel-air mixture for combustion.

The fuel-air mixer is located upstream of the throttle body. The throttle valve controls the volume of air and fuel flowing through the fuel-air mixer.

Natural Gas Fuel System Service

Most natural gas fuel systems require little preventive maintenance other than filter changes and periodically checking the system for leaks. Fuel system pressure should always be relieved before beginning any repair work on a natural gas fuel system. Refer to appropriate operator's manual for specific instructions on each machine for relieving system pressure before service.

Fuel System Safety

 CAUTION: Handle compressed natural gas (CNG) safely. CNG is methane (natural gas) stored at high pressure. It spreads into air quickly.

Natural gas fumes can cause sickness or death. Always work in a well-ventilated area.

Do not smoke when refueling or working on or around natural gas vehicles or equipment.

Keep natural gas vehicles away from sparks, flames, and electrical devices in operation, especially if you suspect a natural gas leak.

 CAUTION: Service compressed natural gas (CNG) and liquid natural gas (LNG) systems safely. Improper installation, service, or operation of natural gas storage and delivery components can result in fire, explosion, and/or serious injury.

Relieve natural gas fuel system pressure before working on the system. Properly tighten connections and check for leaks before pressurizing the fuel system.

 CAUTION: Protect against high-pressure. Natural gas fuel systems operate at high pressures. DO NOT disassemble or remove any natural gas fuel system components under pressure. Explosive separation of components and the escaping natural gas can cause serious injury.

Relieve natural gas fuel system pressure before disconnecting any fuel system component.

 CAUTION: Protect against extremely cold CNG/LNG leakage. Gas escaping from the natural gas fuel system is very cold. Contact with cold escaping gas or surrounding components can cause frostbite or skin damage.

Inspect for leaks by spraying a soap and water solution on joints, fittings, and other areas. Look for bubbles that indicate leakage from the system.

Fuel Pressure Leak-Off Procedure

Fuel Cylinder Manual Shutoff Valve

1/4-Turn Valve

Fuel Cylinder Manual Shutoff Valve

JDPX5792

Fig. 24 — Fuel Valve Locations on Typical Vehicle (CNG System Shown)

IMPORTANT: Always relieve the natural gas pressure by closing each fuel cylinder manual shutoff valve (Fig. 24). DO NOT relieve the natural gas pressure by closing the 1/4-turn valve.

NOTE: *(Fig. 24) is a typical application and does not show all of the shutoff valves. Refer to vehicle operator's manual to help locate all fuel cylinder shutoff valves.*

The valve is closed when turned fully clockwise viewed from the top, and open when turned counterclockwise viewed from the top.

NOTE: *The following is a sample procedure. Refer to the operator's manual for the specific procedure.*

1. Close all fuel cylinder manual shutoff valves.

2. If the engine WILL start, let it run until it dies from running out of fuel. Make sure pressure is completely relieved by attempting to start engine several more times.

3. If the engine WILL NOT start and run, make sure the vehicle is outside, away from heat, flames, or sparks.

4. Slowly loosen fuel metering block inlet fitting just until escaping gas is heard. Let fuel escape until fuel pressure is completely relieved.

Inspect Natural Gas Lines for Leaks

Natural gas tanks, valves, and lines need to be inspected periodically for damage and leaks.

LEAK CHECK PROCEDURE

1. Open fuel cylinder manual shutoff valves.

2. Cycle the ignition to the ON position for 3–4 seconds, then back to the OFF position.

3. Use a non-ammonia soap solution or a commercial leak detector solution and wet all fuel lines and fittings. If bubbles form, the fuel line or fitting is leaking.

4. If a leak is detected, inspect all lines and fittings for damage. Also check for damaged or missing O-rings.

5. Repair and repeat procedure until no leaks are detected.

Coalescing Filter

The coalescing filter should be replaced at intervals recommended by the manufacturer. The style and mounting locations of the filters vary.

Regulator Filter

If pressure regulator is equipped with a filter, it should be periodically inspected and replaced. The style and mounting locations of the filters vary. In the example shown, the filter is installed into the regulator housing.

JDPX5607

Fig. 25 — Fuel Filter Assembly (HFN04)
  A — Mounting Stud
  B — Cap Screw
  C — Fuel Filter Outlet Line
  D — Fuel Filter Assembly
  E — Drain Cock
  F — Fuel Filter Inlet Fitting

REMOVE FUEL FILTER ASSEMBLY

 CAUTION: Natural gas is highly flammable. DO NOT smoke while working on or near natural gas equipment. Natural gas fumes may cause sickness or death. Work in well-ventilated area, shut off natural gas supply, and relieve internal regulator pressure before servicing equipment.

1. Perform fuel pressure leak-off procedure (see "Fuel Pressure Leak-Off Procedure" on page 3-20).

2. Disconnect batteries.

3. Open filter drain cock and drain off any oil or water that is present. Close drain cock.

4. Disconnect natural gas fuel filter inlet line (shown removed) from inlet fitting.

5. Disconnect fuel filter outlet line.

6. Disconnect wires from mounting stud. Remove mounting stud.

7. Remove cap screw and remove fuel filter assembly.

8. Replace parts as necessary.

INSTALL FUEL FILTER ASSEMBLY

1. Install fuel filter assembly using cap screw and mounting stud. Tighten cap screw and mounting stud to specification.

2. Connect wires to mounting stud.

3. Connect fuel filter outlet line. Tighten line to specification.

Compressed Natural Gas (CNG) Fuel Storage

COMMON VENT PIPE

FUEL TANKS

COMMON FUEL LINE

MANUAL SHUTOFF VALVES AND PRESSURE RELIEF VALVES

PRESSURE GAUGE

1/4-TURN SHUTOFF VALVE

FRONT

JDPX5608

Fig. 26 — Compressed Natural Gas (CNG) Fuel Storage/Delivery System

The major parts of the compressed natural gas (CNG) fuel storage system are:

- Fuel tanks
- Relief valves
- Fuel lockoff valve
- Coalescing filter

Natural gas has a higher heating value per pound than gasoline, but being a gas, it has a much lower energy storage density than gasoline. Therefore, to provide a sufficient supply of fuel as compared to a gasoline fuel tank, natural gas must be compressed and stored in high-strength cylinders (Fig. 26). The result is that storage systems for compressed natural gas are bulkier and heavier than gasoline storage containers due to the increased volume and the need to withstand high pressures.

The fuel tanks (Fig. 26) may be constructed of high-strength steel or aluminum, reinforced with fiberglass or composite fibers. The gas is stored in the tanks at 3000 to 3600 psi.

Each tank is equipped with a manual shutoff valve and pressure relief valve. The pressure relief valve is designed to vent at either high pressure or high temperature. Each tank's relief valve is plumbed into a common vent pipe that routes the vented gas out of the vehicle.

A common fuel line connects the tanks to a high-pressure fuel lockoff device and a coalescing filter.

The fuel lockoff device is a valve that shuts off the fuel flow to the engine when the engine is not running, even if the ignition switch is in the ON position. The lockoff device opens when the ignition switch is in the ON position and the engine is either being started or is running.

A coalescing filter removes debris and contaminants from natural gas. The contaminants consist primarily of oil from natural gas compressors. If oil contaminants are allowed to enter the fuel system, the fuel system components can become restricted. The result may be a decrease in engine performance and even damage to engine components.

Liquefied Natural Gas (LNG) Fuel Storage

JDPX5609

Fig. 27 — Liquefied Natural Gas (LNG) Fuel Storage/Delivery System

The major parts of the Liquefied Natural Gas (LNG) fuel storage system are:

- Fuel tank
- Fill check valve
- Relief valves
- Regulator valve
- Fuel gauge
- Vaporizer

Natural gas is converted to an extremely dense gas, liquefied natural gas (LNG), by a cryogenic (or freezing) process in which the gas is cooled to –259°F (–126°C). The LNG fuel storage system is designed to receive and store the liquefied natural gas, then distribute vaporized gas to the engine.

The fuel tank is a cryogenic container designed to maintain the fuel in a liquid state (Fig. 27). The fuel tank is similar to the common Thermos bottle. It consists of an inner pressure vessel designed to hold the cold liquid positioned inside a larger outside vessel. The inner vessel is wrapped with special insulating material. The space between the two vessels is evacuated to form a superior insulation system.

This design prevents almost all heat from reaching the liquid. This allows the tank to keep the natural gas in a liquefied state for a period of time without excess pressure build-up.

Each tank is equipped with overfill protection and a one-way fill check valve at the liquid filling connection to provide safety during the fueling operation. During filling of the tank, the liquid is sprayed into the top of the inner vessel through the top fill spray header. The action of the spraying liquid will reduce the pressure within the vessel, eliminating the need to vent or recover vapor.

The tank filling is terminated automatically when the vessel becomes full. As the top spray ports are covered with liquid, the pressure quickly rises in the vessel to that of the delivery pressure. Once these pressures equalize, filling stops.

The fuel level inside a fuel tank is measured with an electronic fuel gauge. A probe inside the tank reads the column height of the liquid and sends a signal to an electronic converter module that is remotely mounted. The electronic module converts the signal and registers it on an electric fuel gauge.

LNG fuel tank systems operate at a specific pressure, which is maintained by a series of relief valves (Fig. 27). The primary relief valve is designed to safely vent any excess pressure in the tank. The secondary relief valve will open at a slightly higher pressure in the event that the primary relief valve malfunctions or cannot handle the volume of excess pressure.

To use LNG in a natural gas engine, two processes must take place:

1. The gas pressure in the fuel tank must be regulated in order to supply adequate fuel to the engine.

2. The cold liquid must be vaporized.

   Typically, LNG fuel storage systems rely on the pressure build-up that occurs as the temperature of the liquefied gas increases to force the fuel from the tank. For this reason, the temperature of the LNG must rise to about −205°F (−96°C) to maintain a 100 psi pressure in the tank.

3. The economizer regulator valve maintains a specified tank operating pressure.

When the operating pressure is higher than the selected pressure for the tank, the economizer regulator will open (Fig. 28, top). The gas supplied to the engine will be withdrawn from the vapor space in the top of the tank. The gas will travel through the economizer regulator to the vaporizer where it will be warmed before it reaches the pressure regulator.

The action of removing gas from the top of the tank reduces the tank's pressure. When the tank operating pressure is reduced below the selected pressure level, the economizer regulator will close (Fig. 28, bottom). Liquid will then be forced from the bottom of the tank and into the vaporizer.

The vaporizer is nothing more than a heat exchanger located between the fuel tank and the engine. In the fuel vaporization process, warm engine coolant is circulated through the vaporizer. As the LNG flows into the vaporizer, the heat from the coolant turns the liquid into a gas. The gaseous fuel can then be supplied to the engine.

JDPX5610

Fig. 28 — Liquefied Natural Gas (LNG) Fuel Delivery

Diesel Fuel Systems

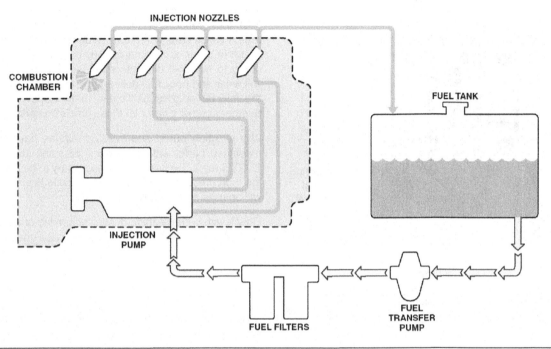

Fig. 29 — Diesel Fuel Systems (Distributor-Type Shown)

The prime job of the diesel fuel system is to inject a precise amount of atomized and pressurized fuel into each engine cylinder at the proper time (Fig. 29).

Combustion in the diesel engine occurs when this charge of fuel is mixed with hot compressed air. No electrical spark is used (as in gasoline engine).

The major parts of the diesel fuel system are:

- Fuel tank — stores fuel
- Fuel transfer pump — pushes fuel through filters to injection pump
- Fuel filters — clean the fuel
- Injection pump — times, measures, and delivers fuel under pressure to cylinders
- Injection nozzles — atomize and spray fuel into cylinders

These parts in a basic system are shown in (Fig. 29).

Operation

In operation, fuel flows by gravity pressure from the fuel tank to the transfer pump (Fig. 29).

The transfer pump pushes the fuel through the filters, where it is cleaned.

The fuel is then pushed on to the injection pump where it is put under high pressure and delivered to each injection nozzle at the exact time needed.

The injection nozzles atomize the fuel and spray it into the combustion chamber of each cylinder.

Various kinds of injection systems are used on different engines. All systems have a low-pressure side and a high-pressure side as shown in (Fig. 29). The low-pressure side is from the fuel tank to the injection pump. The high-pressure side is from the injection pump to the injectors. The high pressure created by the injection pump forces the fuel through the injectors, making a fine mist as fuel is sprayed into the cylinders.

The injection pump times and meters the injection of fuel into each cylinder at the precise moment for good combustion. Note that one type of injection system has a combination injection pump and nozzle which is actuated by a rocker arm similar to those that operate the intake and exhaust valves.

Most diesel fuel systems have a fuel return line, which returns excess fuel from the injectors or from the injection pump to the fuel tank. The excess fuel is used on some systems to help cool and lubricate the pump and injectors.

Filter systems vary from one filter to three filters. If there is only one filter it must be serviced regularly and carefully because there are no other filters to help clean the fuel.

Additional filters, such as second-stage and third-stage filters, are often used to ensure that water and dirt particles will be removed from the fuel (Fig. 30). Second- and third-stage filters also require careful attention, but at longer intervals.

Fig. 30 — Two-Stage Diesel Fuel Filter

Air Bleed Screws

Fuel Outlet

Fuel Inlet

Cotton String Element (First Stage)

Paper Element (Second Stage)

Sediment Bowls

Screen

Drain Screws

JDPX5455

Importance of Service

The diesel fuel system requires careful service in order to keep it operating properly. The injection pump and nozzles are precision parts which can be damaged by small particles of dirt or other contaminants. Any damage to these parts is costly to repair. If dirt enters the injection pump, the pump will wear and poor fuel delivery will result. Dirt will also clog the injector nozzles and make them inoperable. Water is another enemy; it can rust these precision parts.

The injection pump and injector nozzles have very finely machined parts, with clearances as small as 0.0001 inch (0.0025 mm). These parts are necessary to develop and use the high pressures required at the nozzle tips so the engine will operate properly and efficiently.

Check with your machine dealer for service of injector parts. Not all dealers are equipped to service these precision machined parts and it may be necessary for the manufacturer to service them.

It is not possible to eliminate all moisture and dirt particles from the fuel. However, dirt and moisture can be reduced by good maintenance so that your engine will give thousands of hours of operation without repair to the injection pump or the injectors.

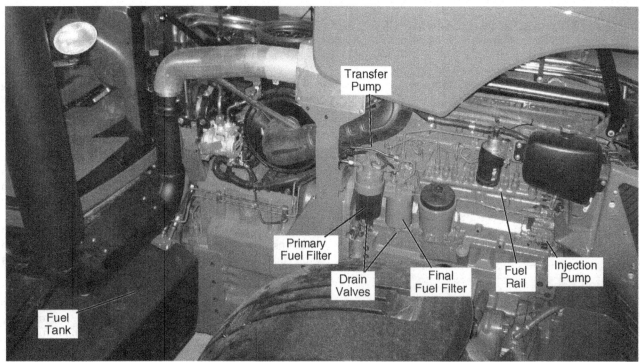

Fig. 31 — Removing Daily Deposits From Diesel System

Transfer Pump

Primary Fuel Filter

Drain Valves

Final Fuel Filter

Fuel Rail

Injection Pump

Fuel Tank

JDPX5617

Servicing the Diesel Fuel System

 CAUTION: Modern diesel fuel systems operate under high pressure. Follow all manufacturer's procedures and safety instructions for relieving system pressure prior to servicing fuel filters or any other fuel system components.

Because servicing the injection pump and injector nozzles require special tools and equipment, you should be mainly concerned with the other components, on the low-pressure side, such as the fuel filters, fuel sediment bowl and fuel tank. If these units are properly serviced, little trouble should be experienced with the injection pump and nozzles.

Tools and Materials Needed

To service the low-pressure side of the system, the following tools and materials are needed.

- Clean, lint-free cloths
- Container of cleaning solvent (not gasoline)
- Container to catch waste fuel
- Set of wrenches (inch or metric, as required)
- Small, soft bristle scrub brush
- Replaceable filters, if needed

Testing Diesel Fuel

A fuel analysis program can help to monitor the quality of diesel fuel. The fuel analysis can provide critical data such as cetane number, fuel type, sulfur content, water content, appearance, suitability for cold weather operations, bacteria, cloud point, acid number, particulate contamination, and whether the fuel meets specification.

Contact your John Deere dealer for more information on diesel fuel analysis.

Importance of Water and Dirt Removal

Water and sediment can seriously damage a diesel fuel injection system. Therefore, diesel engines have rather elaborate systems for removing such impurities from the fuel.

- Sediment grinds away the finely fitted parts of the injection pump.
- Water causes the parts to rust (a very small amount of rust can cause serious damage).
- Water interferes with the proper feeding of fuel and causes rough running of the engine.

Water is more of a problem in diesel fuel than it is in gasoline. Water separates from gasoline rather readily but the weight of diesel fuel is so near the weight of water that they mix readily and separate slowly. With the machine motionless during the night, water has time to separate from the diesel fuel and settle to the bottom of the tank. The trapped water should be removed from the system each morning.

Machine manufacturers take advantage of this situation and have provided for removing the water as shown in (Fig. 31).

Removing Daily Deposits of Water and Sediment

Use the directions in the operator's manual for your machine. Here are instructions for a typical unit.

1. If there is water or an excess of foreign matter in the fuel pump sediment bowl, close the fuel tank shutoff valve and remove the sediment bowl.
2. Clean the bowl and strainer in solvent and wipe dry.
3. Install the bowl and strainer, using a good gasket.
4. Open the shutoff valve and bleed the filters by working the hand primer on the injection pump (see "Bleeding Air from Fuel System after Service").
5. If there is water or an excess of foreign matter at the bottom of a fuel filter bowl (Fig. 31), loosen the drain plug for that filter and drain the water or foreign matter from the filter. Bleed the filters.
6. If water was present in the fuel pump bowl or a fuel filter bowl, drain all the water from the fuel tank to prevent the water from plugging the filter. A sump at the bottom of the fuel tank traps the water.
7. To drain the fuel tank sump, open the drain cock. Normally, only the fuel pump sediment bowl and the filter sediment bowls need to be checked every day. If they are clean, the system should be okay. If they are dirty, perform all the maintenance steps given above.

Servicing Fuel Filters

Refer to your operator's manual for the filter change interval. Normally, a first-stage filter should be changed every 500 hours, and the second-stage filter every 1000 hours or each season. The condition of your fuel will determine whether or not you have to change more frequently.

Fig. 32 — Removing Diesel Fuel Filter

Service the filters as follows:

⚠ **CAUTION: Modern diesel fuel systems operate under high pressure. Follow all manufacturer's procedures and safety instructions for relieving system pressure prior to servicing fuel filters or any other fuel system components.**

1. Be sure fuel shutoff valve is turned off (if equipped). Clean outside of filter and area surrounding filter.

2. Drain fuel from filter if the filter has a drain.

3. Remove filter or filter bowl (Fig. 32). Filters may be held in place with one or more stud bolts or a clip, or be of the spin-on type.

4. If the filter is not the disposable type, clean it in a pan of cleaning solvent (not gasoline).

5. Inspect it for ruptures or damage. Replace element if it is not in excellent condition. ALWAYS replace a disposable filter.

6. Clean inside of filter bowl or body (unless it is a self-contained unit). Use a brush or lint-free cloth for cleaning. Be sure that it is absolutely clean.

7. Install cleaned filter or new disposable filter element. Be sure to use new gaskets where separate gaskets are used. Secure filter to filter body.

8. Replace or clean the second-stage filter if necessary. (The dual filters shown in (Fig. 32) are replaced in pairs.)

9. Replace the drain plug or tighten the drain valve (if opened).

10. Open the fuel shutoff valve (if equipped).

11. Bleed the fuel filters if instructed.

Bleeding Air from Fuel System after Service

Fig. 33 — Bleed Plug for Removing Air from Fuel Filters

Each time you drain the fuel lines or filters, air is left in them. Unless removed, this air may form an air lock when you try to start the engine. This will prevent a normal supply of fuel from reaching the injection pump, and the engine may not start or may run poorly.

Many fuel systems do not require bleeding after a filter change. On some systems, it is recommended to fill the new filters with clean diesel fuel before installation, which reduces the amount of air in the system. Some are equipped with "self-bleeding" fuel systems. The fuel system in (Fig. 31) is equipped with an electric transfer pump mounted on top of the primary fuel filter. The filters are not filled before installation. Turning the key to the ON position starts the electric pump which primes the fuel system. A sample bleed procedure is given below. Follow the instructions given in the machine operator's manual for each application for specific procedures, safety instructions, and bleed locations.

Before bleeding air, be sure fuel tank is nearly full to provide enough fuel and pressure to bleed the system.

Bleed air from the system as follows:

1. If you have changed more than one filter, bleed the filter closest to the fuel tank first.

2. Open bleed plug or plugs on top of filters (Fig. 33).

Fig. 34 — Hand Priming Pump for Bleeding Air from System

3. Open fuel supply valve. This will force air through the bleed plug and replace the air in the lines and filters with fuel (on gravity-flow systems). Some systems are equipped with a hand priming pump or lever to be used in removing air (Fig. 34). Push the hand primer several strokes until fuel free of air bubbles escapes from the bleed plug hole at the filters.

4. Close bleed plug after all air is removed from filters.

5. If air lock is still present (the engine may not start or will run poorly), you will also have to bleed the injection lines (Fig. 35). (Normally, you can bleed half the injection lines and the others will bleed themselves by running the engine until it runs smoothly).

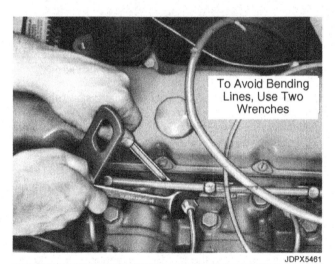

Fig. 35 — Bleeding Injection Lines at Injectors (If Necessary)

⚠ CAUTION: Escaping diesel fuel under pressure can penetrate the skin, causing injury. Before disconnecting lines, be sure to relieve all pressure. Before applying pressure again, be sure that all connections are retightened after bleeding. If an accident occurs, see a doctor immediately. Any fluid injected into the skin must be removed within a few hours or gangrene may result. Doctors unfamiliar with this type of injury should reference a knowledgeable medical source.

6. Loosen injection line nuts only one turn to avoid excessive spray. Use two wrenches as shown in (Fig. 35) to avoid bending or twisting fuel line.

7. Crank the engine with the starter until fuel without foam flows around the connectors.

8. Carefully tighten the line connectors only until snug and free of leaks.

9. Start the engine and run it until it runs smoothly. This will bleed the other injectors.

NOTE: Some diesel fuel systems have a separate fuel pump with primer (Fig. 36). On these systems, loosen filter bleed plugs and pump out air using primer lever on pump. Then bleed air from lines if necessary.

Fig. 36 — Bleeding Air from Diesel Fuel System (Alternate System)

Servicing of Diesel Injection Pumps and Nozzles

Injection pumps and nozzles require special tools and equipment (Fig. 37), so go to your dealer or service center for all adjustments and repair of precision injection units.

Mechanical diesel injection nozzles can be tested by a dealer or service center for correct opening pressure, leakage, chatter, and proper spray pattern to determine if the injection nozzle is functioning correctly.

Fig. 37 — Injection Pump and Nozzle Service Equipment

Engine Governors

The governor is a device which automatically controls the speed of the engine under varying loads (Fig. 38).

Governors do these jobs:

- Maintain a selected speed
- Limit the slow and fast speeds
- Shut down the engine when it overspeeds

(Fig. 39) shows how the governor keeps the engine at a constant speed when the machine is going uphill or downhill. The governor on the engine automatically regulates speed at whatever setting you select on the speed control (throttle) lever.

④ Result: Engine Speed Is Controlled under Variable Loads

① Engine Speed Varies with Load

③ Fuel-Air Mixture Is Changed

② Governor Reacts

JDPX5463

Fig. 38 — Governing System (Gasoline Engine with Centrifugal Governor Shown

2000 rpm   3000 rpm   2000 rpm   3000 rpm

Without Governor (Fixed Throttle)

2000 rpm   2000 rpm   2000 rpm   2000 rpm

With Governor (Maintains Same Speed)

JDPX5464

Fig. 39 — What the Governor Does for the Machine Engine

Most operator's manuals give detailed instructions on how to adjust the governor for high no-load speed. However, some manuals have no governor adjustment and others warn against making any adjustments.

Some engines have governors with the adjustments sealed inside the governor housing to discourage operators from making adjustments.

Since there is some question about whether operators should adjust governors, this discussion does not include procedures for doing the job. But it is intended to help you understand how a governor works, and the importance of proper governor adjustment. This understanding will be helpful whether you service it, or have it done by a competent serviceman.

Importance of Governor Adjustment

Machine manufacturers test their engines and select a maximum speed for each model that provides satisfactory power in relation to fuel consumption, wear, and other factors. The speed selected varies with different makes and models. The maximum idle speed recommended for your machine is given in the operator's manual. It is the one you normally use for checking your governor.

Your operator's manual may also give a full-load speed. It will be less than the high-idle speed even though the speed control lever is in the same position. As load is added, there is some loss of engine speed that the governor does not recover. For example, an engine that has a high no-load speed of 2700 revolutions per minute (rpm) may have a full-load speed of 2500 rpm. The speed loss is different with different engines.

- If a machine is operated much faster than the top speed specified, wear increases rapidly.

- If the engine is operated much slower than the manufacturer recommends, there is less power available and operating costs increase.

If only one high no-load speed is given, the governor is usually considered as being in satisfactory adjustment if the top engine speed is within 20 rpm (faster or slower) of that speed. However, some manuals will indicate a speed range such as 2500 to 2600 rpm. The governor is considered to be in proper adjustment if the high-idle speed is within this range.

Operation of Governor

After you set the speed control lever, the job of the governor is to adjust the amount of fuel-air mixture (fuel only for diesel engines) that the engine receives so the engine speed remains approximately the same even though the load varies. Consequently, the governor must be sensitive to speed changes. (Fig. 40) shows a simplified governor control. Note that the governor is mounted on the engine camshaft where it is directly affected by any slight change in engine speed.

On spark-ignition engines, the governor controls the fuel-air mixture by opening and closing the throttle (butterfly) valve. When you open the speed-control lever (Fig. 40), tension is exerted on the governor control spring. The spring tension turns the governor lever clockwise, opening the throttle valve. More fuel-air mixture can enter the engine, causing it to speed up.

Speed Control Lever Changed To Higher Speed Setting

As Engine Speeds Up, Governor Stabilizes It

JDPX5465

Fig. 40 — Operation of Governor in Controlling Engine Speed

But when the engine speeds up, centrifugal force acts on the flyweights pushing them outward (Fig. 40). They are hinged so that when they move outward, the governor drive plate is pushed out. This rotates the governor arm which, in turn, moves the governor lever in a counterclockwise direction. As a result, the butterfly valve tends to close. This would slow the engine speed except for the tension of the governor control spring. But a balance is reached immediately between the force of the flyweights and the tension of the governor control spring. This balance holds the throttle valve at the proper position to maintain a constant engine speed.

Let's assume more load is put on the engine. The engine speed slows, centrifugal force is reduced on the flyweights, and they pull in. This removes some of the pressure on the drive plate against the governor arm, allowing spring tension to turn the governor lever in a clockwise direction (Fig. 40). The throttle valve opens further, allows more fuel-air mixture into the engine and increases horsepower output (lugging power) without increasing engine speed.

With the throttle valve open further, more fuel-air mixture is fed to the engine. Engine speed tends to increase, but any increase in speed causes the flyweights to move out. This overcomes enough spring tension to set up a new balance between the governor and the governor control spring, which keeps the engine speed constant.

At higher engine speeds, your machine has the capacity to meet a wide range of power demands. This is why it is important to set the speed control lever at a high enough speed to take care of the maximum power needed for a job. When you do this, the engine is ready to start lugging the instant the governor action feeds more fuel into it. If your setting is too low, there is not enough tension on the governor spring to allow the engine to come up to full power.

Governing of Diesels

The operating principle of the governor on a diesel engine is the same as that for a spark-ignition engine, except the diesel engine governor controls only the fuel going to the engine. This is done by various means, such as an arrangement that shortens or lengthens the stroke of the injection pump to meet varying load conditions; or a master valve that meters the fuel supply to meet the varying power demands.

The built-in centrifugal governor in a typical diesel injection pump is shown in (Fig. 41).

JDPX5466

Fig. 41 — Governor in Diesel Injection Pump

Maintaining the Governor

A governor in proper condition will respond quickly to a change in load conditions and will maintain, the correct engine speed without surging. Note the delicate balance that exists between the governor control spring and the governor flyweights. If the spring loses tension, if the governor parts wear or if any of the linkage that connects the mechanism starts to bind, the governor will not work properly.

Check the operator's manual for guidance on whether you should attempt to adjust it or take it to a serviceman.

Test Yourself

Questions

1. (Fill in blank.) Gasoline fuels with higher octane ratings have the least tendency to produce _____ in the engine.

2. Match the two items at left with the definitions at right.

   a. No. 1-D Diesel Fuel

   b. No. 2-D Diesel Fuel

   1. Used in high-speed engines in services involving relatively high loads and uniform speeds.

   2. Used in high-speed engine in services involving frequent and relatively wide variations in loads and speeds.

3. What causes knock in diesel engines?

   a. The fuel igniting too slowly.

   b. The fuel igniting too fast.

4. Name the four basic parts of an LP-gas fuel system.

5. Name two gases that are combined to make LP-gas.

6. What is the number one enemy of the diesel fuel system?

7. Name the three jobs of the engine governor.

8. What are the three basic parts of the low-pressure fuel system on a diesel engine?

9. What part of a diesel fuel system will require the most service by the operator?

Engine Lubrication Systems

41

1. Oil Film Reduces Friction and Wear

2. Oil Cools Moving Parts

3. Oil Helps the Rings to Seal

4. Oil Cleanses the Parts

JDPX5491

Fig. 1 — Lubricating System on Typical Engine

Introduction

When agricultural engines were first used, you could have lubricated the engine with an oil can and a single type of oil. Most oil was supplied in three grades — light, medium and heavy.

But in today's high-speed engines, all this has changed. Speeds, pressures, and temperatures have all increased.

Special oils have been developed for each type of engine, for each type of machine, and for each season.

As a result, lubrication has changed from a simple chore to a science of preventive maintenance.

What Engine Oils Must Do

To keep today's engines running, engine oils must:

• Reduce friction and wear.

• Cool moving parts.

• Help seal the cylinders.

• Keep the parts clean.

To do these jobs, engine oil must also:

• Keep a protective oil film on moving parts.

• Resist high temperatures.

• Resist corrosion and rusting.

• Prevent ring sticking.

• Prevent sludge formation.

• Flow easily at low temperatures.

• Resist foaming.

• Resist breakdown after prolonged use.

Importance Of Service

Changing Engine Crankcase Oil

JDPX5492

Fig. 2 — Effect of Poor Maintenance — Piston Oil Control Ring Plugged by Oil Sludge

Oil loses many of its good lubricating qualities as it gets dirty and its additives wear out. Acid formations, sludge, varnish, and engine deposits contaminate oil and make it unfit for continued use. This in turn can harm vital engine parts (Fig. 2).

On the other hand, just because crankcase oil is black, doesn't mean it's time for an oil change. Additives in the oil are supposed to clean and hold deposits in suspension for removal when the oil is drained.

Changing the oil at a time BEFORE the additives wear out will protect the engine against sludge. For the operator, this time is practically impossible to determine. That's why the best policy is to follow the manufacturer's recommendations on oil and filter changes.

New or rebuilt engines require oil and filter changes after a specified break-in period. Performing this service on time is very important, since foreign materials accumulate in the oil at a faster rate during initial operation than when the engine is broken in.

When changing the oil and filter on any engine, always warm up the engine first. This way the contaminants and foreign materials are mixed with the oil and are drained out with it.

Replacing some oil filters requires installing new gaskets or sealing rings. Be sure the sealing surfaces on the engine and filter are clean.

After installing the filter and filling the engine with oil, run the engine and check for possible filter leaks.

Keep a maintenance record of all oil and filter changes to be sure of regular engine service. Some operator's manuals provide a chart for such record keeping, or use a sticker on the cab window or hood as a reminder (Fig. 3).

JDPX5493

Fig. 3 — Record All Oil and Filter Changes

Preventing Contamination of Oil

Oil contamination will reduce engine life more than any other factor. Some sources of contamination are obvious, while others are not.

Let's review some of these sources of contamination and what can be done about them.

1. The most obvious source of contamination is the storing and handling of the oil itself. Store lubricants in a clean, enclosed storage area. Keep all covers on and cap the spouts on containers when not in use. These practices not only keep dirt out of the oil, but also reduce condensation of water caused by atmospheric changes.

2. Another obvious source is dust that is breathed into the engine with combustion air. It is very important that the air cleaner be cleaned or replaced regularly (see Chapter 2, "Engine Intake and Exhaust Systems").

3. A major source of contamination is a cold engine. When the engine is cold, its fuel burning efficiency is greatly reduced. Partially burned fuel blows by the piston rings and into the crankcase. Oxidation of this fuel in the oil forms a very harmful varnish which collects on engine parts.

   To help prevent this, be sure the thermostat is working to provide fast engine warm-up (see Chapter 5, "Engine Cooling Systems"). An overchoked or misfiring engine will also create contamination from unburned fuel.

Water created by a cold engine contaminates the oil, too. Water vapor, a normal product of combustion, tends to condense on cold cylinder walls. This condensation is also blown by the rings into the crankcase. The engine must warm up before this condensation problem is eliminated.

Water not only causes rusting of steel and iron surfaces, but it can combine with oxidized oil and carbon to form sludge. This sludge can very effectively plug oil screens and passages.

Contamination from a cold engine can be prevented by:

a. Properly warming up the engine before applying a load.

b. Making sure the engine is brought up to operating temperature each time it is used.

c. Using the proper thermostat in the cooling system to warm up the engine as quickly as possible.

4. Antifreeze can be another sludge-forming source of contamination. It can also dilute the oil. To guard against antifreeze contamination:

a. Tighten cylinder head bolts to specified torque during an overhaul.

b. Periodically check the cooling system for internal leaks (see Chapter 5, "Engine Cooling Systems").

c. Guard against detonation and improper use of starting fluids in diesel engine (both can result in head gasket damage).

Other problems can also cause oil contamination:

5. Oxidation is not an obvious source of contamination, but is a very real one. Oxidation occurs when the hydrocarbons in the oil combine with oxygen in the air to produce organic acids. Besides being highly corrosive, these acids create harmful sludges and varnish deposits.

6. Carbon particles are another contaminant created by the normal operation of the engine. The particles are created when oil around the upper cylinder walls is burned during combustion. Excessive deposits can cause the piston rings to stick in their grooves.

7. Engine wear creates contaminants. Tiny metal particles are constantly being worn off bearings and other parts. These particles tend to reduce the oil's effectiveness.

All sources of contamination cannot be eliminated. What, then, can be done to protect the engine?

Start by using a good-quality oil with the proper additives (Fig. 4). Additives are put in the oil for a specific reason, based on the service expected for the oil.

8. It is important to use American Petroleum Institute CJ-4 low ash oil standard of oil on equipment produced after 1993; it will be less likely to clog particulate filters that will be standard OEM equipment after 2007.

JDPX5494

Fig. 4 — Good Quality Oil Already Has Important Additives

Here are some of the important additives:

Anti-corrosion additives protect metal surfaces from corrosive attack. These work with oxidation inhibitors.

Oxidation inhibitor additives keep oil from oxidizing at high temperatures. They prevent the oil from absorbing oxygen, thereby preventing varnish and sludge formations.

Anti-rust additives prevent rusting of metal parts during storage periods, downtime, or even overnight. They form a protective coating which repels water droplets and protects the metal. These additives also help to neutralize harmful acids.

Detergent additives help keep metal surfaces clean and prevent deposits. Particles of carbon and oxidized oil are held suspended in the oil. The suspended contaminants are then removed from the system when the oil is drained. Black oil is evidence that the oil is helping to keep the engine clean by carrying the particles in the oil rather than letting them accumulate as sludge.

However, remember that additives eventually wear out. To prevent any problems, drain the oil before the additives are completely depleted. Your operator's manual will tell you when you should change oil. However, watch both the hours of operation and the elapsed time. Some additives in oil lose their effectiveness after a period of time, even if the engine has not been operated much.

Also, service engine oil filters at recommended intervals. This is usually at the same time the crankcase oil is drained and replaced.

If you use quality oil of the type recommended for the engine, other additive compounds should normally not be added to the engine crankcase.

Buy oil only from the manufacturer of your engine or from a reliable oil supplier. Be wary of claims of "miracle" additives, or oils which "won't wear out." Such oils could damage your engine and void the engine warranty.

Finally, keep the fuel, cooling, ignition, intake, and exhaust systems in good condition so that the fuel is efficiently burned.

Operation of Lubrication System

Fig. 5 — Major Parts of Engine Lubricating System

The major parts of the system are:

- Oil pump
- Crankcase
- Oil cooler (if used)
- Oil filter
- Pressure regulating valve
- Pressure gauge

The oil pump pushes oil through the system (Fig. 5). A reserve of oil is stored in the crankcase for circulation through the system. At the oil filter, dirt is taken out of the oil to help keep it clean. Oil passages take the oil to engine parts where they can provide lubrication and cooling and carry away dirt and deposits. Pressure of the oil is regulated by the pressure regulating valve, which is usually adjustable. After oil moves through the whole system it comes back to the crankcase reservoir again. Finally, the pressure gauge tells the operator if engine oil pressure is normal.

The system described above is a full force-feed type. Let's now look at the major types of systems.

Type Of Systems

An engine lubricating system may be classified as:

- Circulating splash
- Internal force feed and splash
- Full internal force feed

The type of system used depends largely upon the size and design of the engine.

Circulating Splash System

Fig. 6 — Circulating Splash System

In the circulating splash system, an oil pump supplies oil to a splash pan located under the crankshaft (Fig. 6). As the connecting rods revolve, scoops on the ends of the rods dip into troughs in the splash pan, creating the oil splash.

The splashing oil lubricates the moving parts nearby. Other parts are lubricated more by oil mist than by the oil splash itself. This mist is created as the connecting rods spin.

The circulating splash system must have:

1. Proper oil level in the pan
2. Suitable oil for good splashing

There must be enough oil in the troughs of the splash pan for the connecting rods to splash. The oil pump must be working properly to provide this oil.

Because the oil must splash and flow freely, heavy oil will not work. Use only oil of the viscosity recommended by the engine manufacturer.

This system is used mainly on smaller engines.

Internal Force-Feed and Splash System

In the internal force feed and splash system, the pump forces oil directly to a main oil gallery in the engine block rather than to a splash pan.

From the main oil gallery, the oil is forced through passages to the main bearings, connecting rod bearings, camshaft bearings, rocker arm shaft, filter, and pressure sending unit.

The oil escaping from the bearings creates a mist which also lubricates the upper cylinder walls, pistons, and pins.

Pressure of the lubricating oil can usually be adjusted in these systems.

Full Internal Force-Feed System

The full internal force feed system goes one step farther than the system above. Oil is forced not only to the crankshaft bearings, rocker arm shaft, filter and pressure sending unit, but also to the piston pin bearings.

Fig. 7 — Full Internal Force Feed System

The piston pin bushings are lubricated through drilled passages in the connecting rods (Fig. 7). The cylinder walls and pistons are lubricated by oil escaping from the piston pin bushings or the connecting rod bearings.

The force-feed system has one prime need: good oil pressure.

Sufficient oil pressure is required to pump the oil long distances and through many passages. The required pressure for most engines is 25 to 40 psi (170 to 275 kPa), but it may go as high as 65 psi (450 kPa). If the oil pressure drops too low on the gauge or if you receive a low pressure warning, shut off the engine immediately and determine the cause.

Oil pressure is normally adjusted at a pressure regulating valve (Fig. 7).

This type of system is widely used in today's agricultural engines.

Oil Pump

Fig. 8 — Engine Oil Pump in Operation

Pumps for engine lubrication are usually gear types, mechanically driven by the engine. Usually the pump is driven from the camshaft or from the crankshaft. In some large engines, an electric motor is used to drive the auxiliary pump.

The pumps push oil through the system and also trap it so that normal pressure can be built up in the system.

The common external gear pump has two gears in mesh, closely fitted inside a housing (Fig. 8). The drive shaft drives one gear, which in turn drives the other gear. The machined surfaces of the outer housing are used to seal the gears.

As the gears rotate and come out of mesh, they trap inlet oil between the gear teeth and the housing. The trapped oil is carried around to the outlet chamber. As the gears mesh again, they form a seal which prevents oil from backing up to the inlet. The oil is forced out at the outlet and sent through the system.

Oil Filters and Filtration Systems

Oil contamination reduces engine life more than any other factor. To help combat this, oil filters are designed into all modern engine lubricating systems.

Let's look first at the two basic types of filters, then at two types of filtering systems.

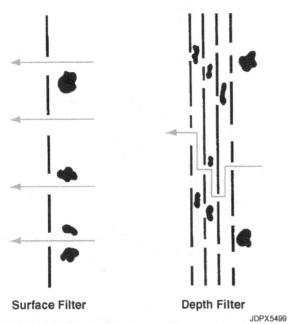

Surface Filter   Depth Filter

JDPX5499

Fig. 9 — Surface and Depth Filters Compared

Types of Filters

Filters are classified as either surface-type filters or depth-type filters depending on the way the oil moves through them (Fig. 9).

JDPX5500

Fig. 10 — Wire Mesh Filter

JDPX5501

Fig. 11 — Metal Edge Filter

Surface filters have a single surface that catches and removes dirt particles larger than the holes in the filter. Dirt is strained or sheared from the oil and stopped outside the filter as oil passes through the holes in a straight path. Many of the large particles will fall to the bottom of the reservoir or filter container, but eventually enough particles will wedge in the holes of the filter to prevent further filtration. Then the filter must be cleaned or replaced.

A surface filter may be made of fine wire mesh (Fig. 10), stacked metal or paper disks, metal ribbon wound edgewise to form a cylinder (Fig. 11), cellulose material molded to the shape of a filter, or accordion pleated paper (Fig. 12).

JDPX5502

Fig. 12 — Pleated Paper Filter

Depth filters, in contrast to the surface type, use a large volume of filter material to make the oil move in many different directions before it finally gets into the lubrication system. The filter made of cotton waste shown in (Fig. 13) is an example of a depth filter.

JDPX5503

Fig. 13 — Depth Filter (Cotton Waste Type)

Now let's look at the complete filtration system.

Types Of Filtration Systems

There are two types of oil filtering systems. They are:

- By-pass system.
- Full-flow system.

Both are shown in (Fig. 14). Note in (Fig. 14A) that in the bypass system only a portion of the oil moves through the filter as it leaves the pump. The rest goes directly to the engine bearings. With this type only about 1/10th to about 1/30th of the oil is by-passed through the filter at any one time. As the filter becomes contaminated, less of the oil goes through and more goes around.

With the full-flow system, as shown in (Fig. 14B), all of the oil moves through the filter unless it is partly or completely blocked because of a dirty filter or cold oil. In that case, oil pressure builds up in the filter until the bypass valve is forced open, permitting unfiltered oil to flow around the filter and directly to the engine bearings. This protects the engine against loss of needed oil.

The full-flow filter, as part of an internal force-feed system, is used on most modern agricultural engines.

JDPX5504

Fig. 14 — Two Types of Engine Oil Filters Compared

Oil Coolers

Lubrication systems of many engines use an oil cooler to help remove the heat created by the engine. Most coolers are the oil-to-water cooling type, using engine coolant to dissipate unwanted heat from the engine crankcase oil.

The oil cooler may be mounted inside the crankcase or on the outside of the engine block.

The full-flow filter as part of an internal force-feed system is used on most modern agricultural engines.

Operation of Oil Cooler

JDPX5505

Fig. 15 — Operation of Engine Oil Cooler

As shown in (Fig. 15), coolant circulates around the plates in the cooler, while the engine oil flows inside the plates. Heat from the oil is conducted through the plates to the coolant, which carries it to the radiator for dissipation.

Another cooler (not shown) uses a small radiator core. The oil is pumped through the core and coolant is circulated around it.

A bypass valve is used with some oil coolers to ensure circulation of the oil if the cooler should become clogged.

Selecting Engine Oils

If you are to receive the best performance possible from a machine, you must use lubricants of the highest quality. The savings to be gained with lower-quality oils are at best small in relation to your over-all operating costs.

JDPX5506

Fig. 16 — Selecting an Engine Oil

How can you be assured of obtaining an oil of high quality and one that's right for the job?

First, follow your operator's manual recommendations for engine oil (Fig. 16). Second, choose oil from a reliable supplier — a reputable brand of oil.

To select the proper oil, you must be able to identify it. Descriptions such as "viscosity" and "service classification" are used to identify types of engine oils.

The Society of Automotive Engineers (SAE) has established the **Viscosity** designation which is a measure of the fluidity of an oil at a given temperature.

The American Petroleum Institute (API) established the **Service Classification** designation which identifies the engine service design of the oil.

Let's look at how oils are rated by these two organizations.

SAE Viscosity

As we stated, SAE rates the oil viscosity — or ability to flow at a given temperature. The lighter or more fluid oils intended for winter use are specified at 0°F (–18°C) and carry a 5W, 10W, or 20W symbol. Heavier oils for warmer operation are specified at 210°F (99°C) and carry SAE 30 and 40 symbols.

Oils vary in viscosity as temperatures change — becoming more fluid as temperatures increase and less fluid as temperatures decrease. The temperature effect on viscosity is not the same for all oils, and a measure of this is often important to the user.

JDPX5507

Fig. 17 — A Multi-Viscosity Oil Can Replace Several Single Viscosity Oils (When Recommended)

Some oils are compounded to behave as light oils at cold temperatures and as heavier oils at high temperatures. These oils are called multi-viscosity oils and include, for example, 5W-30 (Fig. 17). One multi-viscosity oil can replace several single-grade oils. Multi-viscosity oils are preferred as they give protection at both high and low temperatures.

SAE viscosity numbers are widely used as a means of identifying and classifying lubricating oil, and today are found on nearly all cans or drums of oil marketed in the United States (Fig. 18).

Single-Viscosity Oil   Multi-Viscosity Oil

JDPX5508

Fig. 18 — Viscosity Is Marked on Oil Containers

Each number indicates a permissible range or limit of viscosity at specified temperatures. No attempt is made to define the oil's quality, additive content, performance value or suitability for specified service conditions. Therefore, the SAE viscosity should not be the only factor considered when selecting an oil.

Table 2 shows one equipment manufacturer's oil viscosity recommendations for four-cycle diesel engines operating at various temperature levels. Note the upper temperature limits recommended for multi-viscosity oils in industrial equipment applications.

Diesel Engine Oil — Interim Tier 4, Final Tier 4, Stage IIIB, and Stage IV

Use oil viscosity based on the expected air temperature range during the period between oil changes.

John Deere Plus-50™ II is the recommended engine oil.

Extended service intervals may apply when John Deere Plus-50™ II engine oil is used. Refer to the engine oil drain interval table and consult your John Deere dealer for more information.

If John Deere Plus-50™ II engine oil is not available, engine oil meeting one or more of the following may be used:

• API Service Category CJ-4

• ACEA Oil Sequence E9

• ACEA Oil Sequence E6

DO NOT use engine oil containing more than 1.0% sulfated ash, 0.12% phosphorus, or 0.4% sulfur.

Multi-viscosity diesel engine oils are preferred.

Diesel fuel quality and fuel sulfur content must comply with all existing emissions regulations for the area in which the engine operates. (See Fig. 19)

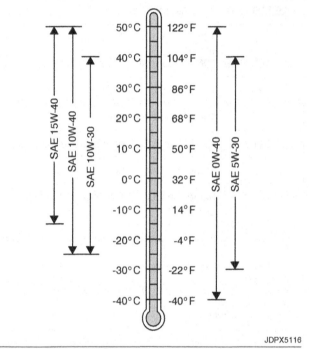

JDPX5116

Fig. 19 — Oil Viscosity Chart

API Service Classifications

The API system is an attempt to clarify the oil specifications and better define oil qualities between the engine manufacturer, the petroleum industry, and the customer. It is a joint effort of the API, ASTM (American Society for Testing Materials), and SAE organizations. Lubricants meeting more than one classification can be so marked.

The API chart (Table 1) gives a brief designation for the SAE family of "S" and "C" designations and what it means in terms of API identification of engine service expected of the oil.

API SERVICE CLASSIFICATIONS FOR ENGINE OILS

SAE LETTER	API Identification
SC	1964-67 Gasoline Engine Warranty Service
SD	1968-71 Gasoline Engine Warranty Service
SE	1972 Gasoline Engine Warranty Service
SF	1980 Gasoline Engine Warranty Service
SG	1989 Gasoline Engine Warranty Service
OB	Moderate Duty Diesel Engine Service
CC	Moderate Duty Diesel & Gasoline Engine Service
CD	Severe Duty Diesel Engine Service 1
CE	Severe Duty Diesel Engine Service 2
CF-4/EG-4	Severe Duty Diesel Engine Service 3

Table 1 — API Service Designations

A summary of all current recommendations, current common names, and new Performance Classifications is given in Table 2. The U.S. Army also has military (MIL) specifications which parallel some of the API designations.

SUMMARY OF CURRENT EQUIPMENT MANUFACTURER RECOMMENDATIONS — ENGINE OILS

Application	Oil Recommendations		Comments
	API Service Classification	Common Current Name	
Gasoline Engine, Passenger Car	SE[a] SF[a] SG/SH/SJ[a]	—	Meet warranty requirements of passenger car manufacturers.
Gasoline Engine, Truck, Bus, and Off Highway	CC/CD/CE/CF4/CGH4[a] SE[a] SF[a] SG/SH/SJ[a]	MIL-B —	Principally concerned with heavy duty, some applications may require improved low temperature performance of SF and SE.
Diesel Engine, Truck, Bus, and Off Highway	CB CC CD[b] CE[b] CF-4/CG-4	Supplement 1 MIL-B Series 3 (S-3)	Recommendation of performance level involves consideration of engine design factors as well as application.
Natural Gas Engine	CI-4[c] CH-4[c] CG-4[c] CF-4[c]	—	Meet Cummins 20074 or Detroit Diesel 7SE272-9510 requirements.

a. Oils meeting the performance requirements of MIL-L-46152B meet the performance requirements of SE, CC, and SF. Oils meeting military specification MIL-L-46167A may be used as arctic oils.

b. Oils meeting the performance requirements of MIL-L-2104C or MIL-L-2104D meet the performance requirements of both CD and CE. Oils meeting military specification MIL-L-46167A may be used as arctic oils.

c. 0.4–1.0% ash content

Table 2 — Summary of Current Equipment Manufacturer Recommendations — Engine Oils

Diesel and Gasoline Engines

Single-Viscosity Oils   Multi-Viscosity Oils

Cold weather oil blends (0W, 5W, 10W) that do not have the listed minimum industry performance (CF-4, ACEAE2), are limited to 100-hour drain intervals.

Natural Gas Engines

Multi-Viscosity Oils   Single-Viscosity Oils

JDPX5509

Fig. 20 — Typical Oil Viscosity Recommendations at Various Temperature Levels

(Fig. 20) shows one equipment manufacturer's oil viscosity recommendations for four-cycle diesel and gasoline engines, and natural gas engines operating at various temperature levels.

Agricultural vs. Automotive Engine Oils

Agricultural machines operate almost continuously under full loads, at constant speeds, over long periods of time.

By comparison, automotive and light truck engines have lighter loads and more idling and stop-and-go driving conditions.

As you can see, each application is very different. For this reason, engineers have recently developed engine oils specifically for off-the-road farm and industrial machines.

If the operator's manual recommends a special engine oil, the engine will probably perform better with that oil than with any other—use it if at all possible.

Diesel Engine Break-In Oil

Many new machines are initially filled with a special oil for the initial break-in period. They contain special additives to allow the piston rings and liners to seat properly while still providing the proper amount of wear protection. Break-in oil is often recommended after major engine service or overhaul. Refer to machine operator's manual or engine technical manual to determine the proper manufacturer's recommendations for engine break-in for new machines and for engines that have been overhauled. The following is a sample engine break-in procedure for a new machine.

Breaking In Engine

Operate the engine at heavy loads with minimal idling during the break-in period.

If engine has significant operating time at idle, constant speeds, and/or light load usage, or makeup oil is required in the first 100-hour period, a longer break-in period may be required. In these situations, an additional 100-hour break-in period is recommended, using a new change of engine break-in oil and a new oil filter.

Check engine oil level more frequently during engine break-in period. If oil must be added during this period, engine break-in oil is preferred.

NOTE: *Some increase in oil consumption may be expected when low viscosity oils are used. Check oil levels more frequently.*

During the first 20 hours, avoid prolonged periods of engine idling or sustained maximum load operation. If engine will idle longer than 5 minutes, stop engine.

After the first 100 hours maximum, change engine oil and replace engine oil filter. Fill crankcase with seasonal viscosity grade oil.

Storing and Handling Engine Oils

Use care in storing and handling oil to keep out dirt and moisture.

Store oil inside whenever possible — in clean, closed cabinets or rooms. It is best to keep oil relatively warm in the winter. Rapid changes in temperature can draw water into oil barrels

If stored outside, lay barrels on their sides. If they cannot be laid on their sides, tilt them slightly and turn the barrel so that the bung is at the high side, away from any water which might collect.

Keep oil bungs drawn tight. Use wooden mallets to make sure.

Rinse oil containers and funnels in fuel after use. Cover them to keep out dirt or store them upside down.

When adding oil, clean all dirt from around the filler cap before removing it. (Do the same before unscrewing an oil filter or a filter cap.)

Servicing the Lubricating System

You must service the engine lubricating system regularly to prevent premature wear and engine damage. This service consists mainly of checking crankcase oil level daily and changing the oil and filter at the proper intervals.

Checking Crankcase Oil Level (Daily)

Check the crankcase oil level daily (Fig. 21).

Don't check the oil level while the engine is running. Try to allow 10 minutes for oil to drain down after engine is stopped.

Remove the dipstick as shown and wipe dry with a clean cloth. Then insert fully and withdraw to check oil level.

Look at the top and bottom marks, which may be labeled "FULL" and "ADD." (Some manufacturers make the dipstick short so that when no oil shows it is time to add.)

Add oil if needed. If oil is down to lower mark, add recommended oil (usually one quart [one liter]) to fill to upper mark on dipstick.

Be sure oil and container are clean.

Oil Level Dipstick

Lower (Add) Mark   Upper (Full) Mark

JDPX5613

Fig. 21 — Check the Engine Oil Daily

Don't overfill; this can cause oil consumption and foaming.

Oil Testing Programs

Many manufacturers offer oil testing programs that help monitor the condition of the engine and other systems by testing oil samples taken from these components. Oil samples can be tested for contaminants such as dirt and water and also for the presence of any metal particles that may indicate wear for specific components. Regular sampling can aid in the early detection of worn components.

Changing Crankcase Oil and Filter

The oil in the crankcase of your engine should be changed every 250 hours or as recommended (refer to your operator's manual for specific times). Periods vary from 60 to 300 hours. Changing the oil filter is usually recommended at the same time. Be sure to change the oil and the filter more often if operating in extremely dirty or dusty conditions.

Tools and Materials Needed

- Wrenches for crankcase drain plug and filter cap if needed (inch or metric, as required).
- Clean, lint free cloths.
- Cleaning solvent (not gasoline).
- New oil of grade and type recommended to your engine and anticipated temperature.
- New oil filter cartridge.
- Container to catch waste oil.

Procedure for Changing Engine Oil and Filter

To change the oil in the crankcase, proceed as follows:

1. Operate the engine until it is thoroughly heated. This permits the oil to drain more completely. More contaminants are removed while the oil is still agitated. If the oil is drained while cold, contaminants may remain in the engine.

Cleaning Magnetic Plug

JDPX5513

Fig. 22 — Removing Engine Crankcase Drain Plug

2. Shut off the engine and remove the drain plug (Fig. 22). Magnetic drain plugs may have metal particles on them. Strike the plug against a solid object to remove the particles. Be careful not to damage threads.

Drain Completely

JDPX5514

Fig. 23 — Allow Crankcase to Drain Completely

3. Allow the oil to drain for several minutes (Fig. 23). This permits oil to drain completely from various parts of the engine.

4. Wipe dirt from filter and surrounding area.

5. Loosen filter bowl or cover and remove (Fig. 24). (If the filter has a drain plug, remove the plug and allow the filter to drain before removing.)

IMPORTANT: Engine must be stopped while filter is removed.

6. Remove old filter cartridge and discard it.

7. Clean inside of filter bowl and base with solvent (not gasoline) (Fig. 25) if the same bowl is used again.

8. Replace and tighten drain plugs in the crankcase and filter if removed.

9. Install new filter gasket, if supplied with filter. With a spin-on filter, apply a light film of engine oil or grease to the gasket or sealing ring before installing it. This will prevent tearing the seal as it is tightened.

Oil Filter

Cover

Filter Bowl

JDPX5615, 5616

Fig. 24 — Removing Two Kinds of Engine Oil Filters

Filter Bowl

Use Cleaning Fluid. DO NOT USE GASOLINE

JDPX5516

Fig. 25 — Clean Inside of Filter Bowl and Base

10. Install new filter cartridge. Do not tighten too much as seals can be damaged. With spin-on filters, turn the filter until the seal contacts the base, then tighten no more than an extra one-half turn. This prevents overtightening, which distorts the seal and causes leaks. On vertical-mounted filters, pre-fill the filter with new oil before installing.

IMPORTANT: **Be sure the new filter is an exact duplicate of the one recommended by the engine manufacturer.**

11. If separate filter bowl is used, replace it and tighten. Do not overtighten.

12. Fill crankcase with new oil. Use the proper amount of oil. Do not overfill. Clean tops of oil containers and use a clean funnel or spout when necessary. Use the viscosity and type of oil recommended in your operator's manual.

13. Start the engine and operate it for a few minutes. This gives the oil an opportunity to coat and protect parts and fill the oil filter.

JDPX5518

Fig. 26 — Check for Oil Leaks after Installing Engine Filter

14. Check for oil leaks around the drain plug and the filter (Fig. 26). Also check the pressure gauge on control console to make certain that the oil pump is working properly.

15. Check oil level on the dipstick after allowing engine to set for a few minutes. If oil is not to the full line, add more until it reaches that level. Do not overfill; this can cause oil consumption and oil foaming.

Testing Engine Oil Pressure

Normal Oil Pressure
Full Oil Spray
Reaches Cylinder

Low Oil Pressure
Weak Oil Spray Does
Not Reach Cylinder

JDPX5519

Fig. 27 — Low Oil Pressure Means Lack of Engine Lubrication

The modern engine must have full oil pressure, or not enough lubricating oil will reach vital engine working parts (Fig. 27).

All modern engines with pressurized lubricating systems have an oil pressure gauge on the operator's console (Fig. 28). Watch this gauge for proper oil pressure. Once the engine is started and running, this gauge should read in the normal range (or go out if it is a glowing indicator). If not, stop the engine at once and find the cause.

Engine Oil
Pressure Gauge

JDPX5520

Fig. 28 — Engine Oil Pressure Gauge on Operator's Console

If **engine oil pressure is too low**, crankcase oil level may be down, oil may be too thin, oil pump or engine bearings may be worn, the gauge may be bad, or the pressure valve may only need adjustment.

Too-high oil pressure is not as common, but can be caused by crankcase oil that is too heavy, a defective pressure gauge, or a stuck regulating valve or one that is out of adjustment.

Anytime the oil pressure is too high or low, stop the engine and test it. To test engine oil pressure:

1. Before checking the engine oil pressure, always check the condition of the oil filter. A dirty filter will drop the pressure reading.

2. Also check the oil level in the crankcase. Low oil level may show up as low oil pressure.

3. Many engines have tapped holes in the block as oil pressure test points. On other engines, the oil pressure sending unit hole is used for testing.

4. Install a master gauge (Fig. 29).

Fig. 30 — Adjusting Engine Oil Pressure (Shim-Adjusted Valves)

To lower pressure, shims are removed to decrease the tension of the spring and allow the valve to open at a lower setting.

Recheck pressure on master gauge. If okay, remove gauge and install plug.

If the oil pressure problem continues, have a serviceman inspect the engine.

Fig. 29 — Oil Pressure Master Gauge

5. Start and run the engine at fast-idle speed.

6. When the engine is warmed up to operating temperature, record the pressure reading on the gauge. Compare this reading with the specifications for the engine.

7. If master gauge indicates pressure is satisfactory, but gauge on operator's console still reads high or low, replace oil pressure sensor and/or gauge which are often supplied as a single unit.

8. Adjust engine oil pressure if necessary.

Some regulating valves are non-adjustable. See engine technical manual to see if adjustment is possible.

Some regulating valves are adjusted by an adjusting screw. Normally, turn the screw in to increase the spring tension and the pressure setting. Turn the screw out to decrease the pressure setting.

Shims and washers are used for adjusting pressure in some regulating valves (Fig. 30).

Test Yourself

Questions

1. What four functions must engine oil perform to keep engines running with a minimum of wear?

2. (Fill in blank.) The Society of Automotive Engineers established the SAE _____ designation which is a measure of the fluidity of an oil at a given temperature.

3. (T/F) When the crankcase oil is black, it is time for an oil change.

4. (T/F) Oil additives rarely wear out.

5. (Fill in blank.) Oil _____ will reduce engine life more than any other factor.

6. Name the three types of lubricating systems.

7. (Fill in blanks.) The two basic types of filtration systems are _____ and _____.

8. How often should the engine crankcase oil level be checked?

9. Why should an engine be operated until it is thoroughly heated before draining the oil?

10. (T/F) Tighten oil filters as tight as possible or they may leak.

Engine Cooling Systems

5

Introduction

Thermostat
If Coolant Cold —
Closes to Circulate in Engine Only
If Coolant Hot —
Opens to Circulate Coolant to
Radiator for Coolant

Pressure Cap
Holds Pressure in System and
Releases Excessive Pressure

Engine Coolant Jacket
Allows Coolant to Circulate
Around Cylinders and Head

Bypass

Air Flow
Removes
Heat from
Coolant

Fan

Coolant
Water + Antifreeze + Inhibitors

Water Pump
Circulates the
Coolant

Hose

Radiator
Reservoir and Heat
Exchanger for Coolant

JDPX5467

Fig. 1 — Basic Engine Cooling System

If a liquid-cooled engine were run without its coolant, the
pistons and bearings would soon weld to their mating parts
and the engine would be damaged beyond repair.

Jobs of Cooling System

The engine cooling system does two things:

- Prevents overheating
- Regulates temperatures

Overheating could "burn up" the engine parts. Some heat is necessary for combustion, but the engine generates too much. So the cooling system is designed to carry off the excess heat.

Regulating temperatures keeps the engine at the best heat level for each operation. Just after starting, the engine must be warmed faster, while during peak operations, the engine must be cooled and kept at a constant temperature.

Parts of Cooling System

A liquid cooling system (Fig. 1) consists of the following:

- Radiator and Pressure Cap
- Fan and Fan Belt
- Coolant Pump
- Engine Coolant Jacket
- Thermostat
- Connecting Hoses
- Liquid or Coolant
- Coolant Filter-Conditioner (if used)
- EGR Cooler
- Coolant Manifold

Now we will see how these parts function in the complete system.

Fig. 2 — Liquid Cooling System on Modern Engine

Operation of Cooling System

The radiator is one of the major components of any liquid cooling system (Fig. 1). It is here that heat in the coolant is released to the atmosphere. The radiator also provides a reservoir for enough liquid to operate the cooling system efficiently.

Coolant from the engine enters the radiator by way of the top tank, then passes down through a series of small tubes surrounded by fins and air passages. Cooled liquid reaching the bottom tank is picked up by the water pump to repeat the complete cycle.

Fig. 3 — Pressure Control Radiator Cap

The radiator cap (Fig. 3) provides pressure control of the cooling system. With a pressure cap, the boiling point of the coolant can be raised (a 7 psi [50 kPa] cap raises the boiling point of water from 212° to about 230°F, or approximately 100° to 110°C. This allows the engine to operate at higher temperatures for better efficiency.

A pressure valve (Fig. 3) in the cap permits the escape of coolant or steam when the pressure reaches a certain point.

The vacuum valve in the cap opens to prevent a vacuum in the cooling system when the system cools.

The fan forces cooling air through the radiator to more quickly dissipate the heat being carried by the coolant into the radiator. The fan is generally driven by a belt from the engine crankshaft, although some engines may use an electrically powered fan.

The coolant pump circulates the coolant through the cooling system. The pump draws hot coolant from the engine block and forces it through the radiator for cooling. When the pump fails to circulate the coolant, heat is not removed from the engine and overheating will occur.

The thermostat provides automatic control of engine temperature at the correct level. This is necessary in order to get the best performance from an engine.

During warm-up, the thermostat remains closed (Fig. 4). The water pump circulates the coolant through the engine coolant jacket only, by way of the bypass.

This quickly warms the engine to its operating temperature before the thermostat opens (Fig. 4).

When the thermostat opens (usually at 180°F to 190°F, 82° to 88°C), hot coolant flows from the engine to the radiator and back. An engine operating at a temperature lower than recommended will use more fuel, have less power, and have increased cylinder wear.

JDPX5472

Fig. 5 — Mineral Deposits from Using Water Alone as a Coolant

The coolant or liquid which circulates in the system to absorb and release heat will be covered next.

Coolants

The primary purpose of the liquid coolant circulating through the engine is to absorb and dissipate the excess heat created by the engine.

While water was once used as a coolant in early engines, it is not recommended today. Use water only in an emergency situation. Drain the cooling system and refill with antifreeze as soon as possible.

An antifreeze solution is the recommended coolant for both gasoline and diesel engines, even in geographical areas where freeze protection is not necessary.

Coolant for Modern Diesel Engines

IMPORTANT: **Some diesel engine manufacturers recommend a specific coolant containing supplement coolant additives (SCAs) which prevent cavitation (corrosive pitting) of the cylinder liners. There are restrictions to the alternatives for these specified coolants. SCAs wear out and must be periodically replaced. ALWAYS consult the machine manual when dealing with a diesel engine.**

Thermostat Closed

Thermostat Open

JDPX5471

Fig. 4 — Thermostat for Cooling System

The cooling system hoses are flexible because they stand up under vibration better than rigid pipes.

A coolant filter-conditioner (used on some engines) contains chemicals which soften the water, maintain a proper acid/alkaline condition, prevent corrosion, and suppress cavitation erosion.

In general, use water as a coolant only in an emergency situation. Drain the water from the cooling system and refill with the recommended coolant as soon as possible.

90%
Rust

10%
Grease and
Water Scale

JDPX5473

Fig. 6 — Rust in Clogging Material

Water as a Coolant

Water by itself is not a satisfactory coolant. Without inhibitor additives it will rust, corrode, and leave deposits in the engine coolant jacket and cause the radiator to plug (Fig. 5) Without an antifreeze solution, it will freeze at 32°F (0°C).

The best water for coolant is clean soft water — distilled water or rain water is the best source. Most ground water is too hard and contains minerals which form scale in the engine. Artificially softened water is better, but there are still dissolved minerals in it. Even distilled water, while the purest of all, needs inhibitors.

The problem is that all waters tend to either corrode or form deposits. Waters that have been softened may tend to corrode metal parts, while harder tap waters tend to form deposits.

The safest rule is to add commercial inhibitors to the water, even in summer, to prevent rust, corrosion, and deposits.

Usually, when the radiator becomes clogged, up to 90 percent of the material is rust (Fig. 6).

Antifreeze

Antifreeze is mixed with water to produce a coolant solution. The prime characteristic of the solution is that it will not freeze. If a coolant freezes, it will expand and may crack the engine block or head and create leaks. It may also weaken the radiator and hoses. During operation of the engine, freezing can prevent circulation of the coolant, causing the engine to run hot.

An effective antifreeze solution will:

*   Prevent freezing at the lowest expected temperature.
*   Flow readily at all temperatures.
*   Inhibit rust and corrosion of system parts.
*   Will be chemically stable.
*   Conduct heat readily.
*   Resist foaming.
*   Have a higher boiling point than water (Fig. 7).
*   Provide lubrication for pump and seals.
*   Will not expand too much.
*   Will not have an unpleasant odor.

Types of Antifreeze

The two types of antifreeze used in engine coolant solutions today are:

*   Ethylene glycol base
*   Propylene glycol base

°F	°C
230°	(110°)
220°	(104°)
210°	(99°)
200°	(93°)
190°	(88°)
180°	(82°)

Boiling Point
212°F (100°C)

Boiling Point
223°F (106°C)

Protecting to
32°F (0°C)

Protecting to
−20°F (−29°C)

Plain Water

Glycol Base Anti-Freeze

JDPX5474

Fig. 7 — Engine Coolant Solutions

FREEZING PROTECTION TABLE

COOLING SYSTEM CAPACITY QUARTS (LITERS)	FULL STRENGTH "PERMANENT" ANTIFREEZE REQUIRED												
	1 °F (°C)	**2** °F (°C)	**3** °F (°C)	**4** °F (°C)	**5** °F (°C)	**6** °F (°C)	**7** °F (°C)	**8** °F (°C)	**9** °F (°C)	**10** °F (°C)	**11** °F (°C)	**12** °F (°C)	**13** °F (°C)
5 (4. 7)	16° (- 9.0°)	-12° (-22.0°)	-62° (-52.0°)										
6 (5.7)	19° (- 7.0°)	0° (-17.5°)	-34° (-36.5°)										
7 (6.6)	22° (- 5.5°)	7° (-14.0°)	-17° (-27.0°)	-54° (-47.5°)									
8 (7.6)	23° (- 5.0°)	11° (-12.0°)	- 7° (-14.0°)	-34° (-36.5°)	-69° (-56.0)								
9 (8.5)	24° (- 4.5°)	14° (-10.0)	0° (-17.5°)	-21° (-29.5°)	-50° (-45.5°)								
10 (9.5)	25° (- 4.0°)	16° (- 9.0°)	4° (-15.5°)	-12° (-24.5°)	-34° (-36.5°)	-62° (-52.0°)							
11 (10.4)	26° (- 3.5°)	18° (- 8.0°)	8° (-13.5°)	- 6° (-21.0°)	-23° (-31.0°)	47° (-44.0°)							
12 (11.4)		19° (- 7.0°)	10° (-12.0°)	0° (-17.5°)	-15° (-26.0°)	-34° (-36.5°)	-57° (-49.5°)						
13 (12.3)		21° (- 6.0°)	13° (-10.5°)	3° (-16.0°)	- 9° (-23.0°)	-25° (31.5°)	-45° (-43.0°)	-66° (-55.5°)					
14 (13.2)			15° (- 9.5°)	6° (-14.5°)	- 5° (-20.5°)	-18° (-28.0°)	-34° (-36.5°)	-54° (-47.5°)					
15 (14.2)			16° (- 9.0°)	8° (-13.5°)	0° (-17.5°)	-12° (-24.5°)	-26° (-32.0°)	-43° (-41.5°)	-62° (-52.0°)				
16 (15.1)			17° (- 8.5°)	10° (-12.0°)	2° (-16.5°)	- 8° (-22.0°)	-19° (-28.5°)	-34° (-36.5°)	-52° (-46.5°)				
17 (16.1)			18° (- 8.0°)	12° (-11.0°)	5° (-15.0°)	- 4° (-20.0°)	-14° (-25.5°)	-27° (-33.0°)	-42° (-41.0°)	-58° (-50.0°)			
18 (17.0)			19° (- 7.0°)	14° (-14.0°)	7° (-14.0°)	0° (-17.5°)	-10° (-23.5°)	-21° (-29.5°)	-34° (-36.5°)	-50° (-45.5°)	-65° (-54.0°)		
19 (18.0)			20° (- 6.5°)	15° (- 9.5°)	9° (-13.0°)	2° (-16.5°)	- 7° (-22.0°)	-16° (-26.5°)	-28° (-33.5°)	-42° (-41.0°)	-56° (-49.0°)		
20 (18.9)				16° (- 9.0°)	10° (-12.0°)	4° (-15.5°)	- 3° (-19.5°)	-12° (-24.5°)	-22° (-30.0°)	-34° (-35.5°)	-48° (-44.5°)	-62° (-52.0°)	
21 (19.9)				17° (- 8.5°)	12° (-11.0°)	6° (-14.5°)	0° (-17.0°)	- 9° (-23.0°)	-17° (27.0°)	-28° (-33.5°)	-41° (-40.5°)	-54° (-47.5°)	-68° (-55.5°)
22 (20.8)				18° (- 8.0°)	13° (-10.5°)	8° (-13.5°)	2° (-16.5°)	- 6° (-21.0°)	-14° (-25.5°)	-23° (-31.0°)	-34° (-36.5°)	-47° (-44.0°)	-59° (-50.5°)
23 (21.8)				19° (- 7.0°)	14° (-10.0°)	9° (-13.0°)	4° (-15.5°)	- 3° (-19.5°)	-10° (-23.5°)	-19° (-28.5°)	-29° (-34.0°)	-40° (-40.0°)	-52° (-46.5°)
24 (22.7)					15° (- 9.5°)	10° (-12.0°)	5° (-15.0°)	0° (-17.0°)	- 8° (-22.0°)	-15° (-26.0°)	-24° (-31.0°)	-34° (-36.5°)	-46° (-43.5°)

(Note: Celsius temperatures above are rounded to nearest 0.5°.)

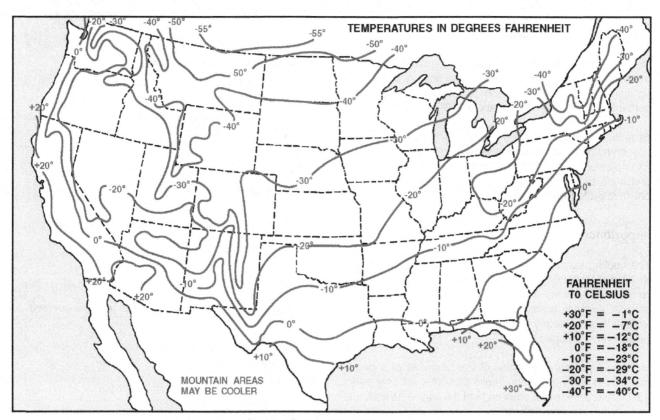

Lowest Temperature Observed
(U.S. Weather Bureau Records — 50 Years)

JDPX5151, 5475

Fig. 8 — Freezing Protection Tables

CAUTION: Glycol base antifreezes can be fatal if swallowed by humans or animals. Always store containers safely away from children and pets. Clean up spilled antifreeze at once.

Operating characteristics of the two glycol base antifreezes are similar. Ethylene glycol antifreeze contains a YELLOW dye. Propylene glycol antifreeze, often referred to as "low-tox," contains a PURPLE dye. While antifreezes will not boil away, they will wear out or become contaminated. Most antifreezes are recommended for only one or at most two seasons before they are replaced.

Freezing Protection for Coolant

When you add antifreeze, protect for the lowest expected temperatures. The map in (Fig. 8) shows the lowest temperature observed in various parts of the United States during the past 50 years (from U.S. Weather Bureau records).

Check your operator's manual for the system capacity of your engine. Then use the chart in (Fig. 8) to find how much full-strength "permanent" antifreeze is required to protect to the lowest expected temperature. For example, a tractor operating in northern Illinois should be protected to approximately –25°F (–32°C). If the tractor cooling system had a 20-quart (75-liter) capacity, then 10 quarts (or 37 liters) of permanent antifreeze would be needed.

Install and maintain a 33 to 50 percent solution (0°F, –18°C freezing protection) for corrosion protection. A 50 percent solution will provide protection to –34°F (–36°C). A 68 percent solution will protect to about –90°F, (–68°C).

Because of the nature of ethylene glycol, a greater concentration of antifreeze will actually give less protection. Examples of this are that an 80 percent solution will provide protection to –57°F (–50°C), while a 100 percent solution provides protection only to –9°F (–23°C).

Importance of Service

The cooling system absorbs about 1/3 of the heat energy developed by the engine fuel. Another 1/3 of the heat energy is used for power, and the remaining 1/3 is dissipated through exhaust gases and crankcase oil. If the cooling system fails to remove its share of the heat, the engine may be severely damaged.

In (Fig. 9) you can see some of the problems of a poorly maintained cooling system. These problems not only affect the cooling system, but other parts of the engine as well, and could result in costly damage.

Damage from Engine Too Hot

If these problems cause the engine to run too hot, the following damage may result:

- Burned valves and spark plugs
- Scored pistons
- Lubrication failure
- Excessive engine wear
- Engine knock, detonation or preignition

Damage from Engine Too Cold

If the engine runs too cold, the following may result:

- Unnecessary wear
- Poor fuel economy
- Crankcase dilution by fuel
- Fouled spark plugs
- Sludge formation in crankcase

Servicing the Cooling System

To maintain the engine cooling system properly, check the coolant level daily and perform other periodic maintenance as explained below.

Tools and Materials Needed

- Commercial flushing compound if cooling system is in good condition.
- Commercial cleaning compound if there is much scale and rust present.
- Soft distilled water.
- Clean container to catch drained coolant.
- Adjustable pliers.
- Screwdriver.
- Wrenches, if needed, inch or metric, as required.
- Goggles or glasses for eye protection.

Services to Be Covered

Maintenance of the cooling system will be covered as follows:

- Checking coolant
- Preventing leaks
- Preventing corrosion and deposits
- Flushing or cleaning system
- Filling system with coolant
- Coolant pump lubrication
- Checking fan belt

Let's discuss each subject in detail.

A —External Leakage
B —Internal Leakage
C —Rust Deposits
D —Heat Cracks
E —Exhaust Gas Leakage
F —Air Suction
G —Clogged Air Passages
H —Stuck Thermostat
I — Sludge Formation in Oil
J — Transmission Oil Cooler
K —Heat Damage
L —Hose Failure
M —Worn Fan Belt
N —Pressure Cap Leakage

JDPX5476

Fig. 9 — Maintenance Problems of the Engine Cooling System

Checking Coolant

Checking Coolant Level

⚠️ CAUTION: When checking the coolant level, wait until the coolant temperature has cooled well below the boiling point before removing the pressure cap.

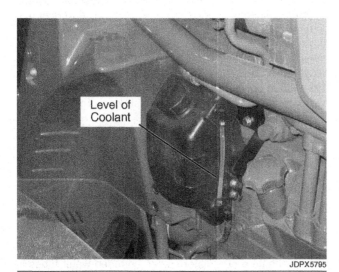

Level of Coolant

JDPX5795

Fig. 10 — Proper Level of Engine Coolant

Allow engine to cool completely. With engine stopped, coolant level should be at or above lower "Cold" line on overflow tank (Fig. 10). Follow manufacturer's recommendations for coolant level checks for each machine application. Never overfill the system. A pressurized system needs space for heat expansion without overflowing. As the coolant expands with heat, any excess coolant will overflow and this wastes antifreeze. Continued overfilling can dilute the antifreeze concentration and there will no longer be adequate freeze protection.

Check the radiator cap and gasket. If in doubt, replace the cap with an exact duplicate (see "Testing Radiator Cap" later in this chapter).

Check for leaks around the radiator, hoses, and hose clamps.

Remove trash from the radiator or radiator screen.

If you have water under pressure, use a hose as shown in (Fig. 11). Direct the stream against the radiator from the side next to the engine. Be sure to get the radiator clean, as mud will make the problem worse if it is not all flushed out.

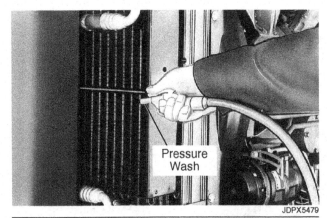
Fig. 11 — Removing Trash from Radiator or Screen

When operating in trashy conditions such as in corn harvesting, check the radiator for trash several times a day.

IMPORTANT: **Never pour hot water into a cold engine or cold water into a hot engine that is not running. You may crack the head or the cylinder block. Do not operate the engine without coolant for even a few minutes.**

Checking Antifreeze Solutions

There are three methods for checking the freeze point of antifreeze solutions:

- Hydrometer
- Test strips
- Refractometer

The hydrometer (Fig. 12) must have a thermometer and a correction table to be accurate, as the density of a liquid changes with the temperature.

Test strips measure the freeze point by changing color when immersed in the solution. The color change is the result of a chemical reaction between the strip and the antifreeze solution. Follow the instructions provided with the test strips.

Some engine manufacturers recommend using a refractometer to measure the freeze point of the solution. Follow the instructions furnished with the refractometer.

If the freeze point does not provide protection for the lowest expected temperature, drain some solution from the system and refill with fresh solution. If it is time for a seasonal change, drain, flush, and refill the entire cooling system.

Cooling system leaks can be caused by other problems: loose cylinder head and other gasket joints, loose hose

Fig. 12 — Checking Freezing Protection Using a Hydrometer

Coolant Testing Programs

Many manufacturers offer coolant testing programs that help monitor the condition of the engine cooling system. Coolant samples can be tested for contaminants, freeze protection point, pH level, and amount of additives in the coolant. Regular sampling can aid in the early detection of worn components and proper coolant condition.

Preventing Leaks

Leaks in the cooling system can mean a loss of valuable coolant. A serious leak could cause the engine to overheat and become damaged.

If antifreeze solution leaks into the engine crankcase (Fig. 13), it can dilute the oil until the engine's lubrication fails. When coolant mixes with oil, it forms sludge and gum which retard lubrication and cause sticking of valves, valve lifters, or piston rings.

To prevent leakage of coolant into the crankcase, check the cylinder head joints periodically to be sure the gasket is okay and the cap screws are tightened to specifications.

Watch oil level in the crankcase. If oil level rises, either coolant or unburned fuel is entering the crankcase. Determine the problem and make corrections immediately.

clamps, fracture of radiator solder, corroded water tubes in the radiator, and rotten hoses and gaskets.

JDPX5481

Fig. 13 — Coolant Leaking into the Crankcase Can Cause Lubrication Failure

Stop-Leak Products

To stop small leaks, at least temporarily, stop-leak compounds can sometimes be used. The main problem is that they give a sense of false security. For example, stop-leak may prevent seepage at a hose connection through the inner lining, but eventually the hose will rot and burst, losing coolant and overheating the engine.

Also, stop-leak compounds will not correct a leaking cylinder head gasket because of the heat and pressures.

Stop-leak compounds can also lead to radiator clogging if water tubes already contain deposits which act as a strainer. If coolant level gets too low, some stop-leak ingredients may harden in the upper radiator and block it.

However, stop-leak compounds are recommended for preventive maintenance in some engines.

Before using a stop-leak, check your operator's manual. Some manufacturers do not recommend them. If used, the compound must be compatible with the antifreeze and the inhibitors, and it must be added correctly and in the right quantity.

NOTE: Do not use coolant system stop-leak additives if the engine is equipped with a coolant filter-conditioner. The stop-leak compound will plug the filter.

NOTE: Some antifreezes now contain stop-leak additives. If this type of antifreeze is approved by the engine maker, no further stop-leak compound is needed in the system.

Air Leaks into Cooling System

Air mixing with the coolant in the system speeds rusting and corrosion. It may also cause foaming, overheating, and overflow loss of coolant.

Air leaks into the coolant may be caused by:

- Leak in the system
- Turbulence in top radiator tank
- Too-low coolant level

Exhaust Gas Leaks into System

A cracked head or a loose cylinder head joint allows hot exhaust gas to be blown into the cooling system under combustion pressures, even though the joint may be tight enough to keep liquid from leaking into the cylinder.

The cylinder head gasket itself may be burned and corroded by escaping exhaust gases.

Exhaust gases dissolved in coolant destroy the inhibitors and form acids which cause corrosion, rust, clogging, and damage to rubber parts.

Excess pressure may also force coolant out the overflow pipe.

Either bubbles or an oil film present in the coolant is a sign of blow-by in the engine cylinders (Fig. 14).

NOTE: Make this test quickly, before boiling starts, since steam bubbles give misleading results.

Pressure Cap Removed

Gas Bubbles Mean Blow-By

Engine Warmed Up and Under Load

JDPX5482

Fig. 14 — Checking for Exhaust Gas Leakage that May Indicate Blow-By

Preventing Corrosion and Deposits

Three types of corrosion can attack the parts of the cooling system:

- Chemical corrosion
- Electrolytic corrosion
- Erosive corrosion

Chemical corrosion is a direct chemical reaction between the coolant and the metal parts of the system. This may be caused by acids in the coolant or various oxidizing agents. An example is the formation of rust on iron parts by the water and oxygen reacting with the metal.

Electrolytic corrosion is a reaction between two different metals joined together, in contact with a solution which conducts electricity. This action is the same as that of a dry-cell battery which produces current by converting a metal into salt. When selecting an antifreeze, be sure that it is not a good conductor, such as a salt solution.

Erosive corrosion is the mechanical abrasion from particles such as rust, scale, and sand as they circulate rapidly through the system with the coolant.

The result of corrosion on metal surfaces is that heat transfer is reduced.

Good engine coolants contain rust and corrosion inhibitors. The inhibitors, however, wear out and must be periodically replaced by adding liquid coolant conditioner to the cooling system.

IMPORTANT: **Some diesel engines require a specific coolant containing supplemental coolant additives (SCA's) which must be periodically replaced. ALWAYS consult the machine manual for coolant and SCA replacement recommendations.**

Preventing Cooling System Deposits

Lime and mineral deposits can be reduced by using distilled or filtered rain water when mixing with the coolant concentrate.

Mineral deposits form rapidly at hot spots in the engine (Fig. 5).

Because heat transfer is reduced, deposits can lead to overheating, knocks, and eventually engine damage.

Using Coolant Filter-Conditioners

NOTE: *Later engines may use the conditioner additives in the coolant itself rather than a filter-conditioner.*

Coolant filter-conditioners (Fig. 15) soften water and remove dirt. The filter-conditioner may be the spin-on type as in (Fig. 15). To change the filter, unscrew the canister from the engine and discard it. Install a new filter as a replacement.

Another type of filter-conditioner contains a replaceable filter element with a sump at the bottom where dirt settles after it collects in the filter. The sump can be drained periodically to remove accumulated dirt and sediment.

The spin-on-type filter contains two elements. The outer paper element filters out rust, scale, or dirt particles in the coolant. The inner element releases chemicals into the coolant to soften the coolant, maintain a proper acid/alkaline condition, prevent corrosion, and suppress cavitation erosion.

The chemicals released into the coolant by the inner element form a protective film on the surface of the cylinder liner. The film acts as a barrier against collapsing vapor bubbles and reduces the quantity of bubbles formed.

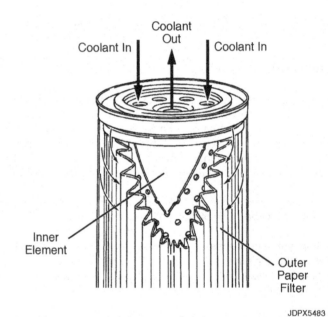

JDPX5483

Fig. 15 — Coolant Filter-Conditioner Softens and Cleans Coolant

Flushing or Cleaning the System

Always flush the system before installing antifreeze. Rust and other deposits in the system can shorten inhibitor life (and also reduce cooling efficiency). When draining the system, if the coolant contains rust and scale, clean the system with an acid-based cleaner. Be sure to follow the manufacturer's instructions.

It is also important to follow the engine maker's instructions when flushing or cleaning their system. For example, some alkaline cleaners can corrode aluminum engines or radiators.

For heavy deposits in the system, more drastic cleaning with an acid-base cleaner may be needed. Allow the solution to remain in the system for two to three hours at operating temperatures and then drain. To neutralize the acid, flush the system with water and lye solution. After running the engine for a while, drain the system and flush it again with clear water to remove all traces of the lye water. This is a very important step.

In severe cases, the radiator must be removed and boiled in a tank cleaner. This is normally done in a commercial radiator shop.

Flushing the System

Incomplete flushing, such as hosing out the radiator, closes the thermostat and prevents thorough flushing of the engine coolant jacket.

For complete flushing, take the following steps:

1. Drain old coolant from the system.

2. Fill the system completely with soft (distilled) water.

3. Run the engine long enough to open the thermostat (or remove the thermostat).

4. Open all drain plugs to again drain the system completely. (Most systems have at least two drains (Fig. 16). Some also have a drain at the engine oil cooler (if equipped). Unless all drains are opened, some coolant will be left in the system.

   Clean out the radiator overflow tube and remove insects and dirt from radiator air passages, radiator grille, and screens.

   Also check the thermostat, radiator pressure cap, and the cap seat for dirt or corrosion.

5. Replace coolant filter-conditioner element (if used) with new element recommended by engine manufacturer.

Engine Drain Plug

Radiator Drain Plug

JDPX5620, 5621

Fig. 16 — Cooling System Usually Has at Least Two Drains

Filling System with Coolant

IMPORTANT: **For diesel engines, consult the machine manual for specified coolant containing the proper supplemental cooling additives (SCAs) or alternative coolant and additives.**

After flushing the system, refill with a complete coolant (containing antifreeze, additives, and soft water) or a recognized brand of antifreeze and soft water.

If not using a complete coolant, see (Fig. 8) for antifreeze dilution table for freezing protection for the lowest temperature expected.

After adding coolant, run the engine for a few minutes until it reaches normal operating temperature. This will allow the thermostat to open and will ensure that the solution has circulated through the entire system for full protection against freezing.

Recheck the cooling system for leaks and to be sure it is filled to the proper level.

Coolant Pump Lubrication

In most engines, the water pump is driven by the same shaft as the cooling fan. Usually, the shaft bearings are factory lubricated and sealed and require no further lubrication. However, some older fan and pump units must be lubricated periodically through a grease fitting (often with a special grease). Here it is important that coolant does not leak into the bearings (Fig. 17).

JDPX5485

Fig. 17 — Coolant Pump with Corroded Bearing and Shaft

Other pumps are lubricated by additives in the coolant. For this reason, most permanent antifreezes already contain a water pump lubricant; so do most inhibitors that are used with plain water. In this case, it is doubly important to change the coolant or add inhibitors at regular intervals. Check the operators manual for the exact intervals and procedures as well as the label on the additives used.

Checking Fan Belt

The fan belt should be neither too tight nor too loose.

Too tight a belt puts an extra load on the fan bearings and shortens the life of the bearings as well as the belt.

Too loose a belt allows slippage and lowers the fan speed, causes excessive belt wear, and leads to overheating of the cooling system.

The condition of the fan belt and its tension should be checked periodically. If belt tension is adjustable, adjust tension as specified in the machine operator's manual. Most modern engines are equipped with an automatic belt tensioner assembly (Fig. 18) that is designed to keep proper belt tension on the belt at all times. When using a belt tensioner assembly, the belt tension is not adjustable, however the tensioner assembly itself needs periodic inspection to ensure proper operation.

Fan Belt

JDPX5622

Fig. 18 — Automatic Belt Tensioner

Belt Tensioner Maintenance

Belt tensioner assemblies require periodic checks to verify that the proper tension is being placed on the belt. The following is an example of checking a belt tensioner assembly for correct operation. Follow the manufacturer's recommendations for each specific application.

CHECKING TENSIONER SPRING TENSION

A belt tension gauge will not give an accurate measure of the belt tension when automatic spring tensioner is used. Measure tensioner spring tension using a torque wrench and the procedure outlined below.

1. Release tension on belt using a long-handle 1/2-in. breaker bar in tension arm. Remove belt from pulleys.

2. Release tension on tension arm and remove breaker bar.

3. Put a mark on swing arm of tensioner as shown in (Fig. 19).

4. Measure 0.83 in. (21 mm) from the mark on swing arm and put a mark on tensioner mounting base (Fig. 19).

Mark on Swing Arm

Mark on Tensioner Mounting Base

JDPX5623

Fig. 19 — Checking Belt Tensioner

5. Rotate the swing arm using a torque wrench until marks are aligned (Fig. 20).

Mark on Swing Arm

Mark on Tensioner Mounting Base

JDPX5624

Fig. 20 — Measuring Belt Tensioner

6. Record torque wrench measurement and compare with the manufacturer's specification. Replace tensioner assembly as required.

Testing of Cooling System

In addition to regular maintenance, several tests will tell you the condition of the cooling system. These are:

• Testing system pressure

• Testing radiator cap

• Testing thermostat

Make these tests whenever the condition of the system components is in doubt. If the tests show major troubles, have the faulty parts replaced.

Testing System Pressure

Because most modern cooling systems are pressurized, all of the components must be tight and in good condition before the system can operate properly.

Overheating and loss of coolant will result unless pressure in the system is maintained.

Test the pressure in the entire cooling system as follows:

Install a pressure tester on the radiator according to the manufacturer's instructions (Fig. 21). Avoid applying too much pressure.

With the tester installed, carefully inspect the radiator, water pump, hoses, drain cocks, and cylinder block for leakage.

Mark all leaks plainly to help locate them when repairs are made by a serviceman.

Testing Radiator Cap

The pressure cap is vital to correct pressure build-up in the cooling system.

Use a reliable tester to test the radiator cap (Fig. 22). The pressure valve should open at a certain pressure (see engine technical manual for specifications).

JDPX5488

Fig. 22 — Testing the Radiator Cap

If the pressure valve does not open as specified or if it leaks before reaching opening pressure, replace the gasket or the whole cap as necessary.

Be sure that both the cap and radiator are free from leaks.

JDPX5487

Fig. 21 — Testing the Cooling System Pressure

Testing of Thermostat

The thermostat must work properly to control the engine temperature at its best level.

Test the thermostat as follows:

1. Suspend the thermostat and a thermometer in a container of water (Fig. 23). Do not let them rest against the sides or bottom.

JDPX5489

Fig. 23 — Testing the Thermostat

2. Heat and stir the water.

3. The thermostat should begin to open at the temperature stamped on it, plus or minus 10°F (5°C). It should be fully open (approximately 1/4-inch, 6 mm) at 22°F (12°C) above the specified temperature.

4. Remove thermostat and observe its closing action.

5. If the thermostat is defective, discard it.

6. Be sure to replace with an exact duplicate of the original thermostat. Notice the temperature stamped on it.

IMPORTANT: **Never operate the engine without a thermostat.**

A thermostat tester can also be used to test the thermostat, if available.

Watching The Coolant Temperature Gauge

All modern engines have a coolant temperature gauge to tell the operator if the engine is operating at a normal temperature (Fig. 24). Watch this gauge during operation. Once the engine is warmed up, the needle should stay in the normal range. If the needle goes over into the red, warning, zone, stop the engine at once. Allow engine and radiator to cool and then check for low coolant level or other causes.

Other machines may have an indicator light which glows red when the engine is too hot.

JDPX5490

Fig. 24 — Engine Coolant Temperature Gauge

Never Stop a Hot Engine

When an engine has been working hard, the pistons, turbocharger, and other parts are very hot and should be allowed to cool gradually to prevent seizing and permanent damage.

IMPORTANT: **Allow a hot engine to idle for a few minutes before shutting it down.**

This will prevent the engine from running after the ignition is turned off. Above all, it will keep the hot pistons and other parts from stewing and cooking in their own oil films, producing deposits. Another problem is that a red-hot valve, open when the engine stops, may warp and later burn.

NOTE: *If overheating is accompanied by an indication of low oil pressure (signal light or gauge reading) stop the engine at once. Running the engine without enough oil could cause more damage than stopping a hot engine.*

Test Yourself

Questions

1. What are the two functions of the engine cooling system?

2. Why isn't water by itself a satisfactory coolant?

3. Which two of the following is best for a cooling system?

   a. Tap water

   b. Well water

   c. Distilled water

   d. Rain water

4. When a radiator becomes plugged, what is the major cause?

5. A 50 percent solution of antifreeze will protect against freezing to:

   a. 0°F (−18°C)

   b. −15°F (−26°C)

   c. −34°F (−37°C)

6. The cooling system absorbs (1/4) (1/3) (1/2) of the heat energy developed by the engine fuel.

7. (T/F) The thermostat keeps the engine from overheating.

8. (T/F) It is all right to remove the radiator cap when the coolant is hot if the cap is removed slowly.

9. (Fill in the blank.) Never pour _____ water into a cold engine or _____ water into a hot engine.

10. (Fill in the blank.) Either bubbles or an oil film present in the coolant is a sign of _____ in the engine cylinders.

Engine Electrical Systems

6

JDPX5524

Fig. 1 — Engine Electrical Systems and Components (Spark-Ignition Engine Shown)

Introduction

If the engine is hard to start or lacks good performance, it could be caused by the engine electrical systems. Poor maintenance of the engine's starting, charging, and ignition circuits is one of the chief causes of these problems.

Engine electrical systems and components are shown in (Fig. 1).

For the engine to run properly, the following conditions must be present:

1. The battery must be fully charged to provide enough power to start the engine.

2. The alternator must be able to recharge the battery when needed.

3. The starter must crank the engine fast enough to start the engine.

4. The coil must provide electrical energy to the spark plugs for igniting the fuel-air mixture.

5. The distributor must direct the electric current to the proper spark plug at the right moment.

6. The spark plugs must be clean and gapped correctly to deliver sufficient spark to ignite the fuel properly.

7. All electrical wires and connections must be clean and secure.

Importance of Service

As with all preventive maintenance, the purpose is to prevent costly operation and damage to the machine. Keeping your engine's electrical systems properly serviced is just as important as any other maintenance job.

Listed below are some of the components which require attention and the results of not servicing them as recommended:

The battery must be kept fully charged and filled with water. It must also be kept clean. Failure to maintain the battery properly can result in brief battery life. The battery can become shorted out and lose its charge.

The alternator requires periodic inspection of its brushes to ensure that sufficient charge is being put back into the battery.

The starter brushes must also be inspected regularly to ensure that the starter is not draining excessive current from the starting circuit (caused by excessive cranking). The engine will be difficult to start with too little electrical power. Also, the starter must be checked for signs of overheating.

The distributor must be timed correctly to direct current to the spark plugs at the proper moment for good combustion. If the timing is late, extremely hot exhaust gases are created which can warp or burn the valves. If the timing is early, power is wasted and severe "knock" (preignition) can damage the pistons, valves, and bearings. Also, poor timing increases fuel consumption.

The breaker points and condenser must be maintained for good current delivery to the spark plugs.

The spark plugs must be clean and gapped correctly to provide sufficient spark to ignite the fuel properly. If the plugs are oil fouled or have deposits on them, the plug will not fire with a good spark and the fuel will not burn completely. Loss of power and fuel economy will result. The spark plug wiring must also be in good condition — clean, free of cracks and shorts.

Operation of Electrical Systems

The complete engine electrical system consists of three circuits:

- Charging circuit
- Starting circuit
- Ignition circuit

Let's look at these circuits briefly.

Charging Circuit

The charging circuit includes:

- Battery
- Voltage regulator
- Alternator

The charging circuit does two jobs:

- Recharges the battery
- Generates current during operation

AC Charging Circuits

AC charging circuits have an alternator and a regulator (Fig. 2).

JDPX5775

Fig. 2 — AC Charging Circuit

The alternator is really an AC generator. It produces alternating current but rectifies it electronically using diodes. Alternators are generally more compact than generators of equal output, and supply a higher current output at low engine speeds. They have replaced generators on most modern engines.

The regulator in AC charging circuits limits the alternator voltage to a safe, preset value. Transistorized models are used in many of the modern circuits.

Operation of Charging Circuit

All charging circuits operate in three stages:

* During starting — battery supplies all load current
* During peak operation — battery helps alternator supply load current
* During normal operation — alternator supplies all current and recharges battery

The battery starts the circuit when it supplies the spark to start the engine. The engine then drives the alternator, which produces current to take over the operation of the ignition, lights, and accessory loads in the whole system.

The battery also helps out during peak operation when the electrical loads are too much for the alternator.

But once the engine is started, the alternator is the "workhorse" which produces current for the ignition and accessory circuits.

The alternator supplies this current as long as the engine is speeded up. When the engine slows down or stops, the battery takes over part or all of the load.

Operation of the charging circuit during the three stages is illustrated in (Fig. 3).

The top diagram shows operation while starting the engine when the battery must supply the current.

The middle diagram shows what happens during peak electrical loads when the battery only helps the alternator.

The bottom diagram shows the system during normal operation when the alternator supplies all power for loads and also recharges the battery.

Detailed operation and maintenance will be covered later in this chapter.

**Battery Supplying
Load Current**

**Alternator and Battery
Supplying Load Current**

**Alternator Supplying Load Current
and Charging Battery**

JDPX5526

Fig. 3 — Alternator Charging Circuit in Operation—Three Stages

Fig. 4 — Basic Starting Circuit

Starting Circuit

The starting circuit (Fig. 4) converts electrical energy from the battery into mechanical energy at the starting motor to crank the engine. A basic starting circuit has four parts:

- The battery supplies energy for the circuit.

- The starter switch activates the circuit.

- The motor switch (solenoid) engages the starting motor drive with the engine flywheel.

- The starting motor drives the flywheel to crank the engine.

Operation of Starting Circuit

The starting circuit is shown in operation in (Fig. 5., Fig. 6, and Fig. 7).

When the starter switch is activated by the operator (Fig. 5), a small amount of electrical energy flows from the battery to the solenoid and back to the ground circuit.

Fig. 5 — Starting Circuit in Operation: (1) As the Starter Switch is Activated

As the solenoid gets this power from the battery, it moves the solenoid plunger and engages the pinion with the flywheel (Fig. 5). The plunger also closes the switch inside the solenoid between the battery and starting motor, completing the circuit and allowing a large amount of electrical energy to flow into the starting motor.

Fig. 6 — *Starting Circuit in Operation: (2) Starting Motor Engages Flywheel*

The starting motor takes the electrical energy from the battery and converts it into rotary mechanical energy to crank the engine (Fig. 7).

Fig. 7 — *Starting Circuit in Operation: (3) Starting Motor Cranks Engine*

But remember that the battery is the only source of power for starting the engine.

In this typical system, we have used a solenoid switch as an example. Motors can also use other types of switches, such as manual or magnetic.

Ignition Circuit (Spark-Ignition Engines)

The ignition circuit creates the spark which ignites fuel-air mixture to power gasoline, natural gas, or LP-Gas engines.

To do this, the ignition circuit must:

- Step up low voltage to high voltage surges
- Time these surges to the engine cycle

The ignition circuit has these parts:

- Ignition coil
- Distributor
- Spark plugs
- Ignition switch
- Ignition control unit
- Engine control unit

The coil transforms the low voltage from the battery to a high voltage for producing a spark. Many modern ignition systems have a separate coil for each individual cylinder.

The distributor does three things:

- Opens and closes the primary circuit, causing the coil to produce high-voltage surges
- Times these surges to engine rotation
- Directs each high-voltage surge to the proper spark plug

The spark plugs ignite the fuel-air mixture within each cylinder of the engine.

The battery is the initial power source for the voltage in the ignition circuit, while the ignition switch turns on the circuit when it cranks the engine.

The primary circuit is the path for low-voltage current from the power source (Fig. 8). It includes these parts:

- Ignition switch
- Coil primary winding
- Sensor and reluctor
- Ignition control unit

The secondary circuit is the high-voltage path for current stepped up by the coil (Fig. 8). It includes these parts:

- Coil secondary winding
- Distributor rotor
- Distributor cap
- Spark plug wires
- Spark plugs

- – – – **Primary Circuit**
———— **Secondary Circuit**

JDPX5772

Fig. 8 — Ignition Circuit

The operation of the electronic circuit is discussed later in the chapter.

Servicing the Battery

Battery maintenance is simple, but it is important that service be performed regularly or the battery will soon fail.

Before we discuss how to service the battery, let's look at how it works. Then it will be easy to understand why the battery requires periodic maintenance.

How a Battery Works

Construction

The battery is made up of a number of individual cells in a hard rubber case (Fig. 9).

The basic units of each cell are the positive and the negative plates.

These plates hold the active materials in flat grids. Charged negative plates contain spongy lead (Pb) which is grey in color. Charged positive plates contain lead peroxide (PbO_2) which has a chocolate brown color.

A plate group is made by welding a number of similar plates to a plate strap (Fig. 10).

JDPX5534

Fig. 9 — Construction of a Storage Battery

Each plate in the interlaced plate group is kept apart from its neighbor by porous separators as shown in (Fig. 9). The separators allow a free flow of electrolyte around the active plates. The resulting assembly is called an element.

After the element is assembled, it is placed in a cell compartment of the battery case.

Hard-top batteries (Fig. 10) have cell connectors which pass through the partitions between cells. The connectors and partitions are sealed so that electrolyte will not transfer between cells. This improves battery performance, since the cell connections are shorter and the cover is more acid-tight.

Fig. 10 — Hard-Top Battery with One-Piece Cover

The main battery terminals are the positive and negative posts. The positive terminal is larger to help prevent the danger of connecting the battery in reverse polarity.

Vent caps are located in each cell cover. The caps have two purposes: 1) they close the openings in the cell cover through which the electrolyte level is checked and water is added and 2) they provide a vent for the escape of gases formed when the battery is charging.

Each cell in a storage battery has a potential of about two volts. Six-volt batteries contain three cells connected in series, while 12-volt batteries have six cells in series (Fig. 11).

For higher voltages, combinations of batteries are used. An example is where two 12-volt batteries are connected in series to serve a 24-volt system (Fig. 11).

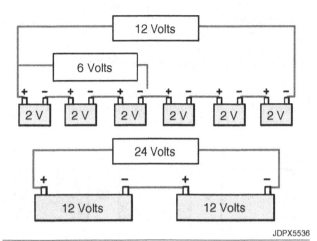

Fig. 11 — Battery Cells and Batteries Connected in Series

Operation of Battery

The battery produces current by a chemical reaction between the active materials of the unlike plates and the sulfuric acid of the electrolyte (Fig. 12).

Current Flow:

Produced by
Dissimilar Plates
in Electrolyte
Solution

Fig. 12 — How a Battery Produces Current Flow

While this chemical reaction is taking place, the battery is discharging. After most of the active materials have reacted, the battery is discharged. It must then be recharged before use.

We'll discuss these two cycles, but first let's see what the electrolyte is made of.

Electrolyte Solution

 CAUTION: Battery electrolyte is a highly corrosive acid and should be handled with extreme care. If electrolyte comes in contact with any part of the body, immediately flush the contaminated area with fresh clean water and seek medical attention immediately. Always wear eye protection when working around batteries. Keep sparks, lighted matches, and open flames away from the top of the battery. Battery gas can explode.

The electrolyte in a fully charged battery is a solution of concentrated sulfuric acid in water (Fig. 13). It has a specific gravity of about 1.270 at 80°F (27°C), which means it weighs 1.270 times more than water. The solution is about 36% sulfuric acid (H_2SO_4) and 64% water (H_2O) as shown.

The voltage of a battery cell depends upon the chemical difference between the active materials and also upon the concentration of the electrolyte.

64% Water	36% Acid	Electrolyte
Sp. Gr. 1.000	Sp. Gr. 1.835	Sp. Gr. 1.270

JDPX5538

Fig. 13 — Battery Electrolyte

Discharge Cycle of Battery

When the battery is connected to a complete circuit, current begins to flow from the battery. The discharge cycle begins (Fig. 14).

This current is produced by a chemical action as shown in the diagram. Study this process to become familiar with the reactions in the battery during discharge.

Note that the material in the positive plates and negative plates becomes similar chemically during discharge, as the lead sulfate accumulates. This condition accounts for the loss of cell voltage, since voltage depends upon the difference between the two materials.

As the discharge continues, dilution of the electrolyte and the accumulation of lead sulfate in the plates eventually brings the reactions to a stop. For this reason the active materials never are completely exhausted during discharge.

When the battery can no longer produce the desired voltage, it is said to be discharged. It must be recharged by a suitable flow of direct current from some external source before it can be put back in service.

Charging Cycle of Battery

The chemical reactions which go on in the battery cell during the charge are the reverse of those which occur during discharge. See (Fig. 14).

These reactions demonstrate the important fact that water actually takes part in the chemistry of a lead-acid storage battery.

The purity of water for battery use has always been a controversial subject, but it always resolves to the fact that distilled water is the best.

Water with impurities hurts the life and performance of a battery. This is because minerals and other impurities build up on the battery plates, reducing the surface area.

JDPX5539

Fig. 14 — Chemical Action in Battery During Discharge and Charge Orders

Maintaining the Battery

To receive the maximum life from the battery, you must:

- Check the electrolyte level every 50 hours
- Clean the battery every 250 hours
- Check the battery electrical condition every 250 hours
- Charge the battery when needed

(Fig. 15) shows a poorly maintained battery. This unit will soon fail completely and all these problems could likely have been avoided by good maintenance.

Every 50 hours of operation, remove all caps from vent wells (Fig. 16). The electrolyte level should be to the bottom of the filler neck — so that the tops of the battery plates are covered (Fig. 17).

 CAUTION: GAS FROM BATTERY ELECTROLYTE IS FLAMMABLE. Keep all sparks and flames away from the battery. If the battery has been charging, hydrogen gas is present. This gas will explode in the presence of a spark or flame and possibly cause serious injury to you or others nearby.

Fig. 17 — Proper Level of Electrolyte in Battery Cells

If any of the cells require water, fill them with distilled water. Use a battery syringe shown in (Fig. 18) to avoid overfilling. If distilled water is not available use clean rain water (better than softened water). Replace caps.

Fig. 15 — Things which Affect the Life of a Battery

Checking the Electrolyte Level

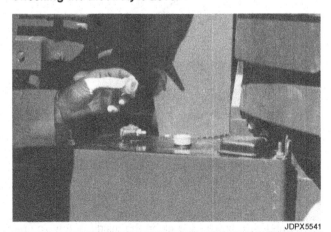

Fig. 16 — Removing Vent Caps to Check Battery Electrolyte Level

Fig. 18 — Adding Distilled Water to Battery

Battery Don'ts

Don't overfill. When the battery is being charged, the electrolyte will overflow through the vents in the caps and onto the top of the battery. This provides a path for leakage of electricity and will also cause corrosion and deterioration of the metal parts.

Don't use hard water. The minerals in hard water will leave deposits on the plates and interfere with the chemical action of the battery.

Don't add acid to the battery unless electrolyte is lost by spilling. To operate properly, a battery must have the correct proportions of acid and water.

Don't add water to the battery just before checking specific gravity. If the level is too low, add necessary water and operate in circuit for a few hours to mix water and electrolyte, then check.

Don't add water to the battery in freezing weather unless it will be operated immediately to allow proper mixing of water with electrolyte.

Cleaning the Battery

Your battery requires cleaning regularly to prevent dirt, moisture, and corrosion from robbing it of its charge.

While the battery is charging, acid spray is carried out of the battery with the hydrogen gas created by the chemical action of the electrolyte. This acid settles on the top of the battery and provides a damp surface for dust and dirt to cling to. Posts and terminals also become corroded.

The small amount of acid is enough to provide an electrical path to the metal frame or to the opposite terminal. This will cause the battery to slowly discharge.

Corroded terminals also prevent the alternator from recharging the battery when needed. Your battery loses its charge due to the poor contact of the cables and terminals caused by a film of corrosion.

Periodically wipe off the battery with a damp cloth, about every 250 hours or when very dirty. If corrosion is present, clean the battery as given below.

Tools And Materials Needed

To clean a battery, the following tools and materials are needed.

- Bristle brush
- Wire brush and sandpaper
  (or battery clamp and post cleaning tools)
- Small paintbrush
- Large common screwdriver
- Battery clamp puller
- Box-end wrenches (to fit terminal bolts)
- Baking soda
- Container of water
- Light grease or petroleum jelly

How to Clean Battery

To clean the battery, proceed as follows:

1. Remove ground strap or cable from battery terminal post (Fig. 19). This prevents short circuits caused by accidentally grounding the other terminal with a tool. Use a battery clamp puller if available.

    Don't pound on terminal; you may crack the battery top or loosen the post.

To remove clamp, loosen bolt and carefully spread jaws of clamp. Use clamp puller if available.

JDPX5544

Fig. 19 — Removing Battery Terminal Clamp

2. Remove the other battery cable.

3. Wipe off the clamps with a cloth. Dip the clamps into a mixture of baking soda and water (two tablespoons of soda to a pint [65 mL per liter] of water). This will clean off some of the corrosion and acid.

4. Clean the inside of the clamps with a round wire brush cleaning tool (Fig. 20), or roll a small piece of sandpaper around your finger, and clean the inside of the clamps. Wipe the clamps clean with a dry cloth.

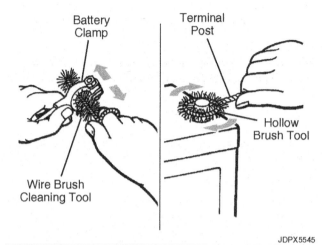

Battery Clamp

Terminal Post

Hollow Brush Tool

Wire Brush Cleaning Tool

JDPX5545

Fig. 20 — Cleaning Battery Cable Clamps and Terminal Posts

5. Use a hollow-brush terminal cleaning tool to scrub the corrosion from the terminal posts (Fig. 20). (A stiff wire brush can be used if no tool is available.)

6. Use a bristle brush to remove loose dirt and corrosion particles from the top of the battery (Fig. 21).

Scrub Brush

Dirt and Corrosion

JDPX5546

Fig. 21 — Removing Dirt with a Bristle Brush

7. Brush a fresh mixture of baking soda and water on top of battery and posts (Fig. 22). This will neutralize the acid. Apply solution until foaming stops.

NOTE: Do not allow any of the solution to enter the breather holes in the caps. The baking soda will weaken the acid in the electrolyte. Also be sure caps are securely tightened before cleaning.

Baking Soda and Water Solution

JDPX5547

Fig. 22 — Neutralizing Acid Deposits

8. Flush off residue with clean water (Fig. 23). Protect battery caps from direct stream of water to avoid flushing dirt into the battery through the vent holes.

If battery is on machine, also flush off surrounding areas with water.

Brush

Flushing Water

JDPX5548

Fig. 23 — Flushing Off Top of Battery

9. Dry the top of the battery with a clean cloth.

10. Inspect the battery for any damage which may require repair or replacement (See Fig. 15).

11. Attach nongrounded cable to proper battery terminal. Be sure the correct connection is made or you may damage the alternator. (Most batteries have terminals of different sizes to avoid mix-ups).

12. Then attach ground cable to the opposite terminal. This will avoid accidental grounding of the other terminal.

IMPORTANT: Do not pound the clamps in place. You may break the seal around the battery posts or crack the battery cover.

Light Grease or Petroleum Jelly

Fig. 24 — Applying Protective Coat of Grease to Terminals

13. Apply a coating of light grease or petroleum jelly (Fig. 24) to the terminals and clamps to protect them against further corrosion.

14. Examine the breather holes in the top of each battery cap to be sure they are open.

Checking Battery Electrical Condition

 CAUTION: Never short across battery terminal posts to check for a spark. This tells you very little about the condition of the battery and an explosion may occur when hydrogen gas is present.

Several devices are available to check the battery more accurately and safely. These include: hydrometer, voltmeter, and charger-tester.

Because the hydrometer is the most commonly used and least expensive, we will cover use of it only.

Checking Specific Gravity

The state of battery charge is indicated by the specific gravity or weight of the battery electrolyte.

The strength of the electrolyte varies directly with the state of charge of each cell.

To find out how much energy is available from the battery, you need only find out what percentage of sulfuric acid remains in the electrolyte. One of the simplest and most reliable ways to do this is to measure the specific gravity or weight of the solution.

Specific gravity can be measured very quickly by means of a battery hydrometer with a thermometer for temperature correction.

Hydrometers are calibrated to measure specific gravity correctly at an electrolyte temperature of 80°F (27°C).

USING THE HYDROMETER

To check the specific gravity of the electrolyte, do the following:

1. Remove battery caps.

2. When checking specific gravity of a battery which has been gassing freely, allow sediment to settle or gas to escape from the sample before taking the reading.

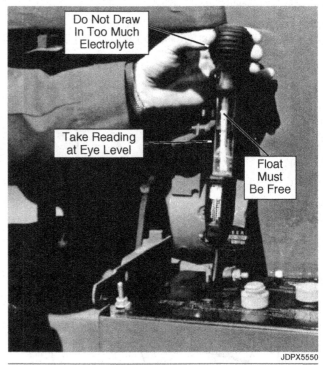

Do Not Draw In Too Much Electrolyte

Take Reading at Eye Level

Float Must Be Free

JDPX5550

Fig. 25 — Check Specific Gravity of a Battery with a Hydrometer

3. Insert the hydrometer into one of the cell openings (Fig. 25). Squeeze the bulb and slowly release it to draw electrolyte into the barrel.

If the electrolyte level is too low to fill the hydrometer, add water to the battery. Operate the engine for a few hours to mix the water and electrolyte so that an accurate reading can be taken.

Hold the hydrometer vertically so the float does not touch the sides. Apply or release some pressure on the bulb until the float in the hydrometer rides freely in the barrel. If the float tends to touch the side of the barrel, shake the hydrometer gently. If the float continues to stick or touch the sides, flush the inside of the hydrometer with soap and water and rinse well before further testing.

If the indicator scale inside the float appears wet or stained, the float probably leaks and your reading will not be accurate.

4. Leave the hydrometer nozzle in the battery cell to avoid spilling acid on the battery or yourself. Be sure your eye is at the level of the liquid when the reading is taken. Readings taken at an angle may be false.

   Note the reading indicated by the level of the electrolyte position on the scale.

5. The specific gravity should read from 1.215 to 1.270 (corrected for 80°F, 27°C electrolyte temperature).

FOR FAHRENHEIT TEMPERATURES

To determine a corrected specific gravity reading when the temperature of the electrolyte is other than 80°F: ADD to the hydrometer reading four gravity points (0.004) for each 10° ABOVE 80°F.

SUBTRACT four gravity points (0.004) for each 10° BELOW 80°F.

This compensates for expansion and contraction of the electrolyte at temperatures above or below the standard.

For example, a specific gravity reading of 1.234 is obtained when electrolyte is at 120°F (Fig. 26). Since this reading was taken with the electrolyte temperature 40° above the standard, a total of 16 (4 x 4) gravity points (0.016) is added, giving a corrected reading of 1.250.

As a further example, suppose a reading of 1.282 is obtained at 0°F. This reading was taken with the electrolyte temperature 80° below the standard. Therefore, a total of 32 (8 x 4) gravity points (0.032) is subtracted, giving a corrected reading of 1.250 (which is satisfactory).

FOR CELSIUS TEMPERATURES

To determine a corrected specific gravity reading when the electrolyte temperature is other then 27°C: ADD to the hydrometer reading seven gravity points (0.007) for each 10° ABOVE 27°C.

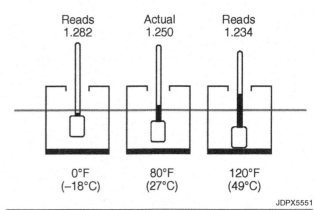

Reads 1.282   Actual 1.250   Reads 1.234

0°F (−18°C)   80°F (27°C)   120°F (49°C)

JDPX5551

Fig. 26 — Correcting Specific Gravity Readings to Allow for Temperature Variations

SUBTRACT seven gravity points (0.007) for each 10° BELOW 27°C.

For example, if a specific gravity reading of 1.234 is obtained when electrolyte is at 49°C (Fig. 26), the electrolyte temperature is 22°C above the standard. A total of 16 (2.2 x 7) gravity points (0.016) is added, giving a corrected reading of 1.250.

Then, suppose a reading of 1.282 is obtained at −18°C. This reading was taken with the electrolyte temperature 45°C below the standard. Therefore, a total of 32 (4.5 x 7) gravity points (0.032) is subtracted, giving a corrected reading of 1.250 (which is satisfactory).

6. Return the electrolyte to the cell from which it was taken.

 CAUTION: Sulfuric acid in battery electrolyte is poisonous. It is strong enough to burn skin, eat holes in clothing, and cause blindness if splashed in eyes. If you spill acid on yourself, flush your skin with water, apply baking soda or lime to help neutralize the acid, and flush your eyes with water for 10–15 minutes. Get medical attention immediately.

7. Check the remaining cells in the same manner as above.

8. Install battery caps and flush the hydrometer with clean water.

9. Compare the temperature-corrected readings with the chart and descriptions below to determine condition of the battery.

Specific Gravity Reading (Adjusted)	State of Charge
1.260 Sp. Gr.	100% Charged
1.230 Sp. Gr.	75% Charged
1.200 Sp. Gr.	50% Charged
1.170 Sp. Gr.	25% Charged
1.140 Sp. Gr.	Very Little Useful Capacity
1.110 Sp. Gr.	Discharged

The table above shows the state of charge of a typical battery at various specific gravity readings.

IF SPECIFIC GRAVITY IS LESS THAN 1.215

When the specific gravity reading is less than 1.215 (after correction for temperature), the battery may be in satisfactory condition although its state of charge is low. Charge the battery before making further tests. (See following in this chapter for details.)

IF SPECIFIC GRAVITY IS ABOVE 1.270

When the specific gravity reading is above 1.270 (after correction for temperature), the battery may be in satisfactory condition although it is above full charge. In use, its specific gravity should return quickly to the normal 1.215–1.270 range. Make further tests to be more certain of the battery condition.

Voltage Chart	
Estimated Electrolyte Temperature	Minimum Required Voltage under 15-Sec. Load (Use 1/2 These Values for 6-Volt Batteries)
70°F (21°C) and above	9.6
60°F (16°C)	9.5
50°F (10°C)	9.4
40°F (4°C)	9.3
30°F (−1°C)	9.1
20°F (−7°C)	8.9
10°F (−12°C)	8.7
0°F (−18°C)	8.5

Table 1 — Voltage Chart

IF MORE THAN 0.050 VARIATION BETWEEN CELLS

A difference of more than 50 specific gravity points (0.050) between cells indicates an unsatisfactory battery condition. This may be due to an internal defect, short circuit, improper activation, or deterioration from extended use. The battery should normally be replaced.

NOTE: Specific gravity readings do not always give a true indication of the state of charge of a battery. If water has been added recently or acid has been lost through accident or leakage, the reading will indicate a lower state of charge than is actually the case. Therefore, never use specific gravity readings alone to decide the condition of a battery. If unsure of the tests, take the battery to your dealer for further testing.

Adjustable Load Test

The following instructions are intended as guidelines. When available, the instrument manufacturer's instructions should be followed.

1. Disconnect battery cables, starting with ground cable.

2. Measure temperature of a center cell. If instrument has an integral temperature compensator, use attached probe. Cover battery with a wet cloth.

3. Connect voltmeter and load test leads to appropriate battery terminals. Make certain terminals are free of corrosion.

4. Connect current transducer (if necessary) to appropriate lead.

5. Apply test load equivalent to 50% of cranking performance rating of battery for 15 seconds.

6. Read the voltage (Fig. 27) at 15 seconds, then remove the load.

7. Determine minimum voltage required at electrolyte test temperature from the Voltage Chart (Table 1).

8. If test voltage is above minimum, return battery to service.

9. If test voltage is below minimum, replace battery.

Fig. 27 — Checking Battery State of Charge

Charging the Battery

The amount of electrical current a battery can produce is limited by the amount of chemical reaction which can take place within it.

When chemical reaction in a battery has ended through defect or long use, the battery is discharged and can no longer produce a flow of electrical current.

The battery can be recharged, however, by causing direct current from an outside source to flow through it in a direction opposite to that in which it flowed out of the battery.

During discharge, current flows from the positive (+) terminal of the battery, through the circuit, and back into the battery at the negative (–) terminal (Fig. 28).

Within the battery, current flow is from the negative to the positive terminal.

To recharge the battery, this flow of current is reversed as shown, restoring the chemicals in the battery to their active state.

The battery then becomes charged and ready to produce electrical current again. The chemical action which takes place within a battery during the discharging and charging was explained earlier in this chapter.

Current Flow During Discharge   **Reversed Flow During Charge**

JDPX5554

Fig. 28 — Current Flow During Discharge and Charge of Battery

Batteries can be recharged in two ways:

• Fast Charging

• Slow Charging

Because most operator-owned chargers are "trickle" chargers, we will only discuss slow charging here.

 CAUTION: A battery produces gasses which can explode. Keep sparks, lighted matches, and open flames from the top of the battery.

SLOW CHARGING

IMPORTANT: During charging, the electrolyte in a sulfated battery will bubble and produce gasses. During slow charging, the electrolyte produces few bubbles compared to fast charging. A badly sulfated battery must be slow charged.

Be sure to follow the manufacturer's instructions for using the charger. The battery charger shown in (Fig. 29) will fast or slow charge and can also be used as a booster battery.

NOTE: Be sure to remove the battery cell caps while charging to allow gas to flow freely from battery.

Charge the battery at a low rate (7% of the battery ampere-hour rating or less) for an extended period of time until fully charged.

A battery is considered fully charged when three consecutive hydrometer readings, taken at hourly intervals, show no rise in specific gravity.

The normal slow-charging period is from 12 to 24 hours.

If a battery's specific gravity has not reached the normal full charge range (1.215 to 1.270) within 48 hours of slow charging, replace the battery.

Badly sulfated batteries, however, may take from 60 to 100 hours to recharge completely.

JDPX5555

Fig. 29 — Battery Charger

Connecting Booster Batteries

Cold weather starting can be made easier by connecting an additional battery (equal voltage) in parallel with the original battery.

 CAUTION: A battery produces gasses which can explode. Make sure all switches are turned off and make the last connection or the first disconnect away from the battery receiving the boost.

The first jumper cable should connect the positive (+) terminal of the booster battery to the positive (+) terminal of the original battery. The second jumper cable should first be connected to the negative (–) terminal of the booster battery and then to the frame of the machine with the battery being boosted. NEVER REVERSE THE CONNECTIONS.

Always break the connection at the booster battery first.

Some portable battery chargers can be used as a booster battery (Fig. 29).

IMPORTANT: Never use a 12-volt booster battery on a 6-volt system as it may damage the system.

Selection of Batteries for Replacement

When replacing batteries, be sure to replace the battery with one at least equal in size to the original.

For cold weather starting, the battery must be powerful enough for the cranking job.

(Fig. 30) shows how the load on the battery gets bigger when it is colder. At –20°F (–29°C), the battery has only 30% of its full cranking capacity. At the same time, greater load is put on the battery by the colder engine when starting.

In effect, at cold temperatures the battery is "smaller" while the engine is "larger."

If the replacement battery is smaller than the original, the engine will surely be harder to start in cold weather.

There are many times in the heat of summer when engines are just as hard to start as in the winter, especially when an air conditioner is added to the engine load. Therefore, use the same method of matching battery power to the engine in hot areas as you would in colder climates.

JDPX5556

Fig. 30 — How Cold Weather Affects the Battery and the Engine when Starting

Other Factors In Battery Selection

When replacing batteries, be sure to replace the battery with one at least equal in size (ampere-hours rating) to the original.

A larger battery than the original may be needed if added accessories put a larger load on the battery.

An extra-output alternator may be the answer in cases where electrical loads are excessive or when operating mostly at slower speeds. This will help keep the battery charged and increase its service life.

The cheapest battery is not always the best buy for replacement. For example, three batteries in the same group size may vary in price, but they also vary in ampere-hours rating, in construction, and in warranty period. Divide the price by the months of warranty, and you may find the most expensive batteries are really the most economical per month of expected service.

A final word on replacing batteries: One out of every four batteries returned for warranty has nothing wrong with it except that it is discharged. Be sure to troubleshoot the battery before you replace it.

Safety Rules For Batteries

1. To avoid injury from a spark or short circuit, DISCONNECT THE BATTERY GROUND STRAP (Fig. 31) when working on any part of the electrical system or engine. This will also prevent accidental starting.

Dual Batteries   **Single Battery**

JDPX5557

Fig. 31 — Installation of Typical Batteries

2. Disconnect the battery cable (Fig. 31) before fast charging the battery in the machine. This is especially important with AC charging systems where the alternator can be damaged.

3. When removing the battery, disconnect the battery ground strap first. When installing the battery, wait until last to connect the ground strap.

4. Never reverse the polarity of the battery connections. In general, systems with AC charging have negative grounds (–), while systems with AC charging can have either, positive (+) or negative (–) grounds. Reversing the polarity may damage some components and wiring in the system.

5. DO NOT ATTEMPT TO POLARIZE THE ALTERNATOR on AC circuits after connecting the battery. No polarization is needed. Any attempt to do so may damage the alternator, regulator, or circuits.

6. If booster batteries are used to start an engine, connect the (+) terminal of the booster battery to the (+) terminal of the dead battery with a jumper cable. Then, connect the second cable to the (–) terminal on the booster battery. Make the last (–) connection to a good ground on the machine with the dead battery. Disconnect in reverse order.

7. Do not attempt to recharge or jump-start a frozen battery. Check for ice in each cell of the battery.

8. When using booster batteries, prevent fire hazards as follows:

   a. When possible, use cables with a switch in the line.

   b. Always "rock" the connector clips to make sure they are making good contact.

   c. Always put the machine in PARK.

   d. Never jump start by touching connectors to the starter motor. The machine can suddenly lurch and crush you.

9. Don't lay tools down by a battery. An accidental nudge and a tool can contact a battery terminal and short circuit the battery.

10. Gas from battery electrolyte is flammable: Keep sparks and flame away from the battery. When charging the battery, gas is created rapidly. Be sure the room where batteries are charged is well ventilated.

11. Battery acid is harmful on contact

    If battery electrolyte spills:

    a. Remove affected clothing.

    b. Rinse affected skin with clear water for 10 or 15 minutes.

    c. Flood eyes with clear water for 10 or 15 minutes. Force the eyes open so water can flush them.

    d. Then see a doctor.

    e. Don't use any medication or eye drops unless prescribed by a physician.

Maintenance-Free Batteries

Maintenance-free batteries operate similarly to the conventional style battery. The construction is somewhat different than other batteries. The plates in maintenance-free batteries are made of lead-calcium which reduces gassing by as much as 97 percent over conventional batteries with lead-antimony plates.

Maintenance-free batteries are vented but most do not have vent caps. This reduces acid spillage and thus reduces the potential for corrosion on the battery terminals.

The vent strip may be removed from the top of some maintenance free batteries to expose the electrolyte. A hydrometer can then be used to check the battery and water may be added if necessary. However, because of the reduced gassing in maintenance-free batteries with lead-calcium plates, additional water normally is not required for the life of the battery.

Most maintenance-free batteries with lead-calcium plates are activated, charged, and ready for service when shipped from the factory. Because of a low rate of discharge, they have a longer shelf life than conventional wet-charged batteries. A maintenance-free battery may have a shelf life of 12 months or longer, depending on storage temperature.

Servicing Spark Plugs

Spark plug service has three basic jobs:

* Inspection
* Cleaning
* Gap adjustment

Most engine manufacturers recommend a specific time interval for ignition services. Follow this timetable very closely.

Fouled or damaged spark plugs can rob a spark-ignition engine of power and economy. For example, if spark plugs are badly fouled, the power and fuel lost in only a few weeks can pay for a new set of plugs.

Spark Plug Operation

Fig. 32 — Spark Plug Construction

A spark plug has two electrodes separated by a gap (Fig. 32). High-voltage current from the distributor enters the top of a spark plug, travels down the center electrode, and jumps the gap at the bottom to make a spark.

The width of the spark plug gap is vital to both the size of the spark and to proper timing of the ignition.

Heat Range of Plugs

The heat range of a spark plug is as important as the gap setting.

The term "heat range" refers to the plug's ability to transfer the heat at the firing tip to the cooling systems of the engine. This is determined by the distance the heat must travel.

As shown in (Fig. 33), the end of a plug insulator that has a long nose or cone is farther from the cooling system. Therefore, heat at the end will travel farther. This type of plug will then run hot.

In contrast, the end of a short insulator cone is closer to the cooling system and heat will transfer faster. This plug will then operate cooler.

Engine design and operating conditions will decide which type of spark plug — hot or cold — should be used. Generally, an engine which operates at fast speeds or heavy loads, and thus hotter, will require a colder plug so that the heat will transfer faster. On the other hand, a hotter plug will be used in an engine that operates at low or idle speeds most of the time. For normal engine operations, a plug that falls somewhere between hot and cold is used.

Fig. 33 — Heat Range of Spark Plugs

The heat range of a plug is usually shown by a number on the plug. A higher number (such as 18) is hotter than a lower one (such as 15).

When the correct heat range is used, the plugs operate at the proper temperatures to burn themselves free of carbon. *If plugs operate too hot, preignition will occur.* *If plugs operate too cold, fouling will result.*

Tools and Materials Needed

To service spark plugs, the following tools and materials are needed:

- Spark plug socket wrench
- Pan of cleaning solvent (not gasoline)
- Wire brush
- Blade-type file
- Wire-type plug gap gauge (inch or metric, as required)
- Set of new plug gaskets (if available)
- Torque wrench (inch or metric, as required)

Removing Spark Plugs

Spark plugs should be removed and serviced every 500 hours, or sooner if recommended in the operator's manual.

Observe these practices when removing plugs:

1. Pull the wire from the plug by grasping the terminal, not by pulling on the wire.

2. Use a deep-well socket to loosen the spark plug. (A special spark plug socket with rubber insert is even better.) Hold the socket straight to prevent breaking the insulator.

3. After loosening the plug but before removing it, always clean the area around the spark plug by blowing, wiping, or brushing. (Be sure to protect your eyes.) This will prevent dirt from falling into the cylinder after removal.

4. Remove the plugs and place them in order to match the cylinder each came from. The condition of the spark plug can tell you a lot about the operation of a particular cylinder. Also remove the plug gaskets (if used).

Inspecting Spark Plugs

Check the condition of all spark plugs removed-even if you are replacing them. The appearance of the plug's firing end can tell you whether your engine is using too much oil, overfueling, misfiring, or overheating. Condition of plugs may also warn you of a wrong grade of fuel or an incorrect spark plug.

Study the chart to become familiar with, spark plug conditions and what they mean.

SPARK PLUG CONDITION CHART

Condition	Identification	Caused By	Condition	Identification	Caused By
Oil Fouling	Wet, sludgy deposits.	Excessive oil entering combustion chamber, worn rings and pistons, excessive clearance between valve guides and stems, or worn or loose bearings.	**High Lead Deposits**	White, powdery deposits.	Highly leaded gasoline (premium gasoline).
Gas Fouling	Dry, black, fluffy deposits.	Incomplete combustion caused by too rich a fuel-air mixture or by a defective coil or ignition wiring.	**Carbon Fouling**	Hard, baked-on black carbon.	Too cold a plug. Weak ignition, defective fuel pump, dirty air cleaner, too rich a fuel mixture.
Burned or Overheating	White, burned, or blistered anti-insulator nose and eroded electrodes.	Engine overheating caused by improper ignition timing, wrong type of fuel, loose spark plugs, too hot a plug, or low fuel pump pressure.	**Silicone Deposit**	Hard and scratchy.	Formed when fine sand particles combine with anti-knock compounds in fuel. Most common in dusty areas. The plugs cannot be cleaned.
Normal Conditions	Rusty brown to grayish tan powder deposit and minor electrode erosion.	Regular or unleaded gasoline.	**Splashed Fouling**	Splattered deposits.	Deposits from misfiring loosened when normal combustion chamber deposits restored after new plugs are installed. During high-speed run, these deposits are thrown into plug.

When inspecting the plugs, look for the abnormal wear shown in the Spark Plug Condition Chart.

Then decide whether to recondition or replace the plugs.

Remember, if one plug is replaced, all the plugs should be replaced to get the full advantage of new plug performance and economy. This does not apply, of course, if unusual conditions cause premature failure to just one in a fairly new set of plugs.

Fig. 34 — Spark Plug Maintenance

Normally, replace the whole set of plugs after long intervals of use. Normal wear can double the voltage requirements of a spark plug even in a short period of time.

Cleaning Spark Plugs

NOTE: Do not use a power wire brush to clean the plugs. Most makers of plugs do not recommend this.

1. Badly fouled plugs should be replaced. It is doubtful if sand blasting or liquid cleaning will remove all the deposits from such plugs.

2. If the plugs have moderate deposits, you may take them to your dealer for machine cleaning. However, if a sandblast machine is used to clean the plugs, some engine manufacturers void the warranty on the engine.

3. Clean wet, oily plugs with a cleaning solvent which dissolves petroleum deposits (but not gasoline).

4. Clean the threads with a wire hand brush.

5. To allow room for filing, bend the ground electrode away from the center electrode.

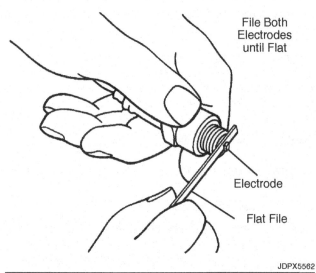

Fig. 35 — Filing Spark Plug Electrodes until Flat

6. File both electrodes (Fig. 35) until they have flat bright surfaces (like a new plug). However, remove as little material as possible.

   These flat surfaces reduce the voltage required to fire the plug consistently. Rounded electrodes require higher voltages to fire the plug.

7. Bend ground electrodes back to original position.

8. Clean or blow metal filings from plug.

Fig. 36 — Checking Spark Plug Gap (With Wire-Type Gauge)

Gap Adjustment of Spark Plugs

1. Whether the plug is new or used, always check the gap before you install the plug (Fig. 36). Refer to your operator's manual for the correct gap (usually 0.020, 0.025, or 0.030 inch; 0.5, 0.6 or 0.8 mm).

2. Don't use a flat gauge to check the spark plug gap. A flat gauge doesn't give an accurate indication of the true gap. A wire gauge will fit the contour of irregular surfaces.

IMPORTANT: **Never bend the center electrode, Doing so may crack or break the insulator tip.**

3. Bend the ground electrode, as necessary, with a gap setter (usually part of the spark plug gauge). See (Fig. 37). Check the gap with the proper thickness gauge.

Fig. 37 — Adjusting Spark Plug Gap

Installing Spark Plugs

As stated earlier, spark plugs are cooled by the coolant in the passages of the engine head. For this reason, be sure the area around each spark plug post is absolutely clean before installing plugs. New spark plugs may result in some increase in power and decrease in fuel consumption.

1. Install the plugs and tighten with your fingers. Be sure to use a gasket — unless the plug has a tapered seat (gaskets aren't required for this type of plug).

   You should use new gaskets when installing plugs. Old gaskets will be flattened by tightening.

   A properly tightened gasket conducts almost 50 percent of the heat flow from the plug to the engine head and coolant.

2. Tighten plug with a spark plug socket and torque wrench. The operator's manual will tell how much torque to apply. For example, the average 14 mm threaded plug is usually tightened to about 25 ft-lbs (34 N•m) torque.

   If the plug is not tight enough against the gasket, the plug will overheat.

However, if the plug is too tight against the gasket, the porcelain insulator may break. Also, the plug could be distorted and change the gap between the electrodes.

3. Check the condition of the spark plug wires before reinstalling. If the insulation is cracked or extremely soft, replace the wires. Defective insulation will allow electrical leaks and misfiring.

   Check the plug connectors for looseness and bad fit. If the connectors are not repairable, replace the wires.

Electronic Ignition

The components of an electronic ignition system (Fig. 38) are much the same as the components of a mechanical ignition system found on older equipment.

Fig. 38 — An Electronic Ignition

The main difference in the two systems is that the electronic battery system uses a solid state ignition control unit with a reluctor and sensor to time spark delivery in place of breaker points and a condenser.

Fig. 39 — Sensor and Reluctor

When the ignition switch is turned on, battery current flows through the switch to the coil and through the primary winding to the ignition control unit. A strong electromagnetic field is developed around the winding in the sensor coil (Fig. 39).

When one of the reluctor projections enters the magnetic field around the sensor coil its presence is sensed, and the sensing element in the ignition control unit breaks the primary circuit. Breaking the primary circuit collapses the electromagnetic field around the primary coil windings. This collapsing field induces a high voltage in the secondary coil. The voltage is routed to the distributor rotor (Fig. 40) through the high-tension lead. If timed correctly, the rotor, at that moment, is in position to contact the wire to the correct spark plug. The current flows to the spark plug and jumps the spark plug gap to make the ignition spark. The entire cycle then starts over to fire the next spark plug in order.

Fig. 40 — Rotor

Electronic Ignition Maintenance

The ignition control unit is sealed and requires no maintenance. There is no service to be performed on the sensor coil and reluctor with the exception of setting the air gap. To set the air gap:

1. Loosen the sensor coil adjusting screw.

2. Align one of the reluctor teeth with the sensor.

3. Insert a nonmagnetic feeler gauge, usually about 0.008 inch (0.2 mm), between the reluctor tooth and sensor. Move sensor against the feeler gauge and tighten the screw.

The rest of the system requires the same maintenance as a mechanical ignition system.

Checking Condition of Distributor

1. Clean outside of distributor housing and cap before removing cap. Use a small amount of cleaning solvent if necessary. Do not use water; it may cause short circuits. Do not allow any dirt to enter distributor. A clean cap will help prevent electrical shorts or crossfiring during operation.

Carbon Paths

Fig. 41 — Carbon Paths on Distributor Caps

2. Remove cap and wipe interior clean with a dry cloth. Dust, moisture, or oil deposits must be removed. If carbon paths are present (Fig. 41), the cap must be replaced. These paths are caused by electricity flowing between terminals or between terminals and a ground. Accumulation of dirt and moisture causes these paths to form. Once the path is formed, it will continue to conduct current and eventually burn through the cap.

Check to see if ventilator holes are open. If ozone gas (created by sparking between the rotor and terminals) is trapped, moisture will combine with the gas to form an acid which will corrode metal parts.

3. Inspect the distributor cap for chips or cracks.

Replace the cap if it is cracked. If the carbon button in the center of the cap is worn excessively, chipped, or cracked, replace the cap.

4. Remove the rotor and clean it. Inspect for cracks or excessive burning of the metal strip. Replace the rotor if these signs of damage are present.

5. If a dust cover is used, remove it and check the condition of the felt seal. If the seal is worn, replace the seal. Dirt may enter past a worn seal and cause rapid wear of the cam lobes or rubbing block on the points.

6. Check the centrifugal advance mechanism. Turn the distributor shaft in the direction of normal rotation. It must rotate freely for a short distance and return to its original position when released. If it doesn't, have it checked by a service shop.

Timing the Ignition Circuit

Timing Ignition by Timing Light Method

To time the engine with a timing light:

1. Locate the timing marks on the flywheel or fan pulley — see the operator's manual.

2. Connect the timing light to the No. 1 spark plug and make any other connections recommended by the timing light manufacturer (Fig. 42). Three types of timing lights are available:

   • Two-wire leads
   • Three-wire leads
   • 110-volt powered

   The two-wire type has one lead connected to the No. 1 spark plug and the other to a ground connection.

   The three-wire type is connected with one lead to the No. 1 spark plug and the other two to the battery terminals.

   The 110-volt type has a lead which is connected to the No. 1 spark plug and the power cord plugs into a 110-volt receptacle.

   Be sure to read the instructions included with the timing light so that you make the proper connections.

Fig. 42 — Timing the Distributor with a Timing Light

3. Determine the correct engine operating speed for making timing adjustments according to your operator's manual.

4. Chalk the proper timing mark so that it is easy to see.

5. Start the engine and adjust it to the proper speed.

 CAUTION: Be careful to avoid getting your hand or the timing light leads caught in any drive belts or the fan blades.

6. Aim the timing light (Fig. 42) at the marking or pointer near the flywheel or crankshaft fan pulley (wherever the timing marks appear).

   Be sure you aim the timing light so that it is aligned with the pointer mark and the centerline of the crankshaft (Fig. 43). This will assure you of a correct reading.

   If the proper timing mark doesn't align exactly with the pointer, proceed with the following steps.

7. Loosen clamps holding distributor (Fig. 42).

8. Turn distributor body slowly back and forth until timing mark is exactly opposite the pointer.

9. Tighten distributor clamps and remove timing light from engine.

10. Recheck idle speed, as timing can affect engine speed.

Fig. 43 — Be Sure to Align Timing Light with Pointer Mark and Center of Crankshaft

Ignition Systems Without Distributors

Distributorless electronic ignition systems operate similar to conventional ignition systems except that the spark is electronically timed. Electronic ignition systems do not have points or a condenser so they require little maintenance. They also produce a hotter spark of longer duration for:

- Quicker starts under adverse weather conditions

- More complete combustion

- Longer spark plug life

There are two types of ignition systems in which the distributor is not used to fire the spark plugs: direct ignition system or distributorless ignition system, both known as (DIS). Distributorless ignition system may also be known as (DLI). In both types of systems, the high voltage generated by the secondary winding of the coil is applied directly to the spark plug.

Some advantages of these ignition systems are these:

- Improved reliability

- Greater ignition spark control

- Electrical interference from the distributor is eliminated

- Ignition timing can be controlled over a wider range

There are two basic methods for generating sparks in these ignition systems.

- Independent ignition (non-waste spark)

- Simultaneous ignition (waste spark)

Independent ignition uses one coil per cylinder. Ignition systems using simultaneous ignition use one coil and two cylinders, which are paired according to piston position.

A typical direct ignition system is shown in (Fig. 44). It is a non-waste spark, camshaft-referenced, inductive ignition system. For a detailed description of the operation of the ignition system of a particular machine, refer to the technical manual for the appropriate machine.

The overall operation of the ignition system is controlled by the engine control unit (ECU). The spark timing is controlled by the ECU based on engine speed, manifold absolute pressure, and engine coolant temperature.

The manifold absolute pressure sensor sends a signal to the ECU to indicate the manifold (boost) pressure. The ECU interprets this signal as an indication of the load on the engine.

The ECU monitors signals from the camshaft position sensor to determine engine speed and piston position. The ECU determines the desired timing advance and then outputs a trigger signal to the ignition control unit (ICU) when a coil should be fired. A synchronized pulse is also sent by the ECU to the ICU so the ICU fires the correct coil.

JDPX3416

Fig. 44 — Electronic Ignition

Electronic Control Units

Electronic control units are used on nearly all modern agricultural equipment. They contain the electronic hardware and software needed to monitor and control a given system. Engine control units are used to control spark timing and fuel delivery by monitoring information such as air and coolant temperature, engine speed, manifold pressure, and others. Electronic control units are also used for other applications such as monitoring solution system operation on a sprayer or to control an automated steering system on a tractor. If a problem occurs in the system, the control unit can store this information as a diagnostic trouble code (DTC). Technicians can later access these trouble codes to aid in the diagnosis of the machine. Electronic control units do not require any maintenance; however, certain precautions should be taken when working with or around them.

- If pressure washing a machine, do not direct spray near any control unit.

- Never disconnect the battery while the key switch is on and the engine is running. This can cause electrical voltage spikes that can damage electronic components.

- Disconnect batteries prior to recharging. Battery chargers can cause electrical voltage spikes that can damage electronic components.

- Never jump start the machine with a voltage higher than the machine is designed to operate on. This can damage electrical components.

- Do not connect or disconnect electrical connectors while the key switch is on or the machine is running. This can cause computer system errors caused by interrupting a computer program while it is running. Electrical voltage spikes that are produced can damage electronic components.

- Do not apply power or ground to any component as a test unless specifically instructed to do so. Connecting the wrong voltage to the wrong point of an electronic system can cause electronic component failures.

- When welding on the machine, make sure to connect a ground lead to the parts being welded. For maximum protection disconnect all electronic controllers before welding.

The high currents associated with welding can damage wiring harnesses that are involved in the ground path. Welding can also cause electrical voltage spikes that can damage electronic components.

Servicing Alternator and Starting Motor

The alternator and starter will normally require little attention. But it is important that they receive service when required or you will have trouble starting your engine, and these components may become damaged.

Operation of Alternator and Starter

The alternator (AC charging circuits) operates continuously while the engine is running (Fig. 45). A regulator controls the alternator output, as required, to charge the battery or supply other electrical components on the engine or machine with power. The alternator produces an alternating current which flows back and forth. This current must be "rectified" (made to flow in one direction) to be usable by the electrical systems. This is done by electronic "check valves" called diodes within the alternator.

JDPX5771

Fig. 45 — Alternator (AC Generator)

The starting motor (Fig. 46) engages the flywheel when the engine is to be cranked for starting. As soon as the engine starts, the starting motor disengages. Running the starter without pause for more than 20 or 30 seconds will cause overheating and damage to the starter. It is designed to handle heavy loads for short periods of time only.

JDPX5077

Fig. 46 — Starting Motor and Solenoid

Most alternators do not require any periodic service except to check electrical connections and belt tension. However, read the following alternator and voltage regulator precautions to avoid damaging these components.

If your alternator or starting motor requires more service than is given in the following procedures, take it to your local service shop.

Precautions for Alternator and Voltage Regulator

Disconnect the battery ground strap from the battery when working on or near the alternator or regulator.

This will prevent damage that might occur if the terminals are accidentally shorted.

When the batteries are connected, observe the following precautions. Failure to observe them will probably result in damage to the alternator, regulator, or both.

- Never attempt to polarize the alternator or regulator. Never ground a terminal or connect a jumper wire to any alternator terminals.

- If electrical problems are encountered, before disconnecting the battery or alternator from the circuit, check for proper polarity. If polarity was incorrect the alternator has probably been seriously damaged. Have it repaired by a qualified service shop.

- Before installing a battery or alternator, be sure of proper polarity. Turn off all switches and accessories. Then, before connecting the battery ground strap, momentarily touch it to the battery post. No sparks should occur. If there are sparks, recheck all connections and installation procedures.

- The alternator field terminal or the field circuit between the alternator and the regulator must never be grounded under any circumstances.

- The alternator output terminal must never be grounded under any circumstances.

- Never disconnect or connect any alternator wires with batteries connected or with alternator operating. Do not operate the alternator on open circuit. The high voltage resulting from open circuit operation will result in damage to the alternator, regulator, or electrical system.

- Always connect additional batteries to each other in the correct polarity: Positive to Positive and Negative to Negative.

IMPORTANT: Disconnect cables from positive battery terminals when charging batteries.

Checking Alternator Belt Tension

The condition of the alternator belt and belt tension should be checked periodically. If belt tension if adjustable, adjust tension as specified in the machine operator's manual.

If equipped with automatic belt tensioner, inspect tensioner assembly as specified in the machine operator's manual.

Watching Gauges During Operation

When operating a machine, glance at the electrical gauges from time to time. They will tell you if the electrical system is charging properly.

The voltmeter shown in (Fig. 47) tells the operator it the battery is being charged and also tells the charged condition of the battery itself. Once the engine is running, the voltmeter needle should stay in the white "normal" range.

Indicator lights are used on some machine consoles. These glow to warn of a low charging rate.

JDPX5603

Fig. 47 — Voltmeter Tells Battery Charge and Condition

When starting the engine, the electrical indicator lights will glow, but they should go out after the engine has been running for a few seconds.

Test Yourself

Questions

1. Which of the following can be results of poor engine timing?

   a. Burned valves

   b. Worn breaker points

   c. Excessive oil consumption

   d. Excessive fuel consumption

2. (T/F) The condition of the spark plugs affects timing.

3. List the three basic circuits of the engine electrical system.

4. What causes a dirty battery to lose its charge?

5. What makes battery charging a potential safety hazard?

6. (T/F) An engine that runs at fast speeds, heavy loads, and hot temperatures requires a hotter spark plug.

7. Which of the following are not causes of spark plug failures?

   a. Damaged plug wires

   b. Cracked distributor cap

   c. Cracked plug insulation

   d. Carbon deposits on the electrodes

   e. Incorrect spark plug gap

Power Trains

7

Introduction

The power train has to absorb tremendous forces in today's farm machines. These components also operate under severe conditions, from the freezing cold of winter to the searing heat of summer, and from engine-staggering loads to rough, start-and-stop operation.

Because the clutch, transmission, and final drives receive such severe use, important periodic maintenance is required to provide transmission of power for the life of the machine (Fig. 1).

The lubricant used in the power train, whether it is hydraulic fluid or gear oil, becomes contaminated by dust, rust, moisture, and metal particles. All of these elements can cause severe damage to gears, bearings, and valves when the power train maintenance is neglected.

Because the transmission lubricant is so important, let's discuss it first.

Selecting Transmission Lubricants

Three basic types of transmissions are used today. Each requires specific types of lubricants. Below is a description of each type of transmission and its lubrication requirements.

- Sliding gear transmissions require gear oils to provide lubrication under extreme pressure conditions.

- Automatic transmission (including torque converters and hydrostatic transmissions) require automatic transmission fluids to provide a medium to transmit power, lubricate, and transfer heat.

Fig. 1 — Parts of a Power Train

• Hydraulic assist transmissions require transmission-hydraulic fluids to provide a medium to transmit power, lubricate, and transfer heat from both the transmission and hydraulic systems of the machine (Fig. 2).

Fig. 2 — Transmission-Hydraulic Oil Reservoir

Let's look at each of these transmission lubricants in more detail.

Gear Oils

The relatively small gears used in today's power trains result in higher loads and more friction between meshing gears. This makes lubrication more critical. Unless a good film of lubricant is maintained between the meshing gear teeth, they will show excessive wear and scoring (Fig. 3).

Normal Wear

Scoring Wear

Fig. 3 — Normal Gear Wear and Scoring Wear

In spur gear units (Fig. 4), where tooth pressures are relatively light, a simple gear oil is often adequate. However, special gears, such as spiral bevel and worm gear units (Fig. 4) can wear very rapidly unless the correct gear oil is used.

Spur Gears
Lower gear loads and less rubbing. Standard gear oils are often adequate.

Worm Gears
Higher gear loads and more rubbing. Special gear oils are often needed.

Fig. 4 — Gear Oils Must Match the Gear Load

For these higher loads, the gear oil must have special anti-friction and anti-weld agents. Oils containing these additives are known as extreme-pressure or hypoid lubricants.

To select the proper gear oil you must know:

• Viscosity requirements

• Service classification requirement

Viscosity Classification

The Society of Automotive Engineers (SAE) gear oil classification is based on the viscosity of an oil.

While the SAE numbers of gear oils are higher than the SAE numbers of engine crankcase oils, gear oils are not necessarily that much higher in viscosity. To avoid confusion, higher numbers are assigned to gear oils (Fig. 6). For example, SAE 80 gear oil actually has about the same viscosity as SAE 20 engine oil.

Multi-grade gear oils are presently available from some suppliers in grades of SAE 75/80 and SAE 80/90.

Some manufacturers recommend engine crankcase oils for use in standard transmission service, while some transmissions may use SAE 50 engine oil as an alternate for SAE 90 gear oil. As a result of this, some gear oil containers are marked SAE 50-90 indicating that the viscosity requirements of SAE 50 engine oil are also met.

Service Classification

The American Petroleum Institute (API) designates gear lubricants by the types of service for which they may be suitable. This is not a rating of performance.

API GL-1 oil is the lowest service, adequate for lower gear speeds and pressures, while GL-5 oil is for the hardest service.

As the GL number rises, so does the type of service.

Fig. 5 — Higher SAE Viscosity Numbers Are Assigned to Gear Oils (To Avoid Confusion)

For example, GL-5 oil is rated for harder service than GL-4.

Lubricants indicated for API Service GL-4 and GL-5 are applicable for use in non-automatic transmissions and final drives, and are generally available locally.

API Service GL-6 is an obsolete designation which may have been specified for some older machines. If so, consult your machine dealer or a reputable oil supplier for the proper substitute.

Refer to your operator's manual for recommended gear oils — the suggested viscosity and service classification should be designated.

Automatic Transmission Fluid

Inside an automatic transmission, the lubricant must perform specific functions under severe conditions. These are:

- Protect heavily-loaded helical and spiral gears with an oil film cushion.

- Perform as a non-foaming fluid in transmitting power.

- Operate as a hydraulic fluid between –30° and 300°F (–35° and 150°C).

Fig. 6 — Distillation Plant for Distilling Crude Oil

- Act as a wet clutch and transmission lubricant to provide smooth, silent engagement, without slipping.

- Resist oxidation under conditions of heat and aeration, while at the same time be compatible to all metals, rubber seals, gaskets, adhesives, facings, and liners in the system.

Automatic transmission fluids are designed to perform under a variety of conditions. Because of this, the following popular types of fluids are used in most automatic transmissions today:

- Type F (Ford Motor specification)

- DEXRON II (General Motors specification)

- Detroit Diesel Allison C-3

- John Deere Hydrostatic Fluid

Do not mix these fluids. Although these fluids are physically compatible, their built-in frictional properties are different to meet different transmission design requirements. Mixing alters the properties of the fluids and should be avoided. Follow the machine manufacturer's recommendations in selecting fluids.

Some special components may require different qualities from an automatic transmission fluid. Torque converters and hydrostatic transmissions are among these.

Torque Converter Fluids

Automatic transmission fluids, Type A and Suffix A, have proven satisfactory for torque converters in heavy-duty trucks, buses, and off-the-road machines.

More recently, the specification has been replaced by DEXRON II from General Motors and Type F from Ford Motor.

However, torque converters may require different qualities from an automatic transmission fluid.

Hydrostatic Drive Fluids

Hydrostatic drives can use automatic transmission fluids, but may require different qualities in the fluid.

Always follow the exact fluid recommendations in the machine operator's manual.

Transmission-Hydraulic Fluids

Some farm and industrial manufacturers have designed machines with a common reservoir for both the transmission and hydraulic systems (Fig. 7). This means that the same lubricating fluid has to serve the gear train as well as the precision hydraulic system.

Common Transmission
Hydraulic Reservoir

JDPX5633

Fig. 7 — Transmission-Hydraulic Systems

This requires special fluids, and these have been developed:

- John Deere Hy-Gard Fluid
- International Harvester Hy-Tran Fluid
- Allis-Chalmers Power Fluid 821
- Case TCH and TFD Fluids
- Ford M2C53-A and M2C134-A Fluids

These fluids are referred to as four-way oils because of the wide range of services they must perform.

Their key properties are:

- Have high oxidation stability for long life and protection.
- Have low pour point for low-temperature service, particularly during cold starting.
- Have high viscosity index for best viscosity under various operating temperatures.
- Contain extreme pressure additives for increased load carrying and wear protection under heavy and shock loads.
- Contain rust and corrosion inhibitors.
- Are compatible with all types of seals.
- Contain foam suppressors.

Some fluids which serve as transmission-hydraulic fluids also operate wet brake or wet clutch systems and require additives to control clutch or brake chatter.

While no transmission-hydraulic fluid will fully meet each specific need for every machine, products are available which will meet the service demands in any one machine for which these oils are specified.

Always use the oil specified by the manufacturer. Through testing, he has determined which oil will give the best service in his machine and his own special designs.

Keeping Transmission Fluids Clean

Good lubricants, which come in cans or barrels, are delivered clean and free from contaminants. It is generally after the containers are opened or stored that trouble develops.

When opening a can or barrel, be sure that the area around the opening is completely free of dust, dirt, lint, or water. If a container, funnel, or hose is required to fill the system, be sure that it is spotless.

When possible, always store barrels indoors, or at least under cover, and be sure the bung is tight. If barrels are stored in the sun without a tight bung, the fluid will expand, forcing some air from the bung. Then as the fluid cools off, the fluid contracts, drawing rain, dew, or other moisture into the barrel and fluid.

The harmful effects of water in lubricants have already been discussed (see "Preventing Contamination of Oil" on page 4-2). For this reason, keep the bungs in barrels as tight as possible, and tip the barrels so that water cannot collect around the bung.

Operation of Power Trains

To help understand why maintenance is important, we will briefly look at how the various power trains work.

Operation of the following components will be covered:

- Clutch
- Mechanical transmission
- Hydraulic assist transmission
- Infinitely variable transmission
- Mechanical front wheel drive (MFWD)
- Hydrostatic drive
- Combine power rear wheel drive system
- Torque converter
- Differential
- Final drives
- Power take-off

Operation of Clutch

The clutch provides the means of disconnecting the engine from its load while starting, shifting, or idling. In (Fig. 8) you can see how the standard dry clutch, found on most machines, operates.

In the engaged position, the pressure plate provides pressure against the clutch plate and forces the plate against the flywheel. Power is transmitted from the engine through the flywheel and clutch plate to the drive shaft or transmission input shaft.

The clutch is disengaged by applying pressure on the pedal, which pushes the clutch release assembly against the release levers. The levers pull the pressure plate away from the clutch plate so that the clutch plate is no longer forced against the flywheel. Now the flywheel and pressure plate are free to rotate independently of the clutch plate and drive shaft.

Notice that in the engaged position, there is clearance (usually 1/16 to 3/16 inch, 1.6 to 4.8 mm) between the clutch release bearing and the clutch release levers. This is to allow for wear of the clutch plate facings.

As the facings wear, the release levers move closer to the clutch release bearing until, eventually, there is no clearance. Adjustment must then be made, or the release levers will press continuously on the clutch release bearing, and pressure will be reduced on the clutch plate.

This will cause the clutch release bearing to fail prematurely. And the clutch will slip also — resulting in a burned clutch and rapid facing wear.

To maintain this necessary clearance between the bearing and the release levers, the clutch pedal free travel must be maintained.

Note that the standard clutch is a dry-disk type and that no lubricant is found in the clutch compartment (except for the grease fitting to the release bearing). Because the clutch operates by friction, the disks and plates must be kept perfectly dry.

Fig. 8 — Operation of Standard Dry-Disk Clutch

JDPX5634

Operation of Hydraulic-Type Clutch

The hydraulic clutch (Fig. 9) is similar to the standard clutch, except that the clutch plate operates wet in a transmission fluid and the clutch is engaged and disengaged hydraulically.

Hydraulic clutches normally don't require free travel or clearance adjustment.

Operation of Mechanical Transmission

The mechanical transmission is a train of gears that transfers and adapts the engine power to the drive wheels of the machine.

The transmission does two jobs:

- Selects speed ratios for various travel speeds.
- Reverses the travel of the machine.

The transmission can also power a special drive such as a power take-off (PTO).

Fig. 9 — Operation of Hydraulic Clutch

JDPX5635

Normally the transmission is located to the rear of the engine and clutch and in front of the differential or ring gear (Fig. 10).

Mechanical transmissions are of three major types:

- Sliding gear
- Collar shift
- Synchromesh

The sliding gear transmission has two or more shafts mounted in parallel or in line, with sliding spur gears arranged to mesh with each other and provide a change in speed or direction.

The collar shift transmission has parallel shafts with gears in constant mesh. Shifting is done by locking free-running gears to their shafts using sliding collars (Fig. 10).

The synchromesh transmission also has gears in constant mesh. However, gears can be selected without clashing, by synchronizing the speeds of mating parts before they engage.

In all three cases, the transmission is shifted by hand or foot. So we call them mechanical transmissions.

The gear train for all these transmissions normally operates in a bath of gear oil. For special lubrication, oil sprays or feeder lines from oil pumps are sometimes used.

JDPX5636, 5637

Fig. 10 — Mechanical Transmission in a Complete Power Train

JDPX5639

Fig. 11 — Hydraulic Assist Transmission in a Complete Power Train

Operation of Hydraulic Assist Transmission

The hydraulic assist transmission (Fig. 11) is a train of gears which can be shifted without interrupting the flow of power.

The gears are kept in constant mesh while two or more hydraulic clutches control the flow of power "on the go."

The parts work together as follows:

• Hydraulic clutches control the power flow

• Gear train transmits the power flow

When the operator shifts gears, hydraulic oil engages the clutches that route power to the selected gears.

A hydraulic clutch is normally an alternating pack of friction disks and plates (Fig. 12).

The clutch is engaged when pressure oil is sent to push the piston against the disks and plates, clamping them together. The disks are splined to the drum, while the plates are splined to the hub. As a result, input power through the hub is sent on through the hub to the output by the engaged clutch.

The clutch is disengaged when oil pressure is released and the piston moves away from the clutch pack. This frees the disks from the plates and the power flow is stopped. Spring action or oil pressure on the other side of the piston may be used to help release the disks and plates.

This hydraulic clutch unit replaces the standard clutch used on mechanical transmissions.

Clutch Engaged
Oil pushes against disks and plates, clamping them and joining input power from drum to hub and output shaft.

Clutch Disengaged
Oil is released and piston moves away, freeing disks from plates. Power flow is stopped.

JDPX5640

Fig. 12 — Hydraulic Clutches Control the Power Flow in Hydraulic Assist Transmissions

The gear train is usually either a countershaft or a planetary unit which feeds power to the output or drive wheels.

The gear train normally operates in an oil bath. This oil is usually the reservoir for the hydraulic circuit which operates the clutch units, so special transmission-hydraulic fluid must be used.

Operation of Mechanical Front Wheel Drive (MFWD)

JDPX5658

Fig. 13 — Mechanical Front Wheel Drive Operation

When the dash switch is in the "engaged" position, spring pressure closes the solenoid valve, preventing the flow of clutch control oil to the clutch. Springs force the clutch disk pack together and power flows forward through the U-jointed drive shaft to the front axle differential drive shaft. The shaft drive gear meshes with the ring gear, turning the limited slip differential unit as shown in (Fig. 13). The differential supplies the required power to the left-hand and right-hand wheel drive shafts.

The wheel drive shaft powers the sun gear of the wheel hub planetary. The sun gear rotates the fixed planetary gears, which walk around the outer ring gear. The planetary system reduces the drive shaft output speed and increases the torque at the front tires.

The wheel drive gear is meshed with the outer ring gear, which is meshed to the wheel hub.

The front wheel housings are linked to a standard tractor steering system. Disengaging the MFWD provides a shorter turning radius.

When the MFWD dash switch is moved to the "disengaged" position, the solenoid valve directs pressure oil to release the MFWD clutch.

With the dash switch in the "auto" position, the MFWD is engaged and disengaged automatically. At speeds under 8.5 mph (14 km/h), the MFWD remains engaged until either brake pedal is depressed. If both brake pedals are depressed, the MFWD will remain engaged.

When the tractor speed exceeds 8.5 mph (14 km/h), a relay is activated, which disengages the MFWD. If both pedals are depressed, the MFWD is automatically engaged to assist braking.

Operation of Hydrostatic Drive

JDPX5642

Fig. 14 — Hydrostatic Drive in a Complete Power Train

The hydrostatic drive is an automatic fluid drive which uses fluid under pressure to transmit engine power to the drive wheels of the machine.

Mechanical power from the engine is converted to hydraulic power by a pump-motor team (Fig. 14). This power is then converted back to mechanical power for the drive wheels.

The hydrostatic drive can function as both a clutch and transmission. The final gear train can then be simplified, with the hydrostatic unit supplying infinite speed and torque ranges as well as reverse speeds.

Hydrostatic transmissions use fluids at high pressures but relatively low speeds. Basically, energy is transferred by the fluid itself in a closed circuit between the pump and motor as shown in (Fig. 15). While the fluid does move through the lines, it is still considered as being at rest or under static pressure. The rise in pressure of the fluid, which will not compress, is what transfers the energy.

JDPX5643

Fig. 15 — Complete Hydraulic System for Hydrostatic Drive

Operation of Combine Power Rear Wheel Drive System

High-Pressure Oil

Low-Pressure Oil

Pressure-Free Oil

Hydrostatic Reservoir

Rear Wheel Drive Filter

Drain Line to Rear Wheel Motors

Hydrostatic Drive Pump

Drain Line to Filter

Flow Control Valve

Drain Line to Filter

Rear Wheel Motors

Forward

JDPX5644

Fig. 16 — Oil Flow Schematic of Power Rear Wheel Drive System

Power rear wheel drive offers extra traction in muddy fields. When the combine needs additional traction, the operator turns on a switch which actuates this drive.

The power rear wheel drive system (Fig. 16) consists of an electrohydraulic control valve, two fixed-displacement rear wheel motors of a planetary gearing or cam lobe design, an oil filter, and connecting hydraulic lines. Hydraulic power for this system is taken from the hydrostatic drive to combine front wheels.

To engage the power rear wheel drive, the operator sends an electrical signal from the console control switch to the power rear wheel drive control valve. This valve responds by opening to allow flow of hydrostatic fluid to the rear wheel motors (Fig. 16). The wheel motors convert this hydraulic energy into mechanical energy through a gear reduction to the wheel rims, propelling the combine.

Operation of Infinitely Variable Transmission (IVT)

The infinitely variable transmission (IVT) is the newest innovation in power trains. It's the first totally new design in decades. Customer acceptance has been very high, with large numbers choosing the new transmission option.

Automotive manufacturers have also introduced infinitely variable transmissions in recent years.

Benefits include better fuel efficiency, higher productivity, reduced wear, greater flexibility, ease of operation, and a host of convenience features. With manufacturers competing for market advantage, features will vary somewhat from model to model.

IVT can automatically shift up and throttle back under light load. This saves fuel, reduces engine wear, and lowers the noise level.

JDPX2337

Fig. 17 — IVT with Two Forward Gears

A—Input Shaft	E—Ring Gear	I—High Clutch	M—Low Clutch
B—Trans Pump	F—Compound Planet Pinions	J—Clutch Output Assembly	N—Reverse Brake
C—Input Gear	G—Input Sun Gear	K—Trans Output Gear	O—Reverse Ring Gear
D—Hydro Gear	H—High-Output Sun Gear	L—DDS Gear	P—Reverse Sun Gear

Designs vary. Perhaps the simplest version (Fig. 17) has only two forward gears and one reverse, plus the hydrostatic input for variable speed. It has two clutches, one brake, and a compound planetary. This design is the basis for much of the following discussion. Other IVTs have more components, but they are just variations on the same theme.

In basic terms, IVT adds a hydrostatic input and automatic controls to a simple power shift transmission. Shifts are seamless. Speed can transition smoothly from zero to maximum.

The heart of the IVT is a compound planetary gear set. It has one ring gear, two sun gears, and compound planet pinions. In (Fig. 18), the ring gear has been removed and the front sun gear has been moved to one side to reveal the remaining gears.

The front sun gear turns at engine speed at all times. The ring gear is controlled by a hydrostatic drive. It turns at variable speed in either direction.

View from Rear of Assembly

JDPX2338

Fig. 18 — Compound Planetary Gears

The planet pinion carrier turns at variable speed, controlled by the two inputs working together. The planet pinion carrier is the input for low gear and reverse.

The planet pinions are compound gears. The small gear in front and the large gear in back are one piece. The rear sun gear is driven by the large gears on the planet pinions. The rear sun gear is the input for high gear.

Medium-Output Speed

JDPX2339

Fig. 19 — Planetary Gear Set with Two Inputs

The sun gear turns at a fixed speed. The ring gear, controlled by a hydrostatic drive, turns either direction at variable speed. The planet pinion carrier is the output.

(Fig. 19) shows the simplest situation. The ring gear is not turning at all. The planetary gear set works like a final drive or any simple planetary.

Slow-Output Speed

JDPX2340

Fig. 20 — Ring Gear Turning Backward

If the ring gear is turned backward, the output slows down. How much it slows down depends on how fast the ring gear turns backward.

The fastest the ring gear can turn backward is exactly enough to offset the sun gear. The planet pinion carrier doesn't turn at all. This holds the machine stopped without using brakes or clutch. It isn't the same as PARK, but it will not let the machine roll, even on a slope.

The IVT has all the benefits of the hydrostatic transmission without the trade-offs. Only one gear in the transmission is driven hydrostatically—not the whole machine. Half the time, the hydrostatic system is holding back instead of pulling. Efficiency is not an issue.

This particular IVT uses a bent-axis design for hydrostatic pump and motor. Bent-axis components are larger and more expensive than swashplate designs, but they are more efficient over a wider range of speeds. This advantage allows the use of only a two-speed planetary gearbox, because the hydrostatic drive can provide more flexibility.

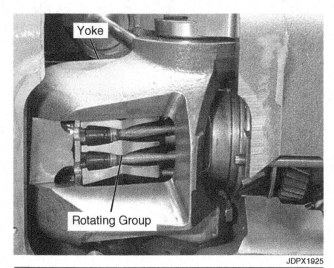

JDPX1925

Fig. 21 — Bent-Axis Hydrostatic Pump

The hydrostatic pump is inside a yoke that swings 45° in each direction from neutral. If the pump is centered, it holds the compound planetary ring gear stationary. By changing the angle of the pump, it can drive the ring gear either direction at varying speed.

Operation of Torque Converter

A torque converter is also an automatic fluid drive (Fig. 22). It transmits engine torque by means of hydraulic force, shifting smoothly through an infinite number of speeds.

Actually a gear train is used with the torque converter to give extra speed ranges. But no gear train could give the infinite variations in speed and torque of a torque converter.

Acting as a clutch, the torque converter connects and disconnects power between the engine and the gear train as a transmission. The converter gives many more speed ratios than are practical with a strictly mechanical gearbox.

To compare a torque converter with a hydrostatic drive, use this rule of thumb:

Hydrostatic drives are driven by fluids at high pressure but at relatively low velocity, while torque converters are driven by fluids at low pressure but at high velocity.

Here are the formulas:

Hydrostatic DRIVE = HIGH pressure + LOW velocity

Torque Converter = LOW pressure + HIGH velocity

The basic torque converter system is shown in (Fig. 22).

A fluid at high velocity strikes a turbine and forces it to turn, driving the wheel. Thus, torque is transmitted by a fluid.

To change this torque, the velocity of the fluid is changed. At low velocity, the fluid will not even move the turbine. At high velocity, the turbine starts turning and the wheel picks up speed.

Inside an oil-filled housing are two parts: the driving half, or pump, and the driven half, or turbine.

As the pump is turned by the engine, centrifugal force causes oil to be forced radially outward, crossing over and striking the vanes of the turbine. This rotates the turbine in the same direction and so couples the power.

The torque or power from the turbines then flows through the gear train, as shown, to the power output.

JDPX5645

Fig. 22 — Torque Converter in Complete Power Train

Operation of Differentials

The differential does two jobs:

- Transmits power "around the corner" to the drive axles.
- Allows each drive wheel to rotate at a different speed and still propel its own load.

The ring gear and bevel gears direct the power to the axles, while the bevel pinions give the differential action (Fig. 23).

When the machine is moving straight ahead, both wheels are free to rotate as shown in (Fig. 23), left.

Engine power comes in on the pinion gear and rotates the ring gear. The four bevel pinions and the two bevel gears are carried around by the ring gear, and all gears rotate as one unit. Each axle receives the same rotation, and so each wheel turns at the same speed.

When the machine turns a sharp corner, only one wheel is free to rotate, as shown in (Fig. 23), right.

Again engine power comes in on the pinion gear and rotates the ring gear, carrying the bevel pinions around with it. However, the right-hand axle is held stationary, and so the bevel pinions are forced to rotate on their own axis and "walk around" the right-hand bevel gear.

Since the bevel pinions are in constant mesh with both bevel gears, the left-hand bevel gear is forced to rotate because it is subjected to the turning force of the ring gear which is transmitted through the bevel pinions.

During one revolution of the ring gear, the left-hand gear makes two revolutions — one with the ring gear, and another as the bevel pinions "walk around" the other bevel gear.

As a result, when the drive wheels have unequal resistance applied to them, the wheel with the least resistance turns more revolutions. As one wheel turns faster, the other turns slower by the same amount. However, both wheels still propel their own loads — but at different speeds.

Differential action can be a disadvantage when the wheels slip. For example, when a farm tractor is plowing, one wheel may lose resistance on slick ground and start spinning while the other wheel holds. Then the driving power is limited by the "wasted" power sent to the wheel that slips.

To prevent this loss of power, differential locks are often used.

Pinion Gear

Bevel Gear and Axle

Bevel Pinions

Bevel Gear and Axle

Both Wheels Free to Rotate

One Wheel Free to Rotate

JDPX5646

Fig. 23 — Differential in a Complete Power Train

Operation of Differential Locks

A differential lock directs power equally to both wheels by locking out the differential. This prevents the usual loss of traction when one wheel is slipping.

Three types of differential locks are used:

- Mechanical
- Hydraulic
- Automatic (no-spin)

The mechanical differential lock (Fig. 24) is the simplest. When the operator moves the control lever, a fork shifts a splined collar on the axle shaft to engage the collar with splines on the differential housing. This forces the axle and housing to rotate as a unit. The bevel gears are thus prevented from turning, and so the differential is locked.

When drive wheels again have equal traction, the lock disengages automatically. The lock can be engaged on the go, but must be released before the machine is turned.

When the operator depresses the control pedal, a hydraulic clutch engages the hydraulic differential lock. When the pedal is released, oil pressure is cut off and the lock releases as soon as both wheels have equal traction. A safety release connects the control pedal to the tractor's brake pedals to unlock the differential whenever the brake pedals are used. This avoids the danger of making sharp turns with the differential lock still engaged.

The automatic no-spin lock (Fig. 25 and Fig. 26) is located inside the differential housing and replaces the bevel gears, bevel pinions, and their shafts. The no-spin lock is normally engaged and still permits relative motion between the wheels on corners. When engaged, it prevents one wheel from spinning when it loses traction, thereby depriving the other wheel of full power.

To Engage Lock

Housing Splines

Fork

Axle Splines

Collar

To Engage Lock

JDPX5647

Fig. 24 — Mechanical Differential Lock

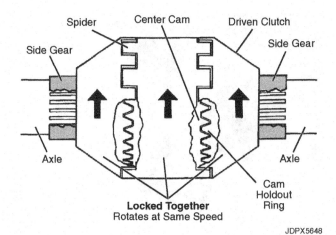

Fig. 25 — Automatic No-spin Lock (Driving Straight Ahead)

Fig. 26 — Automatic No-spin Lock (Left Turn)

However, the no-spin lock does not permit the inside wheel on a turn to slow down — only the outside wheel to speed up. It therefore tends to increase machine turning radius and, in a sharp turn, may prevent the machine from decelerating to a safe turning speed.

Operation of Final Drives

The final drive is the last phase of the power train. It gives the final reduction in speed and increase in torque to the drive wheels (Fig. 1).

Used on most large machines, the final drives are mounted near the drive wheels to avoid the stress of long axle shafts.

By reducing speeds, the final drives lower the stress and simplify the transmission, since extra gears and shafts can be eliminated.

Most final drives must support the weight of the machine as well as withstanding torque and shock loads.

Operation of Power Take-Offs

The power take-off (PTO) is an attachment in the power train of a machine. It drives auxiliary equipment.

PTOs are normally gear-driven from the transmission and send power through a shaft to the PTO outlet where the driven equipment is coupled.

Most modern units are adjustable to drive equipment at standard speeds of either 540 or 1000 rpm.

The PTO is operated by a clutch release, which is sometimes part of the main engine clutch.

Servicing of Power Trains

The power train requires important maintenance, as we will see now.

Servicing of Engine Clutches

Because the foot clutch is the most commonly used on most machines today, we will cover its maintenance only. Hand-operated clutches require somewhat different service and are found on few modern machines. Therefore, refer to your operator's manual for maintenance procedures for this type of clutch.

The clutch on most machines requires two services:

- Lubricating the clutch release bearing
- Adjusting clutch pedal free travel

Lubricating the Clutch Release Bearing

On many of the newer machines, the clutch release bearing is a prelubricated, sealed bearing and requires no further lubrication until major service is performed on the clutch.

However, on some machines the bearing requires regular lubrication. Many manufacturers recommend that this be done every 250 hours. Refer to your operator's manual for suggested intervals.

If the bearing is lubricated too much or too often, excessive grease may be thrown onto the clutch facing and cause the clutch to "chatter" when engaged and may eventually damage the clutch facing.

Too little lubrication will cause the bearing to fail prematurely.

If the bearing on your machine requires periodic lubrication, proceed as follows:

1. Locate the grease fitting. It may be on the side or bottom of the clutch housing (Fig. 27).

JDPX5650, 5651

Fig. 27 — Clutch Release Bearing Grease Fitting

If an external grease fitting is not found, you may have to remove a cover plate to reach inside to lubricate the bearing.

2. Wipe grease fitting clean before attempting to apply grease.

3. Apply lubricant sparingly. One or two short strokes of the grease gun are usually sufficient. Excess grease might leak out and get on the dry clutch disks, causing them to slip.

4. Wipe off excess grease from fitting.

NOTE: Some machines also have power take-off (PTO) clutches which require bearing lubrication.

Adjusting Clutch Pedal Free Travel

Adjustment of clutch pedal free travel is essentially the same for all non-hydraulic clutches, whether they are single or multiple clutch plates, dry or wet type.

Many manufacturers recommend that you check pedal free travel every 250 hours and adjust if necessary. See the recommendations in your operator's manual.

To adjust the clutch pedal free travel, proceed as follows:

1. Refer to your operator's manual for recommended free travel distance. Usually, this may range from 1/2 to 2 inches (13 to 50 mm) or more, depending on the machine and where the distance is measured. Also, determine where the measurement should be taken (for the next step).

2. Check clutch pedal free travel measurement. This is the distance the pedal can be depressed before resistance is noticed. The resistance is caused by the clutch release bearing contacting the release levers.

3. If the measurement checks with those specified in your operator's manual, no adjustment is necessary.

4. If the measurement is different than those specified, proceed with the following steps.

5. Locate pedal adjusting mechanism (Fig. 28). Usually the adjustment is made near the pedal or it may be anywhere along the linkage leading to the clutch release mechanism.

6. Adjust the linkage, as necessary, until the clutch pedal has the proper amount of free travel.

JDPX5652

Fig. 28 — Adjusting Pedal Free Travel at Pedal Arm

Fig. 29 — Basic Train Designs Showing Fluid Reservoirs

JDPX5653

Servicing Transmission, Differential, and Final Drives

Your machine may have a transmission that resembles one of those shown in (Fig. 29) or it may have separate differential and final drives.

Here is an explanation:

1. All gear drive units housed within one compartment. Hydraulic system separate.

2. A one-compartment arrangement which also contains hydraulic pump and uses gear oil for hydraulic system.

3. A two-compartment arrangement with one compartment supplying lubrication to the belt pulley and wet clutch and providing fluid for the hydraulic system.

4. A four-compartment assembly with a separate hydraulic system but with only a partial division between the transmission and differential sections.

5. A three-compartment assembly with one compartment supplying the torque converter and wet clutch with lubricant. Note the hydraulic system is supplied from the power take-off compartment.

6. High-clearance tractors often use a spur-gear drive at the ends of the main axle. Each of these has its own lubricating compartment.

Regardless of its design, the maintenance of the transmission is similar to the following service procedures.

Checking Oil Levels

Operator's manual may recommend checking the transmission oil levels from every 50 to every 250 hours.

OIL LEVEL DIPSTICK

If the machine has a dipstick (Fig. 30) for checking the oil level, remove it and wipe off the excess oil.

Reinsert the dipstick completely and pull it out again to check the oil level.

If the level is below the full mark (or "safe" mark), fill to the proper level with the recommended oil of the proper viscosity. Make the level check with the engine running or according to other recommendations.

Fig. 30 — Transmission Oil Level Dipstick

OIL LEVEL PLUG

If your machine doesn't have a dipstick, remove the oil level plug (Fig. 31) form the transmission case.

On machines with separate final drives, remove the oil level plug from them also. Insert a finger to determine if oil is up to proper level.

If necessary, refill with the recommended oil of the proper viscosity.

Fig. 31 — Transmission Oil Level Plug

Fig. 32 — Final Drive Oil Level Plug

OIL LEVEL SIGHT GLASS

Start engine and warm transmission-hydraulic oil to proper temperature. Shut off engine and wait for oil to drain back to sump. Check oil level in sight glass. Oil level should be between marks on sight glass.

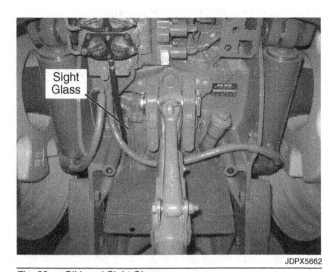

Fig. 33 — Oil Level Sight Glass

Draining and Refilling

The usual draining and refilling period is at least once each year. Others recommend every 1000 hours or less. See your operator's manual.

TOOLS AND MATERIALS NEEDED

• Wrenches for drain plug(s) and filter cap (inch or metric, as required)

• Clean, lint-free cloths

• Cleaning solvent (not gasoline)

• New oil of type and grade recommended by manufacturer

• New filter

• Container to catch waste oil

To drain and refill the transmission, proceed as follows:

1. Drive the machine until you are certain the transmission fluid is well agitated and heated. This helps ensure that most of the sludge and dirt will drain out when the fluid is removed.

2. Park the machine on a level surface. This will ensure a better draining position than if the machine is on a slight incline.

JDPX5656

Fig. 34 — Final Drive Oil Level Plug

3. Remove drain plugs (Fig. 31 and Fig. 32) and catch the old fluid in a container (Fig. 34).

   If the transmission has the differential and final drives in the same housing, you will probably need to remove two plugs. If the final drives are separate, you may have to remove three plugs or more.

JDPX5680

Fig. 35 — Transmission-Hydraulic System Filter Covers

4. Replace transmission oil filter (Fig. 35).

5. Clean dirt and grease from filler plug and surrounding area. Remove plugs.

6. Refill with the proper amount and type of transmission fluid or gear oil, as specified in your operator's manual.

   Do not overfill. This will cause excessive agitation and foaming.

IMPORTANT: **If the machine has one common reservoir for both the transmission and hydraulic systems, use special care in cleaning and in replacing with transmission-hydraulic fluid of the correct type. Precision hydraulic parts can be seriously damaged by dirt, or the wrong fluid.**

7. Replace and tighten plugs.

8. If equipped, clean filler cap and breather (Fig. 30) in solvent (not gasoline). Shake out excess liquid. Add a small quantity of oil to filter and shake out excess. Replace cap.

Adjusting Transmissions

Transmission adjustments are usually performed at the time of major repairs. Gear trains are then adjusted for preload, backlash, or endplay (see "Gear Drives" on page 9-35). Other adjustments, as of shifting linkages, should be made per instructions in the machine operator's manual.

Adjustment of hydraulic power transmission units requires special test equipment and should be done only by a trained serviceman. The basic use of a hydraulic tester for diagnosis is given at the end of "What a Hydraulic Tester Does" on page 8-19.

Precautions for Towing Machines

On some machines, the engine must be turning the transmission gears to obtain proper lubrication. Towing such a machine would result in poor lubrication and high shaft speed. The failure of many transmissions can be traced to towing.

It the transmission gears are operated at excessively high speeds, the gear lubricants will become overheated. Overheating a lubricant causes it to oxidize and thicken. Continuous overheating would result in transmission failure.

When towing a machine there is danger, too, that a brake may grab. The machine may bounce and be hard to steer. It the tires are filled with liquid, the high speed can also damage a tire.

If it becomes necessary to tow a farm machine, do so slowly. It is much better to haul the machine or drive it under its own power. Some machines have a lever that permits the transmission gears to be disengaged so they can be towed. Other machines must have the engine running to maintain power operation of steering and brakes for safety. Refer to the operator's manual for precautions.

Test Yourself

Questions

1. (T/F) Gear oil may have the same viscosity as engine oil.

2. What three types of oils or fluids are used in transmissions?

   a. _____

   b. _____

   c. _____

3. If you must store lubricants in unprotected barrels, how should they be positioned to avoid contamination?

4. Why does clutch pedal free travel change periodically and require readjustment?

5. (T/F) Hydraulic type clutches require periodic free travel or clearance adjustment.

6. Name three major types of mechanical transmissions.

   a. _____

   b. _____

   c. _____

7. (T/F) When the ground speed on a MFWD tractor is below 8.5 mph (14 km/h) and the dash switch is in "auto" position, the MFWD disengages when both brake pedals are depressed.

8. (T/F) Hydraulic wheel motors convert hydraulic energy into mechanical energy.

9. What may happen if you over-lubricate the clutch release bearing?

10. What should you do with the machine before draining old fluid from the power train?

Hydraulic Systems

8

Introduction

JDPX5204

Fig. 1 — Modern Farm Tractor with Full Hydraulics

Hydraulic systems (Fig. 1) provide the "muscles" for doing work. Some machines, like the tractor in Fig. 1, have a hydraulic system that performs several functions: steer, brake, control implements, and operate remote functions.

Other machines may have only one or two hydraulic functions. All the functions may share a common oil supply or they may have their own reservoirs.

The most common hydraulic functions are:

- Steering
- Brakes
- Transmissions ("Power Trains" on page 7-1)
- Implement control
- Remote cylinders
- Hydraulic motors

We'll discuss some of these systems later.

Importance of Service

A well-maintained hydraulic system seldom gives the operator any trouble. Regular checks ensure that the oil level is sufficient. Changing the oil and filters regularly helps prevent problems.

The oil in the hydraulic system is extremely sensitive to contamination. Dust, rust, moisture, and metal particles will damage the hydraulic system.

Hydraulic fluid lubricates and cools the entire hydraulic system. Any contaminant which builds up in the fluid can ruin the whole system.

Routine checks and repair of oil leaks will prevent excessive loss of fluid and overheating. Air leaks will cause the oil to oxidize rapidly, forming harmful gum and sludge. Check for air leaks and repair them promptly.

Selecting Hydraulic Fluids

The fluid in a hydraulic system serves as the power transmitting medium. And as stated above, the fluid is also the system's lubricant and coolant. Selection of the proper oil is essential for satisfactory performance and life. Oil must be selected with care and from a reputable supplier. Be sure to use the manufacturer's recommended oil.

These are some common hydraulic system oils:

- Crankcase oil meeting API service classification CD or SF. The most severe classification is the key to proper selection of crankcase oils for mobile hydraulic systems.
- Antiwear hydraulic oil: There is no common designations for oils of this type. However, they are produced by all major oil suppliers and provide the antiwear qualities of CD or SF crankcase oils.

- Certain other types of petroleum oils are suitable for mobile hydraulic service if they meet the following provisions:
  - Contain the type and content of antiwear compounding found in CD or SF crankcase oils or have passed pump tests similar to those used in developing the antiwear-type hydraulic oils.
  - Meet the viscosity recommendations for expected temperatures.
  - Have the chemical stability for mobile hydraulic system service.

The following types of oil are suitable if they meet the above three provisions:

- API CD Diesel Engine Oil
- MIL-L-2104C
- Type F and DEXRON II
- Hydraulic Transmission Fluid Type C-3

When selecting hydraulic fluids, check the recommendations in the operator's manual. The manufacturer has picked a fluid which meets all the needs of the system, which may vary from simple cylinders to precision hydraulic pumps.

Operation of Hydraulic Systems

A brief introduction to how hydraulic systems work will help you to understand why proper maintenance is so important.

The operation of three common hydraulic operations will be discussed:

- Hydraulic steering
- Power brakes
- Implement control

Hydraulic Steering

Two types of hydraulic steering are used:

- Hydraulic assist steering
- Full power steering

Hydraulic assist steering (not shown) is similar to mechanical steering, except for a hydraulic valve controlled by the steering wheel and hydraulic pistons, which assist the steering mechanism in turning the wheels.

Since full power steering is the most popular today, we will discuss it more fully.

(Fig. 2) shows a power steering system with a metering pump operating during a right turn.

NOTE: *Indications of directions refer to those as seen from the operator's seat. Side A and B will help identify direction of movement in the steering valve housing.*

Fig. 2 — Metering-Pump Power Steering During a Right Turn

When the operator turns the wheel to the right, the gears in the metering pump direct oil in the steering system to the steering valve housing and to the left end of the feedback piston. This oil (under some pressure) moves the steering valve toward side B.

The movement of the steering valve opens the pressure oil circuit to the left end of the steering piston. Oil from the right end of the piston flows back to the steering valve oil gallery and to the reservoir.

Oil from the right end of the feedback piston cylinder is forced out, by piston movement, and returns through the steering valve housing to the metering pump.

This movement of the steering and feedback pistons from left to right causes the spindle to rotate clockwise and turn the front wheels to the right.

When the operator stops turning the steering wheel, the gears in the metering pump stop directing oil to the steering valve. Circuit pressure, from the right end of the feedback piston to the steering valve (caused by movement of the feedback piston), acts against side B of the steering valve. The valve moves toward side A, closing the pressure oil passage from the main hydraulic pump, and stops the turning movement. The valve becomes centered and traps oil in passages to both sides of the steering piston. The trapped oil holds the wheels in the right turn until the operator again turns the steering wheel.

If oil is lost from the control circuit, pressure in the control circuit drops. The reduced pressure causes the make-up valve to unseat and allow return oil from the steering piston to make up oil in the control circuit.

On articulated tractors, the steering and feedback pistons are replaced by hydraulic cylinders which control steering.

To protect against failure of power steering, a check ball and manual steering check valves are used in this power steering system. If the oil supply fails and no incoming oil pushes the check valve open, it closes and traps all oil within the steering circuit.

This allows the operator to steer manually by using the trapped oil as a force to actuate the steering. Pressure is created as the operator turns the steering wheel.

For manual steering, see "Manual Steering" on page 9-5.

Power Brakes

JDPX5800

Fig. 3 — Power Brakes During a Left Turn

On most machines, brakes are located on each drive wheel. For turning, the operator presses down the pedal for the left or right wheel. For stopping, the operator presses down on both pedals at once.

On four-wheel drive machines, a single brake mechanism at the transmission usually controls the whole unit.

Because manual brakes and hydraulic brakes are not powered by the hydraulic system, we will cover them in the next chapter. However, in some systems, oil is supplied to the brake reservoir by the tractor hydraulic system, and bleeding these brakes will be covered later in this chapter.

Let's discuss the operation of power brakes in more detail.

"Power" brakes mean that hydraulic force completely controls the braking of the machine, once the operator presses down the brake pedal to actuate the valving.

Full power brakes on a modern wheel tractor with a closed-center hydraulic system are shown in (Fig. 3). Operation is shown during a left turn.

For a sharp left turn, the operator presses down on the left brake pedal. This causes a rod linkage to push down on the brake valve and open it. Inlet oil under pressure now rushes in through the open valve, forces the outlet check valve open, and flows on to the final drive at the left rear axle (see inset). Here the oil forces the brake pistons and pressure plates to press the revolving brake disk against a fixed plate, and so brakes the left axle and wheel.

When the brake pedal is released, the brake valve is closed again by its spring, and inlet oil is shut off. This relieves pressure on the brake disk at the axle, and braking stops as some oil flows back to the brake valve area. This oil dumps into the brake reservoir after going past the valve and through the valve plunger. When both brake pedals are pressed down at once, oil is sent by both brake valves to both final drives. To ensure equal braking, equalizing valves (not shown) are opened, connecting the two brake valves.

To protect the operator in case of failure of power brakes, oil trapped in the brake valve reservoir by the check valves allows temporary operation of the brakes. On large machines, a hydraulic accumulator stores "charges" of oil for emergency braking.

Implement Control

Two types of implement control systems are used on tractors:

- Power lift (rockshaft)
- Remote control

The power lift is used to control mounted implements, while remote control cylinders are usually placed on a pull-type implement to control a function such as raising the plow bottoms.

Power Lift

The power lift usually is controlled either manually using a control lever or automatically by load sensing.

RAISING PLOW USING CONTROL LEVER

In (Fig. 4), the plow hits hard ground and the operator wants to raise it slightly. So he moves the control lever to the front. This pivots the cam follower forward and presses it against a rod which opens the valve. Pressure oil is now admitted to the cylinder, forcing the piston to the rear. The piston pushes against the shaft arm, rotating rockshaft and lift arm upward. The lift arm is attached to the plow and so the plow is raised slightly to help it pass through the hard ground.

The plow stops rising when the valve is closed again, trapping oil in the cylinder. This happens when the cam follower, working on the sloping cam of the rockshaft, is returned to the rear and releases the rod. The valve is then closed by its spring.

Fig. 4 — Raising an Implement in Depth Control

A — Control Lever	E — Piston	I — Return Valve Ball	M — Draft Link
B — Cam Follower	F — Shaft Arm	J — Valve Lever	N — Plow Furrow
C — Operating Rods	G — Rockshaft	K — Load Control Lever	
D — Pressure Valve Ball	H — Lift Arm	L — Load-Sensing Shaft	

JDPX5801

Fig. 5 — Rockshaft Operating in Draft Control

A — Control Lever	E — Piston	I — Return Valve Ball	M —Draft Link
B — Cam Follower	F — Shaft Arm	J — Valve Lever	N — Plow Furrow
C — Operating Rods	G — Rockshaft	K — Load Control Lever	
D — Pressure Valve Ball	H — Lift Arm	L — Load-Sensing Shaft	

In (Fig. 5), the plow hits hard ground and the load control shaft is pulled rearward by draft links. As a result, the load control arm is pivoted against the cam follower. The cam follower pushes on the rod which opens the valve and admits pressure oil to the cylinder. The cylinder piston pushes against the arm, rotating rockshaft and lift arm upward. The lift arm is attached to the plow, and so raises the plow slightly to help it pass through the hard ground.

With automatic load sensing, the plow will lower itself again when the hard ground is passed. This happens as the tension on the load control shaft is partly released. It flexes forward and pulls back on the linkage to actuate other valves (not shown) which release some oil from the cylinder. This lets the lift arms "settle," lowering the plow again.

The regular depth of the plow can be set at the control lever. The plow will stay at this depth unless a signal is given by the load-sensing device.

We have just described full load sensing or load control.

Two other options are commonly available: If he wishes, the operator can lock out signals from the load sensing linkage by blocking the cam follower at its lower end using a lever (not shown). This is called depth control, since the plow now stays at the depth set by the control lever. The other choice allows the operator to partially block the cam follower using the same lever. This is called load and depth control, since the load signals are now modified by the depth setting.

Some power lifts are designed for dual operations. Two hydraulic cylinders are normally used: one cylinder and valving controls the rear-mounted equipment, and the second operates a front-mounted tool or an attachment. However, the cylinders can be operated in parallel by opening valves which join them to the same pressure oil supply. Two control levers are also used, one for each function. But usually only one function (the rear one) has an automatic load-sensing device.

ELECTRO-HYDRAULIC HITCH

Some newer tractors are equipped with an electro-hydraulic 3-point hitch. It is electrically controlled and hydraulically operated.

The electro-hydraulic hitch uses electrical circuitry and solenoids to control hydraulic oil flow which activates the 3-point hitch.

JDPX5803

Fig. 6 — Hydraulic Load-Sensing Rockshaft

A — Load Control Valve	G — Draft Links	M — Pressure Valve	R — Return Valve
B — Sensing Cylinder	H — Valve	N — Throttle Valve	S — Thermal Relief Valve
C — Load Control Selector	I — Variable Orifice	O — Rockshaft Piston	T — Check Ball
D — Cam Follower	J — Orifice	P — Spring	U — Rockshaft
E — Sensing Cylinder Piston	K — Valve Operating Link	Q — Spring	
F — Draft Arm	L — Valve Operating Cam		

The hydraulic load sensing system (Fig. 6) consists of a load control valve (A) and a sensing cylinder (B). The load control selector (C) is in a position at the top of the cam follower (D) to allow maximum load sensing. The rod end of the sensing cylinder piston (E) is attached to one draft arm (F). The two draft arms are connected by a shaft. The draft links (G) are attached to the draft arms.

As the plow hits hard ground, the soil resistance increases the draft load on the draft arms. The draft force is transmitted to the sensing cylinder (B) by the draft arms and pulls the sensing cylinder piston and valve (H) rearward. More oil then flows into the sensing cylinder through a variable orifice (I), causing sensing pressure on the front of the load control valve (A) to increase. The increase in sensing pressure results in rearward movement of the load control valve (A), cam follower (D), and valve operating link (K) which causes the valve operating cam (L) to rotate clockwise. Note that an orifice (J) allows some oil to escape from the front of the load control valve. This results in a variable pressure on the valve, depending on the amount of oil that enters through the variable orifice (I).

The clockwise rotation of the valve operating cam causes the pressure valve (M) to open and direct pressure oil through the throttle valve (N) to the back side of the rockshaft piston (O). The throttle valve controls the speed of oil flow to and from the rockshaft piston. The piston moves forward and causes the rockshaft (U) to rotate, lifting the draft links (G) and raising the plow. The check ball (T) prevents return oil from the front of the rockshaft piston from entering the return valve housing (R).

When the plow passes the hard ground, the draft force on the sensing cylinder decreases. The sensing cylinder piston (E) and valve (H) move forward, permitting less oil to flow through the variable orifice, decreasing sensing pressure at the front of the load control valve. The spring (P) in the load control valve housing pushes the valve forward. The spring (Q) causes the valve operating cam to rotate counterclockwise and forces the cam follower (D) forward, along with the load control valve. The pressure valve (M) closes and, if necessary, the return valve (R) opens to lower the plow.

When the pressure and relief valves are closed, oil trapped at the rear of the rockshaft may expand if the oil temperature rises. The thermal relief valve (S) senses thermal expansion of hydraulic oil in the system and opens if the expansion is too great.

Remote Control of Equipment

JDPX5804

Fig. 7 — Raising a Pull-Type Plow Using Remote Cylinder Hydraulics

Tractors may operate equipment that is not mounted, but is pulled or pushed. To control this equipment with hydraulics, a remote actuator such as a cylinder or a motor is needed, separate from the tractor connected by flexible hoses.

Let's take the case of a plow again — this time one that is pulled behind the tractor (Fig. 7). The plow is pulling too hard and the operator wants to raise it. This is what happens:

The operator moves the hydraulic control lever to the front as shown. This actuates the control valve which sends pressure oil to the front of the remote cylinder. As this oil pushes the piston to the rear, the cylinder rod extends. Oil from the other side of the piston is forced out and returns through the valve to reservoir. As the cylinder rod extends, it pivots a linkage to the plow axle, rotating the bent axle to the rear, and so raises the plow.

Remote cylinders have hundreds of uses on machines.

Another use of remote hydraulics is the hydraulic motor. For example, a small hydraulic motor can be mounted on a cotton picker as shown in (Fig. 8). The motor converts fluid power into rotary motion, which drives the elevating mechanism. Pressure oil supply usually comes from a machine hydraulic outlet.

We have covered only the most common uses of hydraulics of modern machines. However, our primary aim is to describe maintenance.

JDPX5659

Fig. 8 — Small Hydraulic Motor Used to Drive Basket Compactor Auger on Cotton Picker

Servicing the Hydraulic System

There are four basic maintenance problems with hydraulic systems (Fig. 9):

• Not enough oil in the reservoir

• Clogged or dirty oil filters

• Leaking connections

• Incorrect oil in the system

Fig. 9 — Basic Maintenance Problems with Hydraulic Systems

All these problems can be solved or prevented by knowing the system and maintaining it properly.

Let's discuss some of the practices which will keep the hydraulic system in top-notch condition.

Checking Oil Level

To check the oil level, most hydraulic systems have either a sight glass in the reservoir or a dipstick (Fig. 10). Check the oil level at least every 250 hours. Some manufacturers recommend daily checks.

If the oil level isn't up to the sight glass or the "Full" of "Safe" mark on the dipstick, fill the reservoir with the recommended hydraulic fluid. See "Filling the Hydraulic System" on page 8-15.

At this time, also check for other malfunctions in the system. Look for:

• Oil bubbles or foaming oil. This may mean an air leak somewhere in the system.

• Changes in oil level. If there is a noticeable change in the oil level from day to day, look for leaks or cracks in the external parts of the system.

• Milky oil. This indicates water in the system or in the oil used. Be sure that oil is stored properly.

If the reservoir has a breather cap, clean it in solvent.

Fig. 10 — Two Methods of Checking Hydraulic Oil Level

Checking Oil Cooler

Check the oil cooler (Fig. 11) every 250 hours for accumulation of debris. Oil leaks are a problem, as the oil attracts dirt. Anything that blocks air flow through the cooler can cause overheating of the hydraulic fluid.

Fig. 11 — Location of a Typical Hydraulic Oil Cooler

Checking for Leaks

Fig. 12 — Hydraulic Systems Have Many Lines and Connections

CAUTION: Escaping fluid under pressure can penetrate the skin causing serious injury. Avoid the hazard by relieving pressure before disconnecting hydraulic or other lines. Tighten all connections before applying pressure. Search for leaks with a piece of cardboard. Protect hands and body from high-pressure fluids. If an accident occurs, see a doctor immediately. Any fluid injected into the skin must be surgically removed within a few hours or gangrene may result. Doctors unfamiliar with this type of injury should reference a knowledgeable medical source.

Excessive oil leakage can cause major damage to a hydraulic system if it goes unrepaired. Check all the hydraulic lines and connections for leaks every 50 hours or even daily if your operator's manual recommends it.

Some hydraulic systems are complex (Fig. 12) and have many lines and connections. With several connections in a hydraulic system, the chances are great that leaks will develop.
Look for:

- Pressure oil leaks. Oil leaks in the pressure, side of the system can be located by examining the outside of lines and fittings.

- Air leaks. If the suction side of the system is drawing in air, the oil in the reservoir will bubble and foam.

- Pinched or dented lines. This can cause oil foaming, overheating, and loss of hydraulic power. Replace damaged hoses or tubes at once. Wash lines inside and out with clean solvent before installing them.

Lower all units to the ground and inspect the machine completely. Tighten any leaking fittings using two wrenches to avoid twisting the lines (Fig. 13). Tighten only until snug and the leak stops. Do not overtighten.

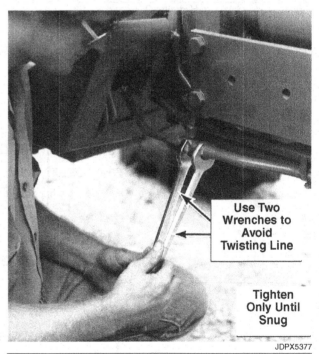

Fig. 13 — Tightening Hydraulic Fittings

H y d r a u l i c   S y s t e m s

Hose Failures

While you are checking for leaks, examine hoses closely. If a hose fails, you may lose all hydraulic fluid in a few moments. This can be dangerous to you and cause damage to the machine.

Look for cracking, splitting, pin-hole leaks, improper hose length, rubbing, heat, twisting, wrong hose selection, wrong fitting, or improper routing.

Replace any hose showing signs of damage with a new hose designed for exact replacement. Don't economize! Selecting a cheaper hose may result in premature failure of the hose.

Fig. 14 — How to Route Hydraulic Oil Hoses

Fig. 15 — Where to Check for Hydraulic Leaks

Component Leaks

If a component of the hydraulic system is leaking, a defective seal may be the problem. Take the machine to a service shop for repair. Do not attempt to repair hydraulic components yourself. Special tools and knowledge are required to repair hydraulic systems.

Refer to "General Maintenance of Hydraulic Systems" on page 8-17 for suggestions on preventing leaks and testing for internal leaks.

Fig. 16 — Connecting Remote Cylinder to Coupler on Machine

Maintaining Remote Cylinders

Remote cylinders require proper care for long service life. This includes correct connection, cleanliness, and bleeding air when necessary.

Connecting Remote Cylinders

1. Install the remote cylinder on the implement as instructed in the operator's manual.

2. Plug the cylinder hoses into the machine couplers (Fig. 16). Some couplers have a rotating lever to lock the hose end into the coupler port.

   When removing hoses from couplers, pull the hose straight out.

After hoses are removed, be sure to insert dust plugs into the coupler ports. Also place dust caps over the cylinder hose ends to protect them from dirt.

Bleeding Air from Remote Cylinders

Any time a remote cylinder is plugged in the hydraulic circuit, all trapped air must be bled. This will prevent sluggish action of the cylinder.

1. Attach the cylinder to the circuit see "Connecting Remote Cylinders".

 CAUTION: **For personal safety, have one person on the tractor operating the hydraulic controls and a second person on the ground supporting the cylinder. Do not stand in front of or behind tractor wheels during this procedure.**

2. Place the cylinder on the ground (or on a hanger) with the piston rod end down as shown in (Fig. 17). (Or on mounted cylinders, place the head end of the cylinder in its working mount, allowing the rod end to move in and out freely.)

3. Start the machine and move the hydraulic control lever back and forth seven or eight times to extend and retract the cylinder. This will bleed the air. (On double-acting cylinders, you may have to turn the cylinder end-for-end and repeat the cycling of the control lever.)

Fig. 17 — Bleeding Air from Remote Cylinder

CAUTION: Be sure machine is locked in PARK position before working around drive wheel.

Draining, Flushing, and Filling System

These services are recommended at least once each year for most machines.

Tools and Materials Needed

- Container to catch waste oil
- Clean, lint-free cloths
- Cleaning solvent (not gasoline)
- Wrenches for drain plug(s) and filter cap (inch or metric, as required)
- New oil of type and grade recommended by manufacturer
- New hydraulic oil filter
- Plastic tube (for bleeding)

Draining the Hydraulic System

- Drain System Periodically
- See Machine Operator's Manual
- Frequency Varies with Operating Conditions

JDPX5382

Fig. 18 — Drain the System Regularly

Periodic draining of the entire hydraulic system is very important. This is the only positive way to completely remove contaminants, oxidized oil, and other injurious substances from the system.

The frequency of draining depends on such things as the temperature of operation and the severity of working conditions. The operator's manual will tell the method to be used and the frequency, depending on conditions. Usually draining, flushing, and refilling is recommended at least once each year.

JDPX5383

Fig. 19 — Transmission-Hydraulic System Drain Plug

To drain the hydraulic system:

1. Operate the hydraulic system until it has reached normal operating temperature.
2. If the transmission case is the reservoir, also drive the machine until normal temperature is reached.
3. Remove drain plug from reservoir and catch oil in a container (Fig. 19).
4. Replace drain plug.
5. If your operator's manual recommends flushing the system before refilling, refer to "Flushing the Hydraulic System," next.

Flushing the Hydraulic System

The nature and amount of deposits in a system may vary widely. Inspection may show any condition between a sticky, oily film and a hard, solid deposit (gum or lacquer formation) which completely chokes small oil passages.

If the system is drained frequently enough, the formation of gum and lacquer will be reduced.

When no gum or lacquer formation is suspected, clean the system as follows: After draining the system, clean any sediment from the reservoir, and clean or replace the filter elements.

It may be advisable to flush out the old oil remaining in the system after draining, particularly if the oil is badly contaminated. For this flushing, use the hydraulic oil recommended for the system involved.

NOTE: Most solvents and chemical cleaners on the market today are NOT recommended for use in flushing hydraulic systems: 1) They are poor lubricants, resulting in damage to moving parts, especially the pump. 2) They are difficult to remove completely from the system. Just a trace of some of the commercial chlorinated solvents may be enough to break down the oxidation resistance of even the best hydraulic oils. Also, in the presence of a small amount of water, some of these solvents will corrode steel and copper.

To flush the system:

1. Operate the equipment to cycle the flushing oil through the system.

   It is important that the valves be manipulated so that the new oil goes through all lines. The time necessary to clean the system will vary, depending on the condition of the system.

2. Run the oil through the system until inspection shows the equipment to be in satisfactory condition, or until it is obvious that the system will have to be disassembled and cleaned manually by a service shop.

3. Drain out the flushing oil and refill the system with clean hydraulic oil of the recommended type.

4. Clean or replace the system filters before refilling the system.

For details, see "Filling the Hydraulic System," next.

Filling the Hydraulic System

Before filling the system, clean or replace the hydraulic oil filter. The filter may be located in the transmission case (Fig. 20) or in a separate reservoir (Fig. 21).

Fill the system as follows:

1. Clean the area surrounding the filter cover before removing cover.

2. Remove the old filter and insert a new one (Fig. 20). Replace filter cover.

3. Fill the reservoir to the specified level with the recommended hydraulic oil. Use only clean oil and funnels or containers. Be sure to replace the filler cap before operating the equipment.

4. Start the engine and warm up the hydraulic system. Then operate the equipment through its working cycle several times to bleed air from the system. (Hydraulic brakes and steering must also be bled individually—see following.)

5. Shut off engine and check oil level again, Add oil if necessary.

Fig. 20 — Typical Transmission-Hydraulic System Filters

Fig. 21 — Typical Hydraulic Oil Reservoir and Filter

Bleeding Brakes

When the brake system is part of the hydraulic system, the brakes must be bled whenever the hydraulic oil is drained and replaced. Also, whenever the pedals feel spongy or have excessive pedal free travel, you must bleed the air from them.

We will describe the procedures for bleeding hydraulic brakes connected to the hydraulic system; for procedures concerning conventional hydraulic brakes (trapped oil type), refer to chapter 9, "Other Components."

The machine may be equipped with either hydraulic brakes or power brakes. Read the following paragraphs on bleeding each type.

Tools and Materials Needed

- Wrenches (inch or metric, as required)
- Screwdriver (if needed)
- Transparent plastic tube (long enough to reach from bleed valve to transmission filler hole)

Bleeding Hydraulic Brakes

To bleed the brakes, proceed as follows:

1. Start the engine and run it at fast idle for two minutes to make sure the brake reservoir is filled with oil.

2. Locate the bleed screws. Usually they are located on top of the axle housing near the differential.

3. Attach a transparent plastic tube to the bleed valve as shown in (Fig. 22).

4. If possible, insert the other end into the transmission oil filler hole as shown. Be sure the end of the tube is submerged in oil.

5. Unscrew the bleed valve 3/4 turn.

6. Slowly depress the brake pedal and allow it to return slowly.

7. Continue operating pedal in this manner until oil in the transparent tube is free of air bubbles.

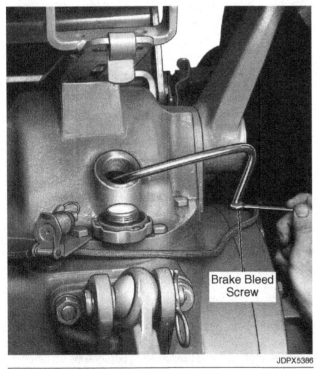

Fig. 22 — Bleeding Hydraulic Brakes

8. With the brake pedal still depressed, close the bleed valve securely.

9. Remove bleed tube and repeat this procedure for the other brake.

Bleeding Power Brakes

If reserve power for braking is provided by a hydraulic accumulator, check the accumulator before bleeding brakes. To check the accumulator, depress brake pedals firmly several times with the engine stopped. The pedal should feel firm for five or six applications. If any trouble is suspected, contact your dealer for service.

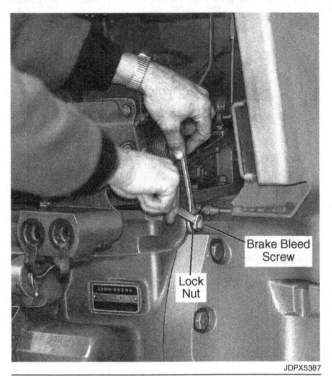

Fig. 23 — Bleeding Power Brakes

To bleed the brakes, proceed as follows:

1. Start the engine and loosen the bleed screw lock nut on both sides of the machine at the drive axle housing (Fig. 23), or follow instructions in your operator's manual.

2. Turn each bleed screw out two turns and tighten the lock nut. Tightening the lock nut prevents oil from leaking around the bleed screw.

3. Depress the brake pedals for a few minutes to bleed air from the brake system.

4. While holding the pedals down, loosen the bleed screw lock nuts and tighten the bleed screws.

5. Tighten the lock nuts, release the pedals, and stop the engine.

6. Discharge the accumulator (if used) and check the pedal free travel. (The accumulator supplies oil pressure to apply the brakes for a short time after the engine has stopped.) If the travel is excessive (refer to your operator's manual), repeat the procedure again.

7. If bleeding the brakes does not correct the problem, take the machine to a service shop for testing and repair.

General Maintenance of Hydraulic Systems

We have covered specific maintenance of the hydraulic system, now let's look at general maintenance:

- Importance of cleanliness
- Preventing overheating
- Preventing leaks
- Safety rules

Importance of Cleanliness

Cleanliness is No. 1 when it comes to servicing hydraulic systems. KEEP DIRT AND OTHER CONTAMINANTS OUT OF THE SYSTEM! Small particles can score valves, seize pumps, clog orifices, and so cause expensive repair jobs.

JDPX5388

Fig. 24 — Pump Pistons Scored by Contaminated Fluid

How do you keep the hydraulic system clean? Let's put it this way:

- Keep the oil clean
- Keep the system clean
- Keep your work area clean
- Be careful when you change or add oil

Preventing Overheating

Heat causes hydraulic oil to break down faster and lose its effectiveness. This why cooling of the oil is needed.

In many systems, enough heat is dissipated through the lines, the components, and the reservoir to keep the oil fairly cool. But on high-pressure, high-speed circuits, oil coolers are needed to dissipate the extra heat.

Overheating the system can:

- Break down the oil
- Damage the seals
- Coat parts with varnish deposits
- Cause extra leakage past working parts
- Reduce the output of the system

To help prevent overheating, keep the oil at the proper level; clean dirt and mud from lines, reservoirs, and coolers; check for dented or kinked lines; and keep relief valves adjusted properly. Also be careful not to overspeed or overload the system, and never hold control valves in power position too long.

If the system still overheats, take the machine to a service shop for testing.

Preventing Leaks

What causes leaks? There are hundreds of causes, but leaks fall into two basic types:

- External leakage
- Internal leakage

Internal leakage does not result in actual loss of oil, but it reduces the efficiency of the system. External leakage does result in direct loss of oil and can have other undesirable effects as well.

External Leakage

External oil leaks not only look bad, they can be expensive and hazardous. A drop of oil every second from a leaking connector can cost you quite a lot of money.

A small leak can also be the signal for a hydraulic rupture that may injure a person, as well as putting the machine out of operation.

Every joint in a hydraulic circuit is a potential point of leakage. This is why the number of connections in a system is kept to a minimum.

Components can leak, but care in assembly and use of new seals and gaskets during overhaul will help to reduce this problem.

The lines that connect the different parts of the system are the number 1 source of external leaks. Here are a few key points:

1. If the reservoir oil level is lower than normal, check all external oil lines for leaks.

2. Pin-hole leaks are hard to detect, yet they can be dangerous. A "vapor" of oil from a small leak can create a fire hazard, or a fine spray of oil against a hot engine can ignite.

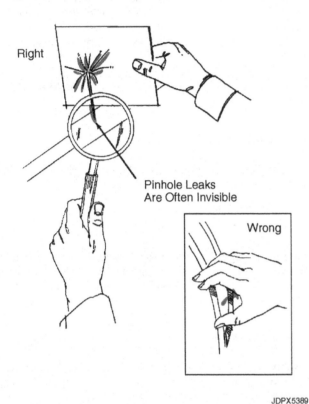

Fig. 25 — Checking Oil Lines for Leaks

⚠ CAUTION: Escaping fluid under pressure can penetrate the skin causing serious injury. Avoid the hazard by relieving pressure before disconnecting hydraulic or other lines. Tighten all connections before applying pressure. Search for leaks with a piece of cardboard (Fig. 25). Protect hands and body from high-pressure fluids. If an accident occurs see a doctor immediately. Any fluid injected into the skin must be surgically removed within a few hours or gangrene may result. Doctors unfamiliar with this type of injury should reference a knowledgeable medical source.

3. The rubber cover on flexible hoses may crack or split without actually leaking. But check very closely for internal damage; the depth of the crack is the deciding factor.

4. Air leaks in suction lines are hard to locate. One way is to pour oil over the points where you suspect leaks. If the noise or bubbling in the system stops, you've located the leak.

5. If line connections are leaking, tighten only until the leak stops. If the connection will not stay tightened, the threads are probably stripped and the connector must be replaced. If the connector will tighten but still leaks, check for a cracked line flare or a damaged seal. But remember, more damage has been done to line connectors by overtightening than from any other cause.

After stopping leaks in a system, be sure to warm up the system and cycle the equipment. Then recheck the trouble spots to be sure the leaks are stopped.

Recheck the system oil level and replace any oil lost through leaks or broken connections.

Internal Leakage

Slight internal leakage as a thin oil film is built into the working parts of a hydraulic system. This lubricates the mating surfaces of valve spools, cylinder pistons, and other moving parts. Oil is not lost through this normal internal leakage since it eventually returns to the system reservoir.

However, too much internal leakage will slow the operation of the system and waste power through the generation of heat. In some cases, it may cause cylinders to creep or drift, or it may cause loss of oil control in the valves.

Internal leakage increases with the normal wear of parts. Leakage is accelerated by using oil which has too low a viscosity, because this oil thins faster at higher temperatures. High pressures also force more oil out of leaking points in the system. This is one reason why excessive pressures can actually reduce the efficiency of the hydraulic system.

Internal leaks are hard to detect. Watch the operation of the system for sluggish action or creeping and drifting. When these signs appear, it's time to have a service shop test the system and pinpoint the trouble.

However, there are two components which can be checked without special hydraulic test equipment — the control valve, and the hydraulic cylinder.

Checking Control Valve For Internal Leaks

If you suspect the system control valve is leaking internally, make the following check.

1. Raise the hydraulic equipment a few feet off the ground, return the control lever to neutral and shut off the engine.

2. Notice whether the equipment settles toward the ground. If the equipment settles, temporarily support it and disconnect the return line between the control valve and reservoir, then plug the line (Fig. 26).

JDPX5390

Fig. 26 — Checking Hydraulic System Control Valve for Internal Leaks

3. Remove the support and examine the open port in the control valve as the equipment settles. If oil leaks from the port, the control valve spool is leaking. Take the equipment to a service shop for repair.

4. Remove plug and connect return line to the valve again.

Checking Hydraulic Cylinder for Internal Leaks

If no oil is leaking from the control valve, check the cylinder as follows:

1. To check a double-acting cylinder, run the cylinder to one end of its stroke. Support the equipment if it is raised, then shut off the engine.

2. Remove the hose from the end of the cylinder that was not pressurized (Fig. 27).

JDPX5391

Fig. 27 — Checking Double-Acting Cylinder for Internal Leaks

3. Start the engine again, pressurize the cylinder, and see if any oil comes out of the open port.

4. Repeat the test in the opposite direction, since it may be possible for the cylinder to leak in only one direction.

5. If oil leaks out the open cylinder port, the packings in the cylinder must be replaced. Take the cylinder to a service shop for repair.

Testing Hydraulic Systems

If you cannot locate troubles with the operational checks above, the system can be checked using a hydraulic analyzer or test gauges. Using this equipment, you can accurately measure oil flow, pressure, and temperature, and quickly isolate faulty components.

What a Hydraulic Tester Does

Hydraulic analyzers are available with pressure loading valves, pressure gauges (high and low pressure), flow meters, and temperature gauges to precisely analyze a complex hydraulic system. The test kit shown in (Fig. 28) is one example.

Test Hoses and Adapters

Cover   Tester

JDPX5392

Fig. 28 — Complete Hydraulic System Test Kit

In testing any hydraulic circuit, the following four checks are of prime importance:

- Temperature: The oil should be checked for correct operating temperature to ensure accuracy of the tests that follow.

- Flow: The flow check determines if the pump is developing its rated output.

- Pressure: These checks test relief valves for proper operation. (In a closed-center system, pressure checks indicate the operation of the main pump.)

- Leakage: The leakage test isolates leakage in a particular component.

These basic checks may be made with most hydraulic testers. Before beginning, however, read the instruction manual furnished with the tester and review the system. You should have a thorough knowledge of the machine's specifications (relief valve pressures, pump output, engine rpm, and operating temperature) to accurately test the system.

To test a machine, you must disconnect some of the oil lines. But remember, DIRT IS THE WORST ENEMY OF A HYDRAULIC SYSTEM. Before disconnecting oil lines, steam clean the machine. And be sure to plug all openings to keep out dirt.

Pump Testing

The pump is the generating force for the whole hydraulic system. This is the place to start testing the system.

This testing procedure is only a basic guideline. When testing actual machines, use your machine technical manual for detailed tests and test results. Remember that the best testing equipment has no value unless the person at the controls knows how to interpret the results.

Installing the Hydraulic Tester

1. Relieve any pressure in the system and disconnect the pressure line between the pump and the control valve. Attach the pressure line to the hydraulic tester INLET port (Fig. 29).

2. Connect hydraulic tester OUTLET port to the reservoir. Whenever possible, connect directly to the reservoir return line because it usually has a return filter. On a closed-center system, always return hydraulic tester oil to a point between the main hydraulic pump and the charging pump to maintain pressure in the system (or to be sure the main pump does not lose its charge).

JDPX5393

Fig. 29 — Testing the Hydraulic Pump

3. Check the oil level and slowly close the tester load valve to load the system. (Do not exceed the system's maximum rated pressure.) Continue loading until the normal operating temperature of the system is reached (see machine specifications).

IMPORTANT: Be sure the tester load valve is OPEN before starting any tests. The load valve can develop tremendous pressure on a component if it is closed too far.

		GALLONS PER MINUTE (LITERS/MINUTE) @ PSI (kPa)									
		0	250	500	750	1000	1250	1500	1750	2000	2250
PUMP TEST		31.0	28.0	25.0	22.0	19.0	16.0	13.0	10.0	7.0	
CIRCUIT TEST	DIRECTION-CYLINDER TRAVEL										

OWNER _____   SERIAL NO. _____

TRACTOR MODEL _____   EQUIPMENT _____

COMMENTS _____

JDPX5394

Fig. 30 — Sample Form for Recording Pump Test Results (Hand-Written Figures are Gallons and PSI)

Operating the Hydraulic Tester

1. With the tester load valve open, record maximum pump flow at zero pressure.

2. Slowly close the load valve to increase pressure and record the flow at 250 psi (1725 kPa) increments from zero pressure to maximum system pressure. Write down your test results so you can refer to them later. Use a test form such as the one shown in (Fig. 30).

3. Open the hydraulic tester load valve until maximum pump flow is again at zero pressure.

4. Shut off the engine.

Pump Test Diagnosis

Pump flow at maximum pressure should be at least 75 percent of pump flow at zero pressure. (On modern variable displacement pumps of the radial piston type, 90 percent can be expected.) A lower reading indicates a badly worn pump.

If pump flow is poor during the free flow test as well as the pressure tests, the pump probably is not getting enough oil. This problem could be caused by low oil supply, air leaks, a restricted pump inlet line, or a dirty reservoir, filter or breather.

If the pump tests okay, then start checking the system components for trouble.

JDPX5395

Fig. 31 — Testing the System Components

System Testing

This testing procedure is only a basic guideline. When testing actual machines, use your machine technical manual for detailed tests and test results. Remember that the best testing equipment has no value unless the person at the controls knows how to interpret the results.

Check the system components by the following procedures.

Installing the Hydraulic Tester

Install a tee fitting in the line between the pump and the control valve and attach the hydraulic tester INLET port to this tee (Fig. 31).

Leave the return line from the hydraulic tester OUTLET port connected in the same way as it was for the pump test.

Operating the Hydraulic Tester

1. Open the hydraulic tester load valve.

2. Start the engine and adjust it to the manufacturer's recommended operating speed.

3. Slowly close the hydraulic tester load valve to load the system. Continue loading the system until normal operating temperature is reached.

4. Open load valve to record maximum system flow at zero pressure.

5. Operate the control valve and hold it in one of its power positions.

6. Slowly close the hydraulic tester load valve and record flow in 250 psi (1724 kPa) increments from zero pressure to maximum system pressure (Fig. 31).

7. Open the load valve until maximum flow is again at zero pressure and repeat the test in the rest of the control valve power positions.

Be sure to make all the tests at the same oil temperature to get readings that can be compared. If oil is too hot from the previous test, allow it to circulate through the system for cooling.

System Test Diagnosis

Here's how to judge the system tests:

1. If flow at each pressure is the same as for pump test: All components are okay.

2. If pressure begins to drop before full load is reached: One of the circuits is bad (such as the bucket roll-back circuit in Fig. 32).

   The pressure drop is caused by leakage. To find out whether the leakage is in the control valve or the cylinder, disconnect the cylinder return line and move the control valve to a power position. If oil leaks from the cylinder return port, the cylinder is at fault and must be repaired. If no oil leaks out, the control valve is probably at fault.

3. It flow drops the same with the control valve in all positions: The system relief valve is probably at fault (see "Relief Valve Diagnosis" on page 8-23). This condition could also indicate a leak in the control valve.

OWNER		SERIAL NO.
TRACTOR MODEL		EQUIPMENT
COMMENTS		

		GALLONS PER MINUTE (LITERS/MINUTE) @ PSI (kPa)									
		0	250	500	750	1000	1250	1500	1750	2000	2250
PUMP TEST		32.0	31.7	31.4	31.0	30.6	30.2	29.8	29.3	28.8	
CIRCUIT TEST	DIRECTION-CYLINDER TRAVEL										
Boom Circuit	Lower	32.0	31.7	31.4	31.0	30.6	30.2	29.8	29.3	28.8	
	Raise	32.0	31.7	31.4	31.0	30.6	30.2	29.8	29.3	28.8	
Bucket Circuit	Dump	32.0	31.7	31.4	31.0	5.0	0.0				
	Roll-Bk.	32.0	31.7	31.4	31.0	30.6	30.2	10.0	0.0		

JDPX5396

Fig. 32 — Transmission-Hydraulic System Filter Covers

Relief Valve Diagnosis

If equipment with circuit relief valves is being checked, you can tell when the valves open because flow will suddenly drop about 3 gpm (11 L/min) (or drop to 0 gpm [L/min] if a full-flow relief valve is used). Often the relief valves will start to "crack" open before they reach their full-pressure settings. This can be noted by comparing the pressure and flow rate readings made in the circuit test above. Any great decrease in flow rate in these valves indicates a faulty valve.

As a general rule:

Faulty SYSTEM relief valves will affect readings in all tests.

Faulty CIRCUIT relief valves will affect only pressure readings in the individual circuits.

Safety Rules for Hydraulic Systems

 CAUTION: Escaping fluid under pressure can penetrate the skin causing serious injury. Relieve hydraulic system pressure before disconnecting any hydraulic lines and fitting or removing components. Tighten all connections before applying pressure. Search for leaks with a piece of cardboard. Protect hands and body from high pressure fluids.

- Always wear eye protection and proper clothing when doing maintenance work on hydraulic systems.
- Always lower the hydraulic working units to the ground before leaving the machine.
- Park the machinery where children cannot easily reach it.
- Block up the working units when you must work on the system while raised. Do not rely on the hydraulic lift.
- Never service the hydraulic system while the machine's engine is running unless absolutely necessary, as for bleeding the system.
- Do not remove cylinders until the working units are resting on the ground or securely on safety stands or blocks. Also shut off the machine's engine.
- When transporting the machine, lock the cylinder stops to hold the working units solidly in place.
- Be sure all line connections are tight and lines are not damaged. Escaping oil under pressure is a fire hazard and can cause personal injury.
- When washing parts, use a non-volatile cleaning solvent.
- To ensure control of the unit, keep the hydraulic system in proper adjustment.

Test Yourself

Questions

1. List three maintenance problems that concern a hydraulic system.

   _____

   _____

   _____

2. Match the symptom on the left with its cause on the right.

   a. Oil bubbles or foaming oil   1. Water in the system

   b. Change in oil level   2. Air leak somewhere in the system

   c. Milky oil   3. Leaks in the external parts of the system

3. (T/F) Tighten leaking fittings as tightly as possible.

4. What is the biggest enemy of hydraulic systems?

5. Give one safety rule that you should follow to avoid injury to yourself or others while working around the hydraulic system.

Other Components

9

Introduction

JDPX5687

Fig. 1 — Modern Machines Consist of Many Components That Require Maintenance

We have covered maintenance of the major basic components of the machine. Now let's look at maintenance of these other components:

- Operator's cab
- Manual steering
- Steering axis and wheels
- Manual brakes
- Tires
- Grease fittings
- Belt drives
- Chain drives
- Gear drives
- Lighting and electrical accessories

Failure to service these components can:

- Cause premature wear or damage to the machine
- Make the machine unsafe to operate
- Make operation of the machine uncomfortable

In addition, we will show how to clean the machine exterior, which should be done at least once each year.

To maintain each of the above components properly, you must be familiar with the basic services that are covered on the following pages.

Operator's Cab

The operator's cab is designed to protect you against dust, cold, and heat. Most cabs today also protect you in rollover accidents and help protect your hearing ability by reducing sound levels. Some even have radios and stereo tape players which give you up-to-date news or soothing music.

If the cab has fresh air ventilation, heating, and air conditioning, you have environmental controls which protect you against adverse operating conditions.

Following are typical cab services that should be performed at least every 250 hours or at intervals recommended in your operator's manual to maintain the maximum comfort in the operator's cab:

- Air filters
- Heater
- Air conditioner

Let's look at the maintenance required for each of these.

Filters

The cab may be equipped with either a fresh-air filter, a recirculating-air filter, or both (Fig. 2). Consult the operator's manual for detailed services.

Fresh-Air Filters

These are usually dry-type paper filters located in either the air intake or the filter cavity in the roof of the cab.

The following tools and materials are needed:

- Compressed air source
- Water pressure source
- Container of warm water
- Non-sudsing detergent

Fig. 2 — Fresh-Air Filter Housing

To clean dry-type paper filter:

1. Remove the filter from housing or access door (Fig. 2).

2. Tap the filter gently on a flat surface, dirty side down (Fig. 3).

   Do not tap on uneven surfaces or the filter element may be damaged.

Fig. 3 — Tapping Filter on a Flat Surface

⚠ CAUTION: Reduce compressed air to less than 30 psi (210 kPa) (2 bar) when using for cleaning purpose. Clear area of bystanders, guard against flying chips, and wear personal protection equipment including eye protection.

3. If you have a source of compressed air, direct it through the filter in the opposite direction of the air flow (Fig. 4). Air flow is usually indicated by arrows.

Fig. 4 — Directing Air through Filter in Opposite Direction of Air Flow

4. If the filter is still dirty, wash it as follows.

5. Soak the filter (Fig. 5) for 15 minutes in warm water (not over 100°F; 40°C) with a special dry filter element cleaner (or a nonsudsing detergent, such as used in a dishwasher).

Warm Water and Cleaner

JDPX5291

Fig. 5 — Soaking Filter in Warm Water and Cleaner

6. Rinse until clean with water from a hose (not over 40 psi; 275 kPa).

7. Shake excessive water from the filter and allow it to dry. Do not use compressed air to dry filter because this will rupture the wet element.

8. Reinstall filter. Be sure to install it with the arrows pointing in the direction of air flow.

Recirculating Air Filters

These filters are usually made of urethane foam and are located in the air recirculators (Fig. 6).

Recirculating Air Filter

JDPX5690

Fig. 6 — Recirculating Air Filter

To clean urethane foam filters:

1. Remove filter and clean by tapping or shaking filter.

2. If filter is still dirty, wash in clean water. Allow filter to dry thoroughly. Do not install wet filters in the air recirculators.

Heater

The heater requires little maintenance. However, check the following:

1. Check the hoses and connections for leaks.

   Tighten clamps or replace hoses if necessary.

2. Check accumulation of dirt and debris in heater core. Clean if necessary.

NOTE: Some applications have the heater core located under the instructional seat as shown in (Fig. 7). In other applications it is located under the cab roof.

Heater Core and Air Conditioner Evaporator Location

Operator's Seat

JDPX5770

Fig. 7 — Heater and Air Conditioner Evaporator Located in Cab

Air Conditioner

Fig. 8 — Basic Air Conditioning System

Service the air conditioning system periodically to maintain maximum cooling.

In (Fig. 8), note how the refrigerant cycle operates.

From the compressor, high-pressure gas is sent to the condenser, where it is converted to liquid and heat is dissipated. The high-pressure liquid flows on to the expansion valve, where it is metered and its pressure is reduced. At the evaporator, the liquid is again converted to gas, absorbing heat from the air. The cycle is then repeated, starting at the compressor.

The air conditioner is a heat transfer unit. Failure of any element will interrupt the heat exchange cycle and cause the whole system to fail. Each basic element is engineered and balanced to the other parts of the system in order to move heat from the inside air to the outside air, where it is dissipated.

Servicing Air Conditioner

Service the system as follows:

1. Check evaporator core for accumulation of dirt and debris (Fig. 7). Clean if necessary.

2. Check condenser core for accumulation of dirt and debris. It must be clean. The condenser is usually located near the radiator (Fig. 9).

3. Check refrigerant level. A sight glass is usually provided near the receiver-drier for this purpose (Fig. 9). Refer to the operator's manual for specific information on this procedure.

   The sight glass should be clear (free of bubbles) before starting the engine and operating the air conditioner.

NOTE: On some agricultural equipment, the receiver-drier is not equipped with a sightglass.

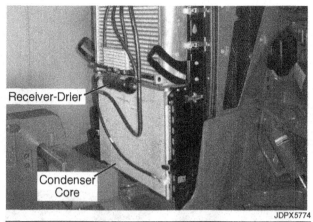

Receiver-Drier

Condenser
Core

JDPX5774

Fig. 9 — Air Conditioner Condenser Core and Receiver-Drier

   a. Start the engine and run it at fast idle.

   b. Turn on the air conditioner to the highest speed and turn the temperature control to the coldest temperature.

     Bubbles will appear in the sight glass for a few minutes after starting the air conditioner.

     At temperatures above 70°F (21°C) the bubbles will disappear and the sight glass should be clear.

     If the bubbles do not stop flowing, the refrigerant level is low. See your service shop for recharging the system. Special equipment and safety are vital to this service.

4. If belt tension if adjustable, adjust tension as specified in the machine operator's manual.

5. If equipped with automatic belt tensioner, inspect tensioner assembly as specified in the machine operator's manual.

6. If water is not draining from the evaporator properly, check the evaporator drain tube trap (Fig. 10) for clogging or a dry trap.

7. If the water has evaporated from a trap, air will be drawn up the drain tube and may hold the condensed water in the evaporator housing. The trap must be primed. To do so, momentarily hold a garden hose against the bottom of the drain tube to fill the trap with water.

Evaporator Water
Drain Tube

JDPX5701

Fig. 10 — Evaporator Water Drain Tube

8. The receiver-drier (Fig. 9) is basically the filter for the air conditioner refrigerant. It removes condensation and other moisture, which can harm the system. While not replaced at regular intervals, it should be replaced when the system is in for major service, or whenever excessive moisture is a problem in the system.

9. Compressor seals may dry out during cold weather when the air conditioner has not been operated for long periods of time. This will cause leaks that will allow refrigerant to escape. To avoid this problem, operate the air conditioner for 5 to 10 minutes at a time at least once a month to prevent seals from drying out. If necessary, rotate the compressor crankshaft a few times by hand.

Heating and Air Conditioning Problems

If the machine cab does not heat or cool properly after regular maintenance has been performed, take it to a dealer for testing and service. Special test equipment and service tools are needed, especially for air conditioners.

Manual Steering

The only maintenance required for manual steering gear is maintaining the oil level in the gear case every 250 hours and adjusting the gear backlash.

Checking Manual Steering Oil Level

Filler
Plug

Steering
Oil Level

JDPX5298

Fig. 11 — Checking Manual Steering Gear Housing Oil Level

Check the oil level in the steering gear housing every 250 or 500 hours, as recommended (Fig. 11). The operator's manual will indicate the proper level and type of lubricant.

Adjusting Steering Backlash

When steering wheel backlash or "play" becomes excessive, adjust it as follows:

1. Turn the steering wheel from one extreme to the other and count the number of turns.

2. Turn the steering wheel back one-half the number of total turns. This will position the mechanism in the mid-position.

3. Loosen the jam nut on the steering gear adjusting screw (Fig. 12).

Fig. 12 — Adjusting Steering Gear Backlash

4. Tighten the adjusting screw until a very slight drag is felt when the steering wheel is turned back and forth through the mid-position.

5. Use a screwdriver to prevent adjusting screw from turning and tighten the nut. Recheck the adjustment.

Steering Axle and Wheels

The steering axle and wheels require periodic adjustment and lubrication to prevent excessive wear and "play." Also, when the steering wheels are guided by tie rods and steering arms, toe-in must be adjusted annually or more frequently if recommended.

Lubricating Steering Axle and Wheel Bearings

Some steering axles and wheels require lubrication every 10 hours of operation. The exception is hand-packed bearings. These must be disassembled, cleaned, and hand packed every 1000 hours or annually. Also, wheel bearings with grease fittings must be cleaned and hand packed at the same intervals. When operating in extremely wet or muddy conditions, these services should be done more often.

Fig. 13 — Lubricating Grease Fittings on Steering Axle and Wheels (Wipe Clean First)

Shown in (Fig. 13) is the location of grease fittings for typical steering axle and wheels. The operator's manual will show you where these are on the machine and how many strokes of lubricant to apply to each. Be sure to wipe fittings clean before applying grease gun.

Cleaning, Repacking, and Adjusting Wheel Bearings

The following procedures describe typical cleaning, repacking, and adjustment of most wheel bearings.

Tools and Materials Needed

- Wrenches (inch or metric, as required)
- Diagonal pliers
- Clean cloths
- Container of solvent (for cleaning, not gasoline)
- Multipurpose grease (or wheel bearing grease if recommended)
- New cotter pins
- Small stiff-bristle brush
- Hydraulic jack
- Support stands
- Source of compressed air (if available)

Two typical types of wheel bearing assemblies are shown in (Fig. 14 and Fig. 15). The spindle-type wheel is used on machines equipped with dual tricycle wheels or wide axles. The axle-type wheel is usually used on machines with a single wheel.

Fig. 14 — Spindle-Type Wheel and Bearings

Removing Bearings on Spindle-Type Wheels

To remove the wheel bearings of a spindle-type wheel:

 CAUTION: Never rely on the jack alone to support the machine. Always use blocking under the machine in addition to the jack.

1. Jack up the machine so that the wheel is off the ground. Be sure to block the other wheels and set the parking brake so that the machine won't move and fall off the jack or support stands. Use blocks or support stands to securely support the machine. (On dual-wheel tricycle front wheels, run one wheel up on a block, freeing the other wheel for service.)

2. Clean dirt from wheel and hub cap.

3. Remove hub cap. It may be either screwed in, bolted on, or pushed into the hub. If bolted on, be careful not to damage the gasket under it. Lay cap, gasket, and other parts as they are removed, in clean pan or container. Avoid laying parts on a dirty surface. Even the slightest amount of dust or dirt is difficult to remove from a bearing, even in a cleaning solution.

Fig. 15 — Axle-Type Wheel and Bearings

4. Remove cotter pin with diagonal pliers. Straighten pin before removing it.

5. Remove adjusting nut (Fig. 16).

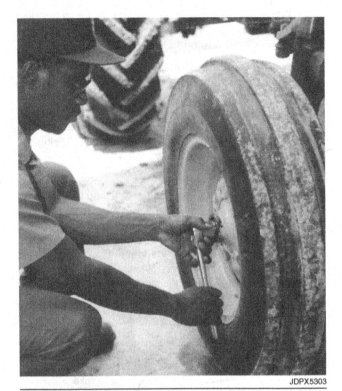

JDPX5303

Fig. 16 — Removing Adjusting Nut

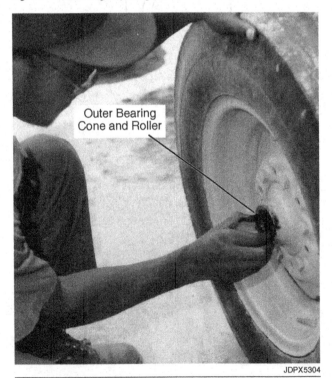

Outer Bearing Cone and Roller

JDPX5304

Fig. 17 — Removing Thrust Washer and Outer Bearing

6. Remove thrust washer and outer bearing (Fig. 17). Shake the wheel gently if necessary to dislodge them. Do not allow the parts to fall to the ground.

7. Carefully pull the wheel off the spindle. Hold your hand behind the wheel to catch the inner bearing if it should fall off when the wheel clears the spindle.

   On some wheels, the bearing and seal will come off with the wheel or remain on the spindle. If the bearing and seal cannot be removed easily from the spindle, leave them on. They can be cleaned while on the spindle.

8. If the grease seal remained in the hub, remove it with your fingers. Then remove the inner bearing.

   If the grease seal cannot be removed with your fingers, proceed with the next step as given below.

9. Turn the wheel over with the inner bearing down. Place a clean cloth or container under the hub to catch the bearing and seal when they fall out.

10. Use a brass drift punch or a wood dowel and gently tap the bearing cone from the hub (Fig. 18). Be careful not to tap on the bearing cage. You may damage the bearings.

   Refer to cleaning the bearings later in this discussion.

Brass Drift or Soft Bar

Hub Cap End

Inner Cone

Bearing

Grease Seal Retainer

JDPX5305

Fig. 18 — Removing Inner Bearing and Grease Seal

Removing Bearings On Axle-Type Wheels

To remove the wheel bearings of an axle-type wheel:

 CAUTION: Never rely on the jack alone to support the machine. Always use blocking under the machine in addition to the jack.

1. Jack up the machine so that the wheel is off the ground. Be sure to block the other wheels and set the parking brake so that the machine won't move and fall off the jack or support stands. Use blocks or support stands to securely support the machine. (On dual-wheel tricycle front wheels, run one wheel up on a block, freeing the other wheel for service.)

2. Clean dirt from the wheel and hub areas.

3. Remove the screws from the bearing lock plates and bend the lock plates away from axle nuts (Fig. 15).

4. Loosen axle nuts and remove dust shields.

5. Remove axle nuts and outer washers. Be careful that the wheel does not fall on you when you remove these parts. The wheel should now come off the yoke easily. Push down on the wheel if it does not come loose.

6. Disassemble axle, seals (felt washers and retainers), bearings, and any spacers and nuts remaining.

Cleaning Wheel Bearings

To clean the wheel bearings and other parts:

1. Swirl the bearing in a container of clean solvent, using a brush to loosen grease deposits.

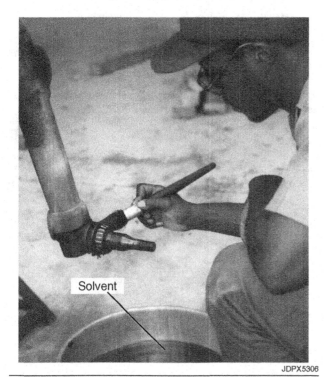

Fig. 19 — Cleaning Inner Bearing on Spindle

If you were unable to remove the inner bearing (spindle-type wheel), clean it and the grease seal while in place. Use a large brush and hold the container of solvent under the parts (Fig. 19). Dip the brush in the container and wash the bearing and seal thoroughly.

2. Clean the bearing cups also. It is not necessary to remove the cups from the hub. Also, clean the hub, cap and spindle or axle.

Fig. 20 — Drying Bearing with Compressed Air

3. Remove solvent from all washed parts using dry compressed air (Fig. 20). If dry compressed air is not available, use a cloth free of dirt, dust, and lint. Hold the bearings so the air blast won't spin the rolling elements or the cage. Spinning a dry bearing can cause minute scoring of the bearing surfaces, which will provide a rough enough surface to cause rapid wear.

NOTE: Do not use air that contains moisture. Moisture will cause the bearings to rust in a very short time.

4. Examine bearings for damage, wear, rust, or corrosion. If it is apparent that any of these defects are serious enough, replace both the bearing race and cup of the affected bearing.

    If the inner bearing (spindle-type wheel) requires replacement and you were unable to remove it before, use a wood dowel and hammer to tap off the bearing.

5. Inspect the grease seals and retainers for excessive wear or damage. Replace any defective seals. The seal keeps out the dirt and moisture as well as retaining the grease.

    If the seal is defective, the bearing life will be short. It is a good practice to replace seals and retainers each time the bearings are cleaned and repacked.

    After you have determined which bearings can be reused and have replaced those that cannot, you are ready to repack the bearings.

Repacking and Assembling Bearings

To repack the bearings with grease and reassemble the wheels:

1. Use multipurpose grease or wheel bearing grease as specified by your operator's manual.

2. Rub a thin coating of clean crankcase oil on your hands to prevent the grease from sticking to them.

3. Place a small quantity of grease in the palm of your hand (Fig. 21). Push the grease into the elements of the bearing, press the bearing against the grease, and rotate the bearing until grease has worked into the bearing thoroughly. Repeat this for each bearing.

Fig. 22 — Wheel Hub Housing Partly Filled with Grease

6. Reassemble the wheel bearings in the reverse order of disassembly. Be sure that grease seals are seated in the hub or retainers properly.

7. Install the wheel and be careful that dirt does not get into the bearing grease.

8. Adjust the wheel bearings as follows.

Adjusting Spindle-Type Wheels

1. Install thrust washer and slotted adjusting nut.

2. Tighten slotted adjusting nut until bearing is seated properly (Fig. 23). Be sure bearings are aligned with the spindle.

Fig. 21 — Packing Grease into a Bearing

4. If the inner bearing was left on the spindle, apply a thick coating of grease to the outer portions of the bearing. Wrap a clean cloth or piece of plastic around the bearing. Twist the ends of the cloth or plastic until it binds tightly around the bearing. This will press the trapped grease into the bearing. (Bearing packer will do an even more thorough job, if available.)

5. Apply a coating of grease to the inside of the hub. This will help to prevent rust and prevent the entrance of dirt and water. Do not fill the entire cavity of the hub unless the operator's manual recommends it. Air space should be left in most hubs to permit the air to expand without building up pressure, which can force grease past the seals (Fig. 22).

Fig. 23 — Adjusting Wheel Bearings on Spindle-Type Wheels

3. Loosen the adjusting nut until the wheel can be turned easily, then turn the wheel and tighten the nut again until the wheel begins to turn with a slight drag.

NOTE: Some manufacturers recommend tightening the adjusting nut to a specific torque. You must use a torque wrench for this adjustment.

4. Loosen the adjusting nut until the nearest slot is aligned with the hole in the spindle. Check your operator's manual for its recommendations. Some manufacturers suggest loosening the nut as much as 1/6 to 1/3 turn.

5. Always insert a new cotter pin. Use diagonal pliers and bend one leg of the pin over the end of the spindle. Cut off any excess length of the other leg and bend it back against the nut. If the cotter pin is not installed properly, it could loosen and fall out, allowing the wheel to come off.

6. Replace the hubcap.

Adjusting Axle-Type Wheels

1. Install the wheel on the yoke.

2. Slide outer washers onto axle until they seat into the hole in the yoke.

3. Attach the lock plates loosely with cap screws.

4. Screw on the axle nuts loosely.

5. Tighten the bearing adjusting nut with a drift and a hammer (Fig. 24) until a slight drag is felt when the wheel is rotated.

6. Back the nut off and lock the adjustment in the closest notch with the lock plate screw.

7. Tighten the axle nuts. The wheel should still rotate with a slight drag.

8. If the adjustment is correct, bend the corner of the lock plates against the axle nuts.

Fig. 24 — Adjusting Wheel Bearings on Axle-Type Wheels

Adjusting Wheel Toe-In (Wide-Axle Machines)

Wheels that steer the machine must have proper toe-in so that the machine tracks in a straight line. This reduces wear on the tires and makes steering easier.

With wide steering axles, wheel toe-in must be checked periodically. "Toe-in" means that the wheels point slightly inward on the front or leading side.

Check the toe-in:

• Whenever steering becomes difficult

• After hitting an obstacle

• After changing wheel spacing

• Before operating the machine at the beginning of the season

To check the toe-in of the wheels that steer the machine:

1. Drive the machine straight ahead for a short distance on level ground. Stop the machine and shut off the engine.

2. Measure the wheel tread at the front and rear of the wheels at hub level (Fig. 25). Usually, proper toe-in is 1/8 to 3/8 inch (3 to 10 mm) less in the front than in the rear. Check the operator's manual for specifications.

   If toe-in does not measure correctly, proceed with the following steps.

Fig. 25 — Measuring Wheel Toe-In

3. On machines with a single tie rod between steering wheels, loosen the tie rod clamps and turn the tie rod until the measurements are correct (Fig. 26). Tighten clamps.

Fig. 26 — Machine with Single Tie Rod Adjustment

4. On machines with a tie rod for each wheel, loosen both clamps on each tie rod (Fig. 27). Turn each tie rod an equal amount until toe-in measurements are correct. Tighten clamps. Both wheels must have equal toe-in.

Fig. 27 — Machine with Tie Rod for Each Wheel

Brakes

Most machines have two brake pedals (Fig. 28) which may be used for stopping (both pedals) or for turning (one pedal on either side to help turn machine).

To keep the machine safe to operate, be sure to maintain the brakes properly. Brakes that are out of adjustment can cause uneven braking or poor braking, which may cause your machine to overturn or crash into something, injuring you or others and damaging the machine.

Knowing how brakes work will help you understand why they need adjustment.

Fig. 28 — Most Machines Have Two Brake Pedals

Operation of Brakes

The machine may be equipped with mechanical brakes, hydraulic (power) brakes, or hydraulic (trapped oil) brakes. Hydraulic powered brakes were discussed in Chapter 8; mechanical and hydraulic (trapped oil) brakes will be described here.

Almost all agricultural machines have brakes for the drive wheels or drive train only.

Mechanical brakes are controlled and actuated by mechanical linkage. Control rods or cables provide the linkage between the brake pedals and the wheel brakes (Fig. 29).

Fig. 29 — Mechanical Brakes

Fig. 30 — Hydraulic (Trapped-Oil) Brakes

Thus far, only the brake controls have been described. The braking action itself is provided by one of the following methods:

- Shoe brakes (internal expanding)
- Disk brakes

For more information on hydraulic brakes, see Chapter 8.

Hydraulic (trapped-oil) brakes are controlled and actuated by hydraulic oil trapped between the brake master cylinder (controlled by the brake pedals) and the slave cylinders, which actuate the brake mechanism (Fig. 30).

The shoe brake is forced against the inside of the brake drum and slows or prevents the drum from turning (Fig. 31). This type of brake is popular on automobiles.

Fig. 31 — Shoe Brakes

Disk brakes are commonly used on agricultural machines, although the other two types are found on some machines. Each brake mechanism consists of two driven brake disks, which have friction facings attached to each side, and two actuating disks, which force the brake disks against a stationary braking surface (Fig. 32).

Fig. 32 — Disk Brakes

The driven brake disks are attached to either differential input shaft or to each drive axle within the differential housing.

Between the brake disks are two actuating disks which are held together by springs. Three steel balls are located in tapered cups on the inside of each actuating disk. When the actuating disks are rotated in opposite directions by levers, the steel balls ride out of their cups and force the brake disks apart (Fig. 32, right).

As the brake disks are forced farther apart, they bind against the stationary braking surfaces of the housing and slow or stop the shaft from turning.

All three of these brakes may be controlled by either mechanical or hydraulic action.

Adjusting the Brakes

Two things can indicate when brakes need adjustment:

- Too much pedal free travel
- Poor or uneven braking action

Adjusting Mechanical Disk Brakes

1. Park on level surface. Chock wheels to prevent machine movement.

2. Unlock brake pedals.

IMPORTANT: New friction disks must be soaked in the specified oil for at least 10 hours prior to installation.

3. If brakes are new, apply at least 70 lb of force to pedals 10 times before adjusting.

4. Apply approximately 20 lb of force to pedal, then measure distance between engaged pedal and disengaged pedal (Fig. 33).

Fig. 33 — Brake Pedal Travel

5. Adjust brake linkage, either the pedal or the brake housing, whichever is recommended in your operator's manual.

Fig. 34 — Adjustment Rod and Turnbuckle (Left Side Shown)

6. Each side of tractor has an adjustment rod with turnbuckle and jam nuts (Fig. 34), so each brake pedal should be adjusted separately. Adjustment mechanism is near the rear end of the rod, above final drive on the left-hand side, and near the front end on the right-hand side. To adjust linkage, loosen jam nuts on each side of turnbuckle.

7. Rotate turnbuckle as needed to increase or decrease length of adjustment rod in order to obtain free travel specification.

8. After pedal travel is within specification, tighten jam nuts on both sides of turnbuckle.

9. Repeat procedure on opposite side.

Adjusting Hydraulic (Trapped Oil) Brakes

Three procedures are required to adjust hydraulic (trapped oil) brakes:

- Bleeding brakes
- Adjusting push rods
- Adjusting brake mechanism

If brake pedal action feels soft or spongy, bleed the brakes using the following steps. The machine should not be raised off the ground.

BRAKE SHOE-TO-DRUM ADJUSTMENT

 CAUTION: Park machine on a flat, level surface and place blocks in front of and behind drive tires.

1. Disengage park brake cable by loosening jam nuts (Fig. 35).

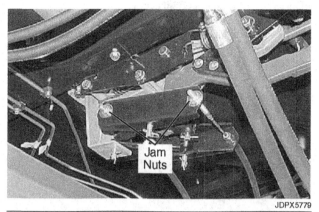

Fig. 35 — Loosen Jam Nuts

2. Remove drive shafts from each side of machine (Fig. 36).

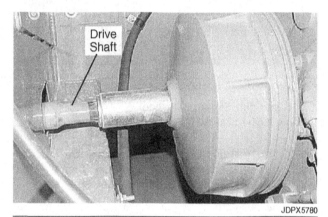

Fig. 36 — Drive Shaft (2 Used)

3. Check brake shoe-to-drum clearance by rotating brake drums back-and-forth.

   A slight drag should be felt.

   If no drag is felt, remove brake drum.

4. Using a brake shoe adjustment tool, check shoe-to-drum clearance.

5. Compare to brake shoe OD and adjust accordingly using star adjusting wheel. Set brake shoes to specification.

   If brakes are too tight, hold self-adjusting arm off star adjusting wheel and back off adjustment wheel. When satisfied with brake drum drag, leave brake drums on.

BLEEDING BRAKE SYSTEM

⚠ CAUTION: Park machine on a flat, level surface and place blocks in front of and behind drive tires.

1. Adjust shoe-to-drum clearance (see "Brake Shoe-to-Drum Adjustment").

⚠ CAUTION: Two persons are required to bleed brakes, one to pump brakes and fill reservoir, and the other to bleed the brakes.

Use only clean DOT 3 brake fluid, or fluid recommended by the manufacturer.

Keep brake fluid off painted surfaces.

2. Check brake system for leaks and loose fittings. Brake system must be free of leaks, and all connections must be tight. Check bleed screws on master and slave cylinders and make sure they are tight.

3. Check fluid in brake reservoir and fill as needed during bleeding. Loosen, but do not remove, reservoir cap to avoid creating a vacuum during bleeding. Prevent dirt from entering reservoir.

4. Install a piece of clean 3/16 in. (5 mm) ID clear plastic tubing, approximately 36 in. (915 mm) long, to right-hand master cylinder bleed screw (Fig. 37). Route hose up so bleed screw is at lowest point and place hose end in a suitable container.

Fig. 37 — Right-Hand Master Cylinder Bleed Screw

5. Loosen right-hand master cylinder bleed screw 1/4 turn.

6. Add brake fluid to remote reservoir and watch fluid flow through plastic tubing until there is a clear flow of fluid with no air bubbles.

7. Close right-hand master cylinder bleed screw.

8. Lock brake pedals together.

9. With clear tubing still installed, loosen right-hand master cylinder bleed screw 1/4 turn.

10. Slowly depress both brake pedals to floor, tighten bleed screw, and slowly release pedals. Repeat until there is a clear flow of fluid with no air bubbles.

11. Close right-hand master cylinder bleed screw.

JDPX5782

Fig. 38 — Slave Cylinder Bleed Screws

12. Install tubing on left-hand slave cylinder bleed screw (Fig. 38). Route hose up so bleed screw is at lowest point and place hose end in suitable container.

13. Loosen left-hand slave cylinder bleed screw 1/4 turn.

14. With pedals still locked together, slowly depress to floor, tighten bleed screw, and slowly release pedals.

    Repeat until there is a clear flow of fluid with no air bubbles.

NOTE: *If system is partially filled before bleed procedure was started, a steady, clear flow of fluid may appear for several initial strokes. If air is located in or near master cylinder, it will take several strokes to move air through lines and out bleed screw.*

15. Close left-hand slave cylinder bleed screw.

16. Unlock brake pedals.

17. Install tubing on right-hand slave cylinder bleed screw. Route hose up so bleed screw is at lowest point and place hose end in a suitable container.

18. Slowly depress right-hand brake pedals to floor, tighten bleed screw and slowly release brake pedal.

    Repeat until there is a clear flow of fluid with no air bubbles.

19. Close right-hand slave cylinder bleed screw.

20. Lock brake pedals together.

21. Install tubing to left-hand master cylinder bleed screw. Route hose up so bleed screw is at lowest point and place hose end in a suitable container.

22. Loosen left-hand master cylinder bleed screw 1/4 turn.

23. With brake pedals locked together, slowly depress to floor, tighten bleed screw and slowly release pedals.

    Repeat until there is a clear flow of fluid with no air bubbles.

24. Tighten left-hand master cylinder bleed screw.

25. Fill brake fluid reservoir to proper level and tighten cap.

26. Unlock brake pedals.

ADJUSTING MASTER CYLINDER

Follow this procedure only if parts in the brake system have been replaced or if excessive free play between the pedal and the master cylinder is noticed.

JDPX5781

Fig. 39 — Master Cylinder Adjustment

1. Loosen nut. Slide rubber boot off master cylinder and onto push rod to expose inside of cylinder (Fig. 39).

IMPORTANT: Outer edge of piston must be touching snap ring in the cylinder. Clean all dirt from between cylinder and snap ring.

2. Screw push-rod in or out of yoke until push-rod just contacts piston in the cylinder, then turn push-rod 1/4 turn away from piston.

IMPORTANT: Use your fingers to adjust each push-rod. Do not move piston away from snap ring.

3. Hold push-rod carefully in place when tightening lock nut. Slide rubber boot back on cylinder.

Repeat for the other cylinder.

Tires

Fig. 40 — *Big Tires Are Expensive — Take Care of Them*

Tire replacement can cost thousands of dollars for larger machines. If tires are not properly inflated or are abused, their life can be shortened greatly. For example, underinflation can reduce tire life by up to one-quarter. This alone could cost hundreds of dollars. Tire abuse such as spinning wheels can wear tires even faster.

Maintaining tires properly takes only a few minutes periodically. Here are the key maintenance items:

- Tire inflation
- Ballast
- Tire failures
- Safety tips

Let's look at each one.

Tire Inflation

Proper inflation is vitally important to proper service life of the tire. Tires are designed to operate with a certain sidewall deflection or "bulge." Correct air pressure helps provide proper traction, flotation, and support of loads, and prevents excessive flexing of the tire, which could cause sidewall cracking. See (Fig. 41) for typical tire construction.

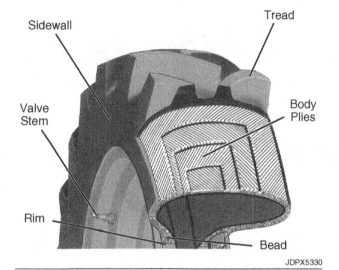

Fig. 41 — *Typical Tire Construction*

Overinflation

Fig. 42 — *Overinflated Tire*

Overinflated tires don't fully contact the ground (Fig. 42). The center of the tread wears. And, because the tire is more rigid, it is more liable to be damaged by curbs, rocks, etc.

 CAUTION: Overinflation and overloading my lead to a violent tire explosion which may result in severe equipment damage, serious injury, and death.

Underinflation

JDPX1407

Fig. 43 — Underinflated Tire

Underinflated tires flex excessively (Fig. 43) every time the wheel turns, resulting in high internal heat and premature failure. Underinflation is indicated by excessive wear of the tread on the sides while the center is relatively unworn.

Proper Inflation

JDPX1408

Fig. 44 — Correctly Inflated Tire

Correctly inflated tires (Fig. 44) permit all of the tread to contact the ground, yet are not soft enough to flex excessively.

Pressure Gauge

JDPX1154

Fig. 45 — Low-Pressure Tire Gauge

Proper inflation must be maintained at all times and all seasons. An accurate pressure gauge is required. Two types of pressure gauges are available for either dry or liquid testing: high-pressure and low-pressure. Always use the proper gauge when checking pressure. Normally, high-pressure gauges are not satisfactory for checking low-pressure tires, as the gauges are usually calibrated in five-pound increments. Low-pressure gauges are better for low pressure; they are calibrated in one-pound increments.

Accuracy is most important. Accuracy can only be determined by checking a gauge against a gauge of known accuracy. For this reason, keep one accurate gauge for the sole purpose of checking the accuracy of other gauges. Low-pressure gauges (Fig. 45) are especially susceptible to inaccuracy.

Tire Inflation Rules

Here are four rules that must be observed for proper tire inflation:

1. Always check and inflate tires when they are cold. This is very important because tires become heated through use and the air expands thus the pressure increases.

2. Never "bleed" air pressure from warm or hot tires. This always results in the tire pressure being too low when its temperature becomes normal and often results in tire damage when put under load. Instead of bleeding air from hot tires, reduce the load, the speed, or both.

3. If a tire becomes low while operating, adjust pressure the same as other tires of the same size on the machine. Recheck the pressure after about 30 minutes of operation to be sure it is still correct.

4. Always use a liquid-type pressure gauge when checking pressure in tires with liquid ballast. Check pressure with the valve stem at the bottom. Always wash the gauge with clean water after checking the tires.

1 ft (0.3 m) =
1/2 psi (3.4 kPa)
Add to
Pressure Reading

JDPX5331

Fig. 46 — Optional Method of Checking Air Pressure with Valve Stem at Top

If it is impossible or undesirable to check the pressure with the valve stem at the bottom, locate the stem at the top (Fig. 46).

For actual pressure, add about 1/2 psi (3.4 kPa) to the pressure gauge reading, as shown, for each foot the liquid is above the lower valve stem position.

Proper Amount of Tire Inflation

Recommended tire inflation varies with size, ply, and load on tire (Fig. 47). An average recommendation for a six-ply front tractor tire is 36 psi (250 kPa) (more with front-mounted equipment). An average six-ply rear tractor tire is 16 psi (110 kPa) (more with heavy ballast or rear-mounted equipment). Always follow your operator's manual for the exact tire pressure.

Inflating Tires

To check tire inflation:

1. If the tire contains ballast, be sure the valve stem is positioned correctly as described in the rules above (see "Tire Inflation Rules" on page 18), or use the method shown in (Fig. 46).

2. Remove valve cap and check air pressure. Be sure to hold the gauge firmly against the valve stem to get a correct reading.

3. Check pressure again if you think a poor contact was made.

TIRE INFLATION		
6-Ply		
Front tires	Lowest	Highest
All 7.50 sizes	20 psi (140 kPa)	36 psi (250 kPa)
6.50	20 (140)	44 (300)
5.50 and 6.00	20 (140)	48 (330)
4-Ply		
Front tires	Lowest	Highest
All 7.50 sizes	20 psi (140 kPa)	24 psi (165 kPa)
6.50	20 (140)	28 (195)
5.50 and 6.00	20 (140)	32 (220)
5.00	20 (140)	36 (250)
4.00	20(140)	44(300)
8- and 10-Ply		
Rear tires	Lowest	Highest
18.4 8-ply	16 psi (110 kPa)	20 psi (140 kPa)
23.1 8-ply	16 (110)	16 (110)
23.1 10-ply	16 (110)	20 (140)
24.5 10-ply	16 (110)	18 (125)
6-Ply		
Rear tires	Lowest	Highest
All 18.4	16 psi (110 kPa)	16 psi (110 kPa)
16.9	16 (110)	16 (110)
14.9	14 (95)	18 (125)
13.6	14 (95)	20 (140)
12.4	12 (80)	22 (150)
11.2	12 (80)	24 (165)
4-Ply		
Rear tires	Lowest	Highest
All 13.6	14 psi (95 kPa)	14 psi (95 kPa)
12.4	12 (80)	14 (95)
11.2	12 (80)	16 (110)
9.5	12 (80)	18 (125)

JDPX5785

Fig. 47 — Tire Inflation Chart

4. Add or release air as needed to obtain correct air pressure.

Do not exceed the maximum recommended air pressure. Some tire manufacturers recommend that you put a few more pounds in tires under the following conditions:

- If mounted equipment puts most of the weight on one side of the machine, put a few extra pounds of pressure in the tires on that side, but do not exceed maximum pressure ratings.

- If the tractor is used for plowing with one set of wheels in the furrow, inflate the furrow tires a few extra pounds (usually about 4 psi [30 kPa]) to avoid excessive buckling of tires (Fig. 48). Again, do not exceed maximum pressure.

JDPX5332

Fig. 48 — Tire Tends to Buckle in Furrow

- If the machine is to be operated on a paved or hard road for several hours, inflate all tires to the maximum recommended pressure.

Now let's take a look at how tire ballast affects traction and available horsepower.

Tire Ballast

Tire ballast or weight can help give the most effective traction and power. The machine weight by itself may not be sufficient for full traction and drawbar pull. However, improper tire ballast can cause premature tire wear.

Farm tractors are the prime users of wheel ballast, so the discussion of ballast will refer mainly to them.

See "Tractor Performance" on page 9-24.

Too Much Weight

Too Little Weight

Proper Weight

JDPX1155

Fig. 49 — Tire Traction Patterns (Farm Tractor in Loose Soil Shown)

Tire traction can be judged by looking at the tire tread pattern after pulling under load as shown in (Fig. 49).

Too Much Weight

When too much weight is used, the tire tracks will be sharp and distinct in the soil and there will be no evidence of slipping.

This is bad, as the tires are literally geared to the ground and do not allow the flexibility of engine operation that is obtained when some slippage occurs.

Too Little Weight

When the tires have too little weight, they lose traction. The tread marks are entirely wiped out and forward progress is slowed. Not only is less work done but the tires wear excessively. Reduced speed caused by excessive slippage can also cause over-application of chemical pesticides.

Proper Weight

When the tires have proper weight, a small amount of slippage occurs. Usually, between 10 and 15 percent slippage is considered ideal in the field. When the tire is properly weighted, the soil between the cleats will be shifted but the tread pattern is still visible in the tire track as shown. Proper weighting allows the engine to perform at its best with maximum flexibility.

Adding Ballast to Tires

See your local service shop for adding ballast to tires. The tires can be filled about three-fourths full of liquid to add weight. Usually a mixture of water and calcium chloride solution is used to prevent freezing. Dealers are equipped to mix and add solution to the tires. A special valve is needed to permit air to escape from the tire while the solution is being added.

If water is used instead of calcium chloride solution, it must be removed during winter in colder climates. Water also provides less weight per unit of volume than does calcium chloride solution.

Cast iron weights can also be attached to wheels for extra weight. Dual or triple tires are another way of improving traction and adding weight on larger tractors.

Remember that tire inflation should be higher when more ballast is added. See the operator's manual for recommended amounts under different operating conditions.

Dual and Triple Tires

Dual and triple tires are frequently added to improve traction and flotation of large tractors. Dual tires generally cost less than large single tires which would provide equal "footprint" or soil contact area. The extra weight of the added tires and wheels increases traction in adverse conditions. Extra tires also increase total load-carrying capacity (for more ballast, spray tanks, etc.). Total weight must not exceed load rating of the tires.

Tires used in dual or triple configurations must be matched in diameter and circumference to avoid uneven distribution of load. All drive tires on four-wheel-drive machines should also be matched. Circumference of tractor drive tires, mounted and inflated, should not vary more than 1-1/2 inches (40 mm). Tires of uneven size can cause excessive tire slippage, axle breakage, difficult steering, and other problems.

Adding dual or triple tires increases strain on axles and housings and is not recommended on some tractor models. Check with your tractor dealer or manufacturer if the operator's manual does not indicate acceptability of extra tires.

We have discussed basic tire maintenance. Now let's look at some tire failures which are caused by poor maintenance or abuse.

Tire Failures

As we have said, tire failures may be caused by abuse, underinflation, overinflation, or just plain careless operation.

If tires aren't inflated properly, they are more subject to damage than under any other condition.

Inspect tires regularly for the following signs of damage. If the machine is operated as it should be, you probably won't find any tire damage as described here. However, the following will reveal what kind of damage is caused by abuse, underinflation, or overinflation.

Tire Abuse

Tire abuse is any operation or lack of attention that will cause damage to tires.

Avoid driving over objects, such as large rocks or tree stumps, or anything that may penetrate the tire or break the tire cords. An impact break is shown in (Fig. 50).

JDPX1170

Fig. 50 — Break Caused by Tire Hitting an Object. Fabric Was Unable to Withstand the Shock.

Avoid spinning the tires. Engage the clutch slowly to prevent the tires from spinning. Use ballast and weights when pulling heavy loads to prevent spinning damage shown in (Fig. 51).

JDPX1176

Fig. 51 — Tire with Spinning Wear

Adjust the tire spacing to avoid stubble damage (Fig. 52) when operating in harvested corn or soybean fields.

JDPX1177

Fig. 52 — Farm Tractor Tire with Stubble Wear

Locate small cuts in the tire and bevel them to prevent stones and other small objects from embedding in the tire and causing leaks or broken cords (Fig. 53).

Check your machine for parts that may be rubbing or gouging the tires as they turn. Hitching or turning too short may cause this problem.

JDPX5783, 5784

Fig. 53 — Small Cut in Tire Lug (Left) Beveled Out to Prevent Imbedded Stones (Right)

Underinflation

If your tires become underinflated, the sidewalls may buckle and break as shown in (Fig. 54). This can occur when operating under heavy drawbar pull and when plowing with tires in the furrow. See the instructions on inflation described earlier.

Avoid operating on roads or other hard surfaces for long periods of time. If you must, inflate the tires to the maximum recommended pressure.

Fig. 54 — Damage Caused by Underinflation

Overinflation

Avoid overinflating tires. Do not exceed the maximum pressure rating.

Breaks in the tire cord (Fig. 55) can occur much easier when striking an object with tires inflated above normal pressures.

Also, the center portion of the tire tread will become worn more rapidly than the outer portions.

Fig. 55 — Damage Caused by Overinflation

Safety Tips for Tires

Fig. 56 — Large Farm Tires Are Potential Safety Hazards

⚠️ CAUTION: An inflated tire can be very dangerous. Under pressure, for example, an 18-22.5 16 PR tire with 75 psi (515 kPa) pressure develops 103,789 Energy Foot-Pounds (140 717 J), and if it exploded, that energy could lift a 20,000 pound (9090 kg) tractor more than 5 feet (1.5 m) off the ground.

When inflating large tires, use a clip-on chuck and extension hose long enough to allow you to stand to one side and NOT in front of the tire assembly.

Before a jack is placed in position, block the tire and wheel on the other side of the machine. ALWAYS crib up with blocks or a stand just in case the jack should slip. NEVER use the jack alone.

Without proper tire repair equipment, tire service can be dangerous. Have tires serviced by a tire service shop that can do the job safer, easier, and quicker.

Tractor Performance

A tractor will provide the best performance and power hop can be controlled when it is equipped with tires that are large enough, relative to the tractor weight, to provide a "soft" ride (low stiffness). In most situations, the tires should be inflated to operate at rated deflections. This means that they should be inflated to the minimum pressures required to support the static weight being carried on each axle. The bigger the tire air volume the better — best results will be obtained if there is more tire on the tractor than might have been thought necessary in the past. A tractor being set up for heavy tillage work should be thought of in terms of bigger tires and moderate to light weight, instead of smaller tires and heavy weight. The three major items to be considered are:

- Total tractor weight and static weight split (weight distribution on front and rear axles)

- Type of ballast used (cast and/or liquid weight)

- Tire inflation pressures

No one item can be considered independent of the other two in order to achieve optimum tractor performance. A properly set up tractor will provide the following benefits:

- Improved traction (reduced slip and higher fuel efficiency)

- Reduced compaction

- Improved flotation

- Improved ride

- Reduced tire wear

- Improved sidehill stability

- Better control of power hop on MFWD and 4WD tractors

Static Weight Split and Ballast

Two-Wheel Drive Tractors

Two-wheel drive tractors will achieve optimum operating efficiency when static tractor weight split is set at approximately 25–35% on the front axle and 75–65% on the rear axle. The upper end of the range on the front axle should be used when heavy rear-hitch-mounted implements are used. To achieve the correct static tractor weight split, cast weights are recommended. Liquid ballast of up to 75% fill can be used in the rear tires, but ride comfort is best if cast weights or a combination of liquid and cast weights is used.

 CAUTION: Installing liquid ballast requires special equipment and training. Have the job done by a tractor dealer or a tire service store.

IMPORTANT: **Liquid ballast has a dramatic stiffening effect at low inflation pressures; therefore, a partial liquid fill used in combination with cast weights will provide the best ride. Do not exceed 75% liquid fill (valve-stem level).**

MFWD Tractor

Mechanical front wheel drive (MFWD) tractors should have a static tractor weight split of 35–40% on the front axle and 65–60% on the rear axle. To achieve the recommended static tractor weight split, use cast weights on the rear and a combination of liquid and cast weights in the front.

 CAUTION: Installing liquid ballast requires special equipment and training. Have the job done by a tractor dealer or a tire service store.

IMPORTANT: **Liquid ballast has a dramatic stiffening effect at low inflation pressures; therefore, liquid ballast in the rear tires should be avoided when a power hop condition exists. If rear liquid weight is used, do not exceed 40% fill (valve stem at four o'clock position) and preferably not more than 25–33% fill. If front liquid weight is used, do not exceed 75% fill (valve-stem level). The liquid fill must be the same in all tires on the same axle.**

Four-Wheel Drive Tractors

Four-wheel drive tractors should have the following static tractor weight split:

- 51–55% on the front axle and 49–45% on the rear axle for standard towed implements.

- 55–60% on the front axle and 45–40% on the rear axle for hitch-mounted implements.

- 55–65% on the front axle and 45–35% on the rear axle for towed implements causing high down-loads on drawbars.

To achieve the recommended static tractor weight split, use a combination of liquid and cast weights in the rear and cast weights on the front.

 CAUTION: Installing liquid ballast requires special equipment and training. Have the job done by a tractor dealer or a tire service store.

IMPORTANT: Liquid ballast has a dramatic stiffening effect at low inflation pressures; therefore, liquid ballast in the rear tires should not exceed 40% fill (valve stem at four o'clock position) and preferably not more than 25–33% fill. The liquid fill must be the same in all rear tires. Added ballast is not normally required on the front axle; however, if required, cast weights are preferred.

Verify the correct static tractor weight split by weighing each tractor axle or by consulting your tractor dealer.

Inflation Pressure Adjustments

IMPORTANT: All tires on the same axle must be inflated to the same pressure.

The recommended tire inflation pressure is dependent upon static load and the number of tires mounted on the axle. The "Rated Deflection" as determined by the tire manufacturer must be maintained in order for the tire to operate at optimum traction. The inflation pressure of large radial tires should be set to the pressure shown in the Extended Inflation Pressure Table for Large Radial Tires. See (Fig. 57). For radial front tires and all bias tires, use the appropriate table provided by the tire manufacturer for the recommended inflation pressure.

Conventional Size Radial Drive Wheel Tires

Tire Size Designation	Inflation (psi)	6	7	8	9	10	12	14	16	18	20	22	24	26	28	30
18.4R38	Single (lbs.)	NR	NR	3520	3740	3960	4400	4800	5200	5680	6000	6400	6600			
	Dual (lbs.)	2640	2820	3100	3290	3480	3870	4220	4580	5000	5280	5630	5810			
	Triple (lbs.)	2460	2620	2890	3070	3250	3610	3940	4260	4660	4920	5250	5410			
18.4R42	Single (lbs.)	NR	NR	3740	3960	4180	4680	5080	5520	6000	6400	6600	6950			
	Dual (lbs.)	2710	3010	3290	3480	3680	4120	4470	4860	5280	5630	5810	6120			
	Triple (lbs.)	2530	2800	3070	3250	3430	3840	4170	4530	4920	5250	5410	5700			
18.4R46	Single (lbs.)	NR	NR	3860	4180	4400	4940	5360	5840	6150	6600	6950	7400	7850	8050	8550
	Dual (lbs.)	2900	3200	3400	3680	3870	4350	4720	5140	5410	5810	6120	6510	6910	7080	7520
	Triple (lbs.)	2710	2980	3170	3430	3610	4050	4400	4790	5040	5410	5700	6070	6440	6600	7020
20.8R38	Single (lbs.)	NR	NR	4300	4540	4800	5360	5840	6400	6800	7150	7600	8050			
	Dual (lbs.)	3200	3480	3780	4000	4220	4720	5140	5630	5980	6290	6690	7080			
	Triple (lbs.)	2980	3250	3530	3720	3940	4400	4790	5250	5580	5860	6230	6600			
20.8R42	Single (lbs.)	NR	NR	4540	4800	5080	5680	6150	6800	7150	7600	8050	8550			
	Dual (lbs.)	3290	3680	4000	4220	4470	5000	5410	5980	6290	6690	7080	7520			
	Triple (lbs.)	3070	3430	3720	3940	4170	4660	5040	5580	5860	6230	6600	7010			
24.5R32	Single (lbs.)	NR	NR	5080	5520	5840	6400	7150	7600	8250	8800	9100	9650			
	Dual (lbs.)	3780	4120	4470	4860	5140	5630	6290	6690	7260	7740	8010	8490			
	Triple (lbs.)	3530	3840	4170	4530	4790	5250	5860	6230	6770	7220	7460	7910			
30.5LR32	Single (lbs.)	NR	NR	6150	6600	6950	7600	8550	9100	9650						
	Dual (lbs.)	4470	5000	5410	5810	6120	6690	7520	8010	8490						
	Triple (lbs.)	4170	4660	5040	5410	5700	6230	7010	7460	7910						

NR – Not Recommended
Goodyear Tire & Rubber Company

Metric Size Radial Drive Wheel Tires

Tire Size Designation	Inflation (psi)	6	7	9	10	12	13	15	17	20	23	26	29
420/80R46	Single (lbs.)	NR	NR	3520	3860	4080	4400	4680	5360	5840	6400	6800	7150
	Dual (lbs.)	2560	2820	3100	3400	3590	3870	4120	4720	5140	5630	5980	6290
	Triple (lbs.)	2390	2620	2890	3170	3350	3610	3840	4400	4790	5250	5580	5860
710/70R38	Single (lbs.)	NR	NR	2900	3150	3350	3650	3875	4375	4875	5300		
	Dual (lbs.)	2140	2330	2550	2770	2950	3210	3410	3850	4290	4665		
	Triple (lbs.)	1995	2175	2380	2585	2745	2995	3180	3590	4000	4345		

NR – Not Recommended
Goodyear Tire & Rubber Company

JDPX1151

Fig. 57 — Extended Inflation Pressure Table for Large Radial Tires

Monitoring Tractor Performance

IMPORTANT: **A radar monitor is recommended to precisely measure wheel slip and ground speed.**

When performing field operations that load the tractor close to a traction or power limit, closely monitor the following:

- Wheel slip: Should not exceed 15% under normal conditions. Typical wheel slip is 5–12%.

- Engine speed: The engine should operate in the speed range specified by the manufacturer. Under normal conditions at full throttle, the speed should be near rated rpm but may drop a few hundred rpm for short durations when operated under certain conditions such as a high draft load. You may also "shift up and throttle back" if this does not cause the engine to labor. Follow your tractor manufacturer's recommendations.

- Ground speed: 5 mph or higher is preferred, but no less than 4 mph continuously. Follow your tractor manufacturer's recommendations.

If the tractor maintains engine and ground speed within the recommended limits but wheel slip is high, one or more of the following should be performed.

- Reduce draft by reducing implement working depth or width.

- Add ballast but maintain correct tractor weight split.

- Consider larger diameter tire.

If the tractor is able to maintain a minimum of 4 mph and the wheel slip is within the acceptable range, reduce implement draft by reducing depth or width.

Power Hop

Under high drawbar loads, in certain soil conditions, MFWD and 4WD tractors may experience these simultaneous conditions:

- Loss of traction

- Bouncing and pitching ride

The occurrence of these two conditions at the same time is termed power hop (or wheel hop). Power hop may become so severe that the operator loses the ability to safely control the tractor. To regain control, the operator should reduce engine speed and/or reduce implement draft until power hop subsides. However, these actions are only a temporary measure. To permanently control power hop, the tractor ballast and tire inflation pressures should be adjusted as described under the previous "Monitoring Tractor Performance" section.

Power hop is strongly influenced by tractor weight split, amount, and distribution of liquid ballast on each axle, and tire inflation pressures. If power hop is still present after following all the procedures outlined in "Monitoring Tractor Performance," then the inflation pressure in the front tires should be raised in 2 psi increments until power hop subsides.

IMPORTANT: **When raising the tire inflation pressure, do not exceed the tire manufacturer's recommended maximum inflation pressure rating. Make sure that all tires on an axle are inflated to the same pressure.**

If power hop cannot be quelled following the previously outlined procedures, consult the tire manufacturer or the tractor manufacturer for additional guidance.

Grease Fittings

Many of the bearings on today's machines are sealed with lubricant for the life of the bearing. Some bearings still require periodic lubrication, but these are few in relation to the number of lubrication points used on machines several years ago.

Fig. 58 — Lubricating at Grease Fittings (Wipe Fitting Clean First)

It is an easy task to grease your machine when it requires it (Fig. 58). Your operator's manual recommends how each bearing or shaft should be lubricated and how much. Usually, pictures tell you exactly where each fitting is located so that you will have no trouble finding them. Fittings on axles and wheels were covered earlier in this chapter.

Some grease fittings require daily or 10 hours service, while others are serviced at 50 or even 250 hour intervals. Common fittings which need daily service are on steering, clutch, and brake mechanisms, especially the mechanical types.

If you don't lubricate the bearings or shafts when required, these parts will wear out prematurely. Grease is not expensive and repair costs will be saved by keeping the machine properly lubricated.

Operation of Grease Fittings

When the grease gun is pushed down over the fitting, a seal is developed (Fig. 59). Pressure from the gun forces grease past a ball check valve in the head of the fitting. When the grease gun is removed, the check valve ball springs close to keep out dirt.

Some special fittings measure quantity or pressure, while others relieve excessive pressure, but these are not common on agricultural machines.

Grease Bank Systems

On some machines which have many fittings requiring regular lubrication, a central grease reservoir and pump is used. A few strokes of the pump forces grease through small individual tubes to each bearing. The reservoir must be kept filled, and each bearing should be inspected regularly to be sure grease is reaching all bearings.

To provide easier access for lubrication of some hard-to-reach bearings on certain machines, small tubes are installed from the bearings to a central easily-reached location on the machine. Individual grease fittings on each tube are filled with grease in the conventional manner. These systems cost less than the central-reservoir type, and it is easier to tell if each bearing is being greased.

Grease tubes in each of these systems must be protected from moving machine parts to avoid tube damage and loss of lubrication.

Types of Grease

The development of multi-purpose grease has made it possible for the machine operator to use one grease for almost all fittings and hand-packed bearings.

Many operator's manuals recommend wheel bearing grease for packing wheel bearings, but multi-purpose grease is now considered to be satisfactory for some wheel bearing lubrication.

JDPX5335

Fig. 59 — How Common Grease Fittings Operate

Rules for Lubricating Bearings

If you follow the rules listed below, you can expect bearings and shafts to provide maximum service.

- Always lubricate parts with recommended lubricant. Multi-purpose grease is satisfactory for most applications.

- Use clean lubricants. Be sure to store lubricants in clean, air-tight containers.

- Always wipe off dirt and grease fittings before attaching grease gun. After lubricating, wipe off excessive grease.

- Hold grease gun directly in line with fitting while pumping slowly. Remove gun by swinging through a 30° arc.

- Do not lubricate bearings too often. Sometimes excessive grease can leak onto other parts and damage them — for example, drive belts, brake linings, and clutch linings.

- Never apply too much pressure or lubricant to bearings with seals. You may rupture the seal, allowing grease to escape and dirt and moisture to enter bearing.

- In cold weather, grease at the end of the day while the bearings are warm — they will accept grease more readily.

- Make it a habit to grease your machine at the recommended intervals.

Belt Drives

JDPX5336

Fig. 60 — V-Belt Drive Using Multiple Belts

Almost every power-driven machine has either belts, chains, or both. These drive components must be maintained to keep them from wearing out prematurely. Belts can stretch and slip — chains wear and rust.

First, let's look at the maintenance for belts.

 CAUTION: Be sure to reinstall any guards or shields that are removed to adjust or replace belts.

Maintaining V-Belts

 CAUTION: Never attempt to check or adjust belts while they are running. Always shut off the machine before servicing belts.

V-belts are the most common belt drive today, so our main discussion on maintenance will be for these drives.

We will discuss the following about belts:

- Tension
- Alignment
- Removal and installation
- Wear

Tools and Materials Needed

- Wrenches (inch or metric, as required)
- Straight edge
- Ruler (inch or metric, as required)
- Spring scale

Belt Tension

Proper belt tension is one of the most important things in maintaining belts.

Too little tension will cause slippage or slip-and-grab, causing the belt to break. If the belt does not break, slip will cause excessive cover wear, burned spots, and overheating.

Too much tension will cause belt heating and excessive stretch as well as damage to drive components, such as sheaves and shafts. The extra tightness will also place heavier loads on the bearings.

Remember that V-belts should ride on the sides of standard sheaves, not on the bottom of the groove.

Watch the tension on a new belt during the first 24 hours of operation. This is when the initial seating and stretch occurs.

Check belt tension by deflecting the belt on one side with a spring scale (Fig. 61). Measure the deflection at the recommended pounds (kg) pull. Your operator's manual will give you this specification.

Another method is to depress the belt halfway between the sheaves and use a ruler at right angles to a straightedge to measure deflection (Fig. 62).

Fig. 61 — Checking Belt Tension Using a Spring Scale

Fig. 62 — Checking Belt Tension Using Ruler and Straightedge

Belt and Sheave Alignment

Check sheave alignment regularly. Be sure that the shafts are parallel and the belt aligns with each sheave.

Common types of misalignment (exaggerated) are shown in (Fig. 63). All are caused by shafts not parallel or sheaves not aligned.

To check alignment, place a straightedge between the sides of the sheaves (Fig. 64). The straight edge must touch the sheaves at the four points indicated. Rotate the sheaves and check at different points. If variation is noticed, either the sheaves or shafts are bent. Replace the defective parts.

JDPX1554

Fig. 63 — Sheaves Not Aligned Can Damage the V-Belt

JDPX1555

Fig. 64 — Check Alignment of Belt Sheaves

Belt Removal and Installation

Before removing any drive belt, loosen the tightener. Do not force the belt off the sheaves.

When installing any drive belt, loosen the tightener. Never force the belt onto the sheaves (Fig. 65). You may break the strength cords in the belt and weaken the belt so that it fails rapidly.

WRONG!
Never Force
a V-Belt onto
a Sheave

JDPX1572

Fig. 65 — Never Force a V-Belt onto a Sheave

Base Cracking — Damaged Belt

Slip Burn — Damaged Belt

Fabric Rupture — Damaged Belt

Gouged Edge — Damaged Belt

Cover Tear — Damaged Belt

Ruptured Cords — Damaged Belt

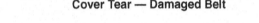

Worn Sides — Damaged Belt

JDPX1577A, 1578, 1579, 1581, 1582, 1583, 1584

Fig. 66 — Fabric Rupture—Damaged Belt

Do not tighten the belt too much. Slight tension is always recommended on a V-belt.

On multiple belt drives, always replace all belts with a matched set of belts, even though only one fails. Otherwise, the new belt may pull the whole load, because the older ones are probably stretched.

Troubleshooting V-Belt Wear

The examples shown in (Fig. 68) will help you to recognize some of the signs of V-belt wear or damage.

Table 1 on page 9-31 explains the causes of typical belt wear so that the problems can be corrected.

Maintaining Flat Belts

Many of the maintenance tips for V-belts also apply to flat belts.

Here are some of the rules:

*   Some flat belts, usually leather or canvas, may require belt dressings to prevent slippage and deterioration.

*   Flat belts normally need more tension than V-belts.

*   Pulley alignment is even more important with flat belts than for V-belts because flat belts can run off the pulley easier (Fig. 67).

Crown on Pulley
Helps Hold Belt

JDPX 1525

Fig. 67 — Crown Helps Keep Flat Belt on Pulley

*   To install flat belts, move the power unit forward, place the belt on the pulleys, and back up carefully to tighten the belt. Start the belt slowly to make sure it is running straight before increasing the speed.

*   Never force a belt off a moving pulley.

V-BELT WEAR TROUBLESHOOTING CHART

Problem	Cause	Remedy
Base Cracking	Normal aging	Replace belt.
	Weather rotted inner fabric	Replace belt.
Fabric Rupture	Prying belt onto sheave	Replace belt, loosening belt tighteners before installing.
	Worn sheaves	Check condition of sheaves. Replace belt.
	Belt too tight	Replace belt. Adjust belt tension properly.
Cover Tear	Belt coming into contact with some part on machine	Locate interference point and eliminate it.
Slip Burn	Belt operated too loose; when operated under load, the belt grabbed and snapped	Replace belt. Adjust belt tension properly.
Gouged Edge	Damaged sheave or interference from some part of the machine	Check condition of sheaves and check for interference. Replace belt.
Ruptured Cords	Driven sheave locked and drive sheave burned area of belt because belt would not rotate with sheave	Avoid overloading drive and lubricate bearings to prevent bearing seizures. Replace belt.
Worn Sides	Long operation without enough tension	Replace belt. Check belt tension regularly and adjust properly when required.

Table 1 — V-Belt Wear Troubleshooting Chart

Chain Drives

 CAUTION: Be sure to reinstall any guards or shields that are removed to adjust or replace chains.

Chain drives are used on some machines. They can eliminate the slippage that belt drives may give in some applications. Where timing is important, chains are often a must.

Because chains are under much stress, they must be maintained properly or they will fail in a short time.

Chain drives have one or more sprockets and an endless chain (Fig. 68).

One sprocket is normally mounted on a power shaft and is the driving sprocket for the complete drive. The second sprocket is driven, in turn, by the driving sprocket as shown.

A third sprocket may be used to adjust tension on the slack side of the chain.

Maintaining Chain Drives

JDPX1599

Fig. 68 — Parts of a Chain Drive

We will discuss the following about chains:

- Tension
- Lubrication
- Alignment
- Removal and installation
- Wear
- Cleaning

Tools and Materials Needed

- Wrenches (inch or metric, as required)
- Straightedge
- Lubricating oil
- Solvent
- Container of oil to soak chain
- Chain detaching tool

Chain Tension

Chain tension — or "slack" — is vital to the proper operation of chain drives. Unlike belts, chains require no initial tension and should not be tightened around the sprockets. Properly adjusted chain drives should permit slight flexing by hand in the slack strand of about two percent of the center distance (Fig. 69).

Too much tension causes the working parts to carry a much heavier load than is necessary and work much harder without delivering any more power. This causes rapid chain wear because of more pressures in the joints. In addition, shaft bearings are overloaded.

Too little tension is also harmful. On long centers, particularly, too much slack will cause vibration and chain whipping, reducing the life of the chain. On long centers, the slack strand should be supported or taken up by idler sprockets or guides.

Correct Amount of Chain Slack

Chain Too Tight, Binding

Chain Too Loose, Whipping

JDPX1645, 1646, 1647

Fig. 69 — Chain Slack (Tension)

ADJUSTING CHAIN TENSION

 CAUTION: Never attempt to adjust chains while they are operating. Always shut off the machine before servicing chain.

For horizontal and inclined drives, the chain sag should be about 1/4 in. (6.35 mm) per 12 in. (305 mm) between shaft centers (with one side of the chain taut).

Vertical drives and those subject to shock loading, reversal, or rotation should be adjusted so that both spans of the chain are almost taut.

For drives on fixed centers, chain tension is usually controlled by an adjustable chain tightener, either an idler sprocket or a shoe.

To adjust chain tension:

1. Determine the amount of sag by pulling one side of the chain taut, allowing all the excess chain to accumulate in the opposite span.

Adjust
Tension at
Idler

JDPX1648

Fig. 70 — Adjusting Chains

2. Place a straightedge over the slack span and pull the chain down at the center (Fig. 70). Measure the amount of sag from the top of the chain to the underside of the straightedge.

3. If necessary, adjust the shaft centers or the tightener to provide the manufacturer's recommended amount of sag for proper chain slack.

Chain Lubrication

Lubrication of chains is perhaps the most important factor in long service life. Running dry, exposed chains have been known to wear out in less than 200 hours. Manual lubrication can extend wear life three to ten times over life with no lubrication.

Dripping oil on the outside of the chain may not be enough. Oil must reach the vital bearing surfaces pointed out in (Fig. 71), top. To do this, oil must penetrate the gap between the inside and outside plates of roller chains. This can be helped by oiling the chain while it is warm and then running it for a short time. Always oil the chain at quitting time each day, and let it sit overnight.

Fig. 71 — Lubrication Points on Chains

JDPX1650

Chains which collect dirt and dust should still be oiled regularly. A "paste" of oil and dirt still wears less than dry dirt packed into the chain joints. Lubrication also helps prevent rust.

NOTE: *For abrasive soil or sandy conditions, some manufacturers may not recommend lubrication of chains. However, this is the exception, not the rule.*

Chain and Sprocket Alignment

Proper alignment of sprockets and shafts is necessary for maximum wear life. Rapid wear will result from misalignment due to rubbing of chain parts against sides of sprocket teeth and excessive friction wear in the joints caused by whipping and twisting of chains.

Align the sprockets axially on the shafts, using a straightedge (Fig. 72). Take care to apply the straightedge to a finished surface on the side of the sprocket. For long center distances, a stretched wire or cord can be used instead of a straightedge.

JDPX1635

Fig. 72 — Aligning Sprockets Using a Straightedge

Chain Installation

To couple the ends of a chain:

1. Loosen the chain tighteners to provide sufficient "working slack."

2. Bring the chain ends together over one sprocket, using the sprocket teeth to hold the chain.

JDPX1636

Fig. 73 — Installing Roller Chain

Chain Detaching Tool

Always Support a Chain Before Attaching It

JDPX1640

Fig. 74 — Chain Detaching Tool for Roller Chain

3. Insert the pin or pin link to couple the chain into an endless strand (Fig. 73).

4. Adjust the chain tighteners to provide the proper tension for operation.

The preceding method is especially useful for coupling drive chains.

When it is necessary to couple a chain in the span between the sprockets, draw the ends together with a block and tackle or other device. Then follow steps 3 and 4 above.

Keep chain straight when coupling. A link coupled when the chain is crooked may cause the chain to twist in operation.

To provide a solid back-up for the chain, assemble it in a straight line on the floor or a table. Then feed the chain onto its drive.

 CAUTION: Keep all chain guards and shields in place during operation.

Chain Removal

The chain detacher is a convenient bench tool for uncoupling roller chain (Fig. 74). It is designed to prevent damage to the chain during disassembly.

The best rule when detaching any chain is: Support the chain while detaching it. This will avoid bending of links.

Chain and Sprocket Wear

New Chain   **Worn Chain, Stretched**

Chain Mates with All Sprockets   **Chain on Tips of Teeth**

JDPX1657

Fig. 75 — Comparing New and Worn Roller Chains

As chains wear and stretch, they do not mate properly with their sprocket teeth. Badly worn roller chains ride so far out of the tooth pockets that they may be off the working faces (Fig. 75, right).

As a rule, when a chain is worn until it has lengthened by three percent or more, it should be replaced.

When new chains are installed on excessively worn sprockets, the new chain will wear rapidly. Sprockets should be replaced or reversed if possible when the teeth develop a hooked appearance.

Cleaning Chains

Periodic cleaning of chains is good economy under even the best operating conditions. Follow these steps:

1. Remove chain from sprockets.
2. Wash chain in solvent.
3. Drain solvent and soak chain in oil.
4. Hang chain to drain off excess lubricant.
5. Install chain.

Gear Drives

JDPX5344

Fig. 76 — Gear Drive

Gears are the most common way to transmit power for heavier loads. With gears in mesh, all slippage is gone. Even the linkage of the chain is eliminated, giving more power potential.

Operation

"Servicing Transmission, Differential, and Final Drives" on page 7-19 covers the basic gear types and their uses. Refer to that chapter for the basics of gear drive operation.

This discussion will cover only the small, open gear drives which require special lubrication or adjustment.

Lubrication of Gears

Gear lubricants range from simple mineral oils to complex formulas containing many ingredients.

For the type of oil to use, consult your machine operator's manual.

Common gear lubricants are:

Spur gears — may use a good grade of petroleum oil, but not always.

Bevel gears — may use an extreme-pressure (E.P.) lubricant.

Worm gears — may use an SCL lubricant, which offers even greater lubricant qualities.

Methods of Lubricating Gears

Enclosed gears (see "Gear Oils" on page 7-2) are usually lubricated by the gears moving through a sump of oil and may have additional run-off troughs to lubricate the upper gears.

Open gears can be lubricated by:

1. Splash pan which the gears run through.
2. Hand lubrication by brushing or squirting with oil can (Fig. 77).
3. Automatic lubrication by a drip oiler.

Check the operator's manual for the proper intervals and types of lubricant.

JDPX5345A, B, C

Fig. 77 — Three Ways of Hand Lubricating Open Gears

Adjusting the Gear Drive

When a gear drive is operated, reaction loads from gears, etc., are transmitted to the bearings and the various parts deflect.

For this reason, the gear drive may periodically require adjustment for the proper fit between parts.

Three kinds of adjustments are used:

- Backlash — clearance or "play" between gears in mesh
- Endplay — end-to-end movement in a gear shaft due to bearing clearances
- Preload — a load within the bearings set up by adjustment

These adjustments should only be made following instructions in the machine service manual and using proper tools and equipment.

Backlash in Gears

Too much backlash in gear trains is the result of: 1) improper mesh between gears or 2) lack of support in bearings.

The result of too much backlash can be broken gear teeth or bouncing of gears under impact forces.

JDPX5346

Fig. 78 — Checking Backlash on Gear

Backlash is often adjusted to a specified reading on assembled gears (Fig. 78).

The dial indicator is mounted so that it registers the full rotary movement of the ring gear shown. To adjust the backlash reading, shims are often used.

Endplay in Gears and Shafts

Too much endplay is caused by lack of bearing support for the thrust produced by the gears rotating.

Preloading is often used to take up the slack and load the bearings.

JDPX5347

Fig. 79 — Checking Endplay on Gears and Shafts

To check endplay (Fig. 79), a dial indicator is mounted against the side of a gear or the end of a shaft. The gear or shaft is then pried in both directions and the readings noted. The difference between the two readings is the endplay.

Shims or adjusting nuts are widely used to adjust endplay.

Preloading of Gear Drives

If the loads are heavy or the thrust too great, gear trains are often preloaded to reduce the deflection of parts. This preload must fit the design of the bearings and the strength of the parts.

If bearings are preloaded too tight, they will heat up and fail. If they are set too loose, the supporting parts will deflect too much, causing them to wear rapidly.

Gear drives are preloaded by shims, thrust washers, adjusting nuts, or double-race bearings.

Lighting and Electrical Accessories

This section covers some of the extra equipment which completes the electrical system on machines.

The basic electrical system was covered in chapter 6 on batteries and charging, starting, and ignition circuits.

Now let's fill in the remainder of the system with the lighting and other electrical accessories:

- Lighting circuits
- Circuit breakers and fuses
- Wiring harnesses
- Gauges
- Meters
- Switches
- Electric motors
- Electronic components

Let's take a closer look at each of these accessories.

Lighting Circuits

Lights are used on most modern agricultural machines. They are required by state or local governments for night driving or towing in most areas. To avoid trouble, know your local regulations.

On modern machines, the lights are often two or four headlights and one taillight (Fig. 80). This usually requires a 12-volt system.

In addition, a flashing warning lamp or lamps is required in most states. This lamp warns other traffic that a slow-moving vehicle is on the road. A slow-moving vehicle (SMV) emblem is also required in many states.

On many agricultural implements, special lighting is used for night work in the field. On a self-propelled combine, for example, a special flood lamp is used to light up the area where the grain is being cut and fed into the combine. Another flood lamp shows the operator when the grain tank is full of grain.

JPDX5110

Fig. 80 — Lighting on a Tractor

Layout of the Lighting Circuit

The lighting circuit is normally a part of the complete electrical system. It operates on power from the battery with help from the charging circuit.

JDPX5349

Fig. 81 — Layout of a Typical Lighting Circuit

The parts of a typical lighting circuit are shown in (Fig. 81). They are the various lamps which are operated by a light switch. The switch is connected to the battery or charging circuit by the wiring harness. Other accessories shown are an electrical outlet socket and indicator lamps. The circuit is protected from a current overload by the circuit breakers and fuses.

On most machines, the starter switch must be turned on before the lights can be operated by light switch.

Also, some machines have indicator lamps which light up when the starter switch is turned on and then go out when the engine is running, showing that the alternator, oil pressure, etc., are normal.

On machines with two or four batteries, a "split-load" lighting circuit is sometimes used. This divides the load equally between both batteries when the lights are turned on.

Lamps

Lamps used for lighting of modern machines are:

- Halogen or xenon bulbs (for headlights and flood lights)
- Sealed-beam units (for headlights and flood lights)
- Light bulbs (for other lights)

Halogen or Xenon Bulb Lighting

Halogen bulbs are used for most headlight and flood light applications in modern machines. High-intensity discharge (HID) xenon lamps are also used.

Lights using these bulbs throw out a high-intensity beam and should always be dimmed when approaching a vehicle at night.

These bulbs also require special handling for best performance and safety.

JDPX5787

Fig. 82 — Halogen or Xenon Bulb and Headlight Lens

Sealed Beam Lighting Units

Sealed beam units consist of a single bulb and lens assembly. The entire unit is replaced when needed.

Safety Rules when Replacing Halogen Bulbs

JDPX5786

 CAUTION: Halogen bulbs contain gas under pressure. Handling a bulb improperly could cause it to shatter into flying fragments.

To avoid possible injury:

- Turn off the light switch and allow the bulb to cool before changing bulbs. Leave the switch off until bulb change is complete.

- Wear eye protection when changing a halogen bulb.

- Handle the bulb by its base. Avoid touching the glass.

- Do not drop or scratch the bulb. Keep moisture away.

- Place used bulb in the new bulb's carton and dispose of properly. Keep out of reach of children.

Safety Rules when Replacing High-Intensity Discharge (HID) Xenon Lights

When replacing xenon bulbs or ballast, always comply with the following safety instruction:

JDPX5786

 CAUTION: Turn OFF light switch and allow the bulb to cool before changing bulbs. Leave switch OFF until bulb change is complete.

Never insert foreign objects or fingers into the bulb holder (high-tension voltage — potential for FATAL ACCIDENTS).

The ballast unit must never be operated when the bulb is missing, as this may cause a dangerous flash-over at the bulb sockets, resulting in serious damage (high-tension voltage — potential for FATAL ACCIDENTS).

If a xenon bulb ever bursts inside a closed space (e.g., workshop), leave the area, making sure it is well ventilated, and wait 20 minutes before returning. This will eliminate the risk to health caused by gases.

High-tension voltage is conducted by the electrical connection between the work lights and the ballast unit; this connection must never be broken (high-tension voltage — potential for FATAL ACCIDENTS).

Make sure that the power supply line between the work lights and ballast unit is never twisted more than 90 degrees and/or bent more than a length of 0.8 in. (20 mm).

Wear eye protection when changing xenon bulbs.

The bulbs contain xenon gas under pressure and metallic salts. Handling a bulb improperly could cause it to shatter into flying fragments.

Do NOT use any bulbs that have fallen on the ground or have scratches on their surface, as there is a risk of them shattering.

Make sure that the bulb is seated correctly in its holder in the light.

Check the light for signs of damage and make sure the seals are seated correctly.

IMPORTANT: Handle the bulb by its base. Avoid touching the glass.

Place used bulb in the new bulb's carton and dispose of properly. Keep out of reach of children.

Do not drop or scratch the bulb. Keep moisture away.

Use a clean cloth and alcohol to remove any fingerprints from the glass bulb.

Adjusting Headlights

When headlights are used on public roads, be sure they are adjusted so that the glare of the lights will not shine into the eyes of approaching drivers.

Adjusting the headlights on a typical tractor is shown in (Fig. 83). This procedure can be used for other machines also.

JDPX5350

Fig. 83 — Adjusting Headlights

Position the machine, as shown, on level ground squarely facing a wall 25 feet (7.5 m) away.

Turn the headlights on "bright" and check the height of the beams on the wall. The centers of the light beams should be 1 to 4 feet (0.3 to 1.2 m) high, depending upon the height of the headlights. Keep the intense part of the beams at least 5 inches (15 cm) below the center of the light from which it comes.

The headlights should also be parallel to the tractor centerline. Look down the center of the machine to see if the centers of the beams are at equal distances from the centerline (about four feet [1.2 m] apart or two feet [0.6 m] off center on most tractors).

On machines with dual headlights, also check the outer flood lamps on "dim" to see that they shine downward and outward to illuminate the desired area as shown in (Fig. 83).

To adjust the lights, loosen the lamp mounting bracket and rotate them as desired. Then retighten the mounting bracket. Remember: Only the lamp mounting bracket is adjustable, not the sealed-beam unit itself.

On other machines with headlights mounted higher than those on a tractor, always adjust the lamps downward far enough to avoid glare to oncoming traffic.

Light Bulbs

Miscellaneous lights such as taillights, dash lamps, and indicator lamps are normally equipped with single- or double-contact bulbs.

When replacing bulbs, use the same style and part number as the old one. Otherwise, the system can be damaged or the bulb may burn out rapidly.

Special light bulbs for special lighting effects may be required for some taillights, flasher lamps, or indicator lamps.

Indicator lamps are often used in place of gauges for generator, oil pressure, and temperature checks.

If the indicator lamp lights up or glows while the engine is running, this shows a failure in the system being monitored. For example, an oil pressure light may glow when the engine is low on oil.

When an indicator lamp comes on, be sure to stop the engine at once and check out the possible causes. But also remember that a burned-out indicator lamp never lights up, even while the engine is being ruined!

Failures of Lamps

Failure of lamps may be caused by a defective unit, a broken wire, a disconnected wire, a corroded connection, a switch failure, or an open circuit breaker.

 CAUTION: High-intensity discharge (HID) xenon lighting operates under very high voltages. For failures of lighting circuits equipped with high-intensity discharge (HID) xenon lighting, refer to machine technical manual for machine-specific safety and testing procedures.

To check a light bulb, visual inspection is best. A good bulb will be clear, while a burned-out bulb may be dark. Where the bulb glass is not dark, the filament wire will be visible. If it is broken, the bulb is defective.

To check a lighting circuit, test the faulty part for voltage drop. If you don't have a voltmeter, take the machine to a service shop for testing.

If the voltage is correct but the lamp is dim, look for a poor wiring connection between the lamp and the main wiring harness. Also check for a poor ground at the lamp mounting. Remember that the frame of the machine serves as the ground, and good contact must be made to complete the circuit.

If there is no voltage across the lamp, look for a broken wire, poor contact in the light switch, or a disconnected wiring connector. Replace or repair any defective parts.

If the lights all go out suddenly, check for a tripped circuit breaker or a blown fuse. For details, see "Circuit Breakers" and "Fuses" later in this section.

Flashing Lamps

Fig. 84 — Flashing Lamp

When a flashing warning lamp (Fig. 84) is prohibited by local regulations, disconnect the flasher unit and the short wire connected to the flasher. (See the operator's manual.) If you want to burn the warning lamp continually, connect the wire from the lamp directly into the lighting circuit wiring harness.

Circuit Breakers

A circuit breaker (Fig. 85) protects an electrical circuit from current overload. The breaker acts as a switch and opens when the current passing through the circuit exceeds the rated level. The breaker may close automatically, after the switch is shut off for a short period. Some breakers have to be closed manually. Both automatic and manual reset circuit breakers are used in electrical systems.

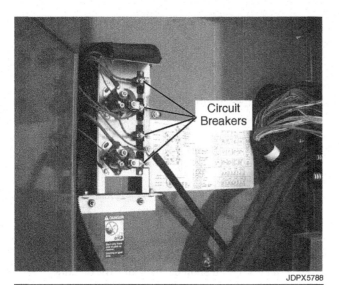

Fig. 85 — Circuit Breakers for a Lighting Circuit

In general, circuit breakers are used when heavy loads may be instantly placed on the circuit.

To check for a defective circuit breaker, use an ohmmeter or a voltmeter. If an ohmmeter is used, a good circuit breaker will show zero resistance.

A defective breaker will show full resistance. If a voltmeter is used, and the circuit breaker is defective, the battery side will show voltage and the load side will not.

Again, if you don't have these instruments, take the machine to a service shop for testing.

Some circuit breakers are equipped with a reset opening. When the breaker trips, it may be reset by inserting a small wire in the opening and pushing against the spring tension (Fig. 86).

Fig. 86 — Resetting a Circuit Breaker

Fuses

Fuses protect an electrical circuit from current overload. When too much current passes through the circuit, the fuse blows, breaking the flow of current and preventing damage to the circuit.

A fuse consists of fine wire or thin metal strip enclosed in glass or fire-resistant material (Fig. 87). Most fuses used for modern agricultural and industrial equipment are automotive blade-type fuses (Fig. 88). They have a contact on each end and are held in place in a panel or individual fuse holder. The fuse panel keeps many fuses in one location and aids in fuse replacement (Fig. 89). The fuse holder is usually a two-piece tube assembly that can be easily separated for installing or replacing fuses.

Fig. 87 — Glass Fuse (Blown and Normal)

JDPX5117
Fig. 88 — Blade Fuse (Normal, Smoked, Blown)

JDPX5790
Fig. 89 — Fuse Panel

Blown fuses are usually caused by:

- A short circuit in the electrical circuit caused by defective wiring or a defective component (lights, motor, etc.).
- An overload in the circuit caused by a surge of electricity passing through the circuit.
- Poor contacts in the electrical circuit or the components.
- Overheating in the circuit caused by overloads or poor contacts.
- Use of incorrect size fuses in the circuit.
- Fuse located too near a hot area such as an engine or a heater.
- Vibrations near the fuse, causing the contacts to come loose.

Types of Fuses

Two types of fuses are widely used in machine electrical circuits:

- Quick-blowing fuses
- Slow-blowing fuses

A quick-blowing fuse blows instantly whenever a too-heavy load occurs.

A slow-blowing fuse will allow an overload for a short period before it blows.

Finding Cause of Blown Fuse

By looking at a blown fuse, you can often tell what failure in the circuit caused it to blow.

Refer to (Fig. 90) for a general check for causes of blown-out fuses, whether from overload or from short circuit.

QUICK-BLOWING FUSES

If an overload — glass case will be clear because fuse link overheats and simply melts away.

If a short circuit — glass will be dark, stained by the fuse link which suddenly "burns up."

SLOW-BLOWING FUSES

If an overload — fuse link will break at solder, which has melted.

If a short circuit — fuse link will break at small wires because of sudden heat.

Quick-Blowing Fuse
- If blown from overload, glass will be clear
- If blown from short circuit, glass will be dark

Slow-Blowing Fuse
- If blown from overload,
  fuse will be broken at solder here
- If blown from short circuit,
  wires will be burned out here

JDPX5355
Fig. 90 — Determining the Cause of a Blown Fuse

Remember that a fuse is meant to protect against overloads. It will also protect against short circuits, but these are abnormal and should be repaired at once.

If a quick-blowing fuse tends to blow out frequently due to small overloads, replace it with a slow-blowing type of the same size.

If the fuse still keeps on blowing, the circuit is overloaded and is not meant to handle the loads being placed on it.

Always replace a blown fuse with one of the same size.

Never use a fuse with a higher amperage rating as it may result in serious damage to the circuit it protects.

Fuses and Circuit Breakers — Where Used

Fuses are cheaper but not reusable. So they are used mainly in circuits where "blow outs" from heavy loads are not common.

Circuit breakers are more expensive but can be reset without replacement. So they are used in heavy-duty circuits where sudden heavy loads are expected — or where safety is a factor.

Wiring Harnesses

A wiring harness is the trunk and branches which feed the electrical circuit. Wiring leads from one part of the circuit enter the trunk or sheath, joining other wires, and then emerge at another point in the circuit (Fig. 91). The harness sheath is normally made of rubber, cloth, electrical tape, or plastic tubing.

Be careful when installing a wiring harness. The harness must not interfere with moving parts of the machine. Also make certain that the clips which hold the harness do not pinch through the harness and cut the wires. This can cause a short in the circuit.

Fig. 91 — Wiring Harness

Individual wires in a harness may be replaced by cutting off the defective wire at each end of the harness. Discard the removed ends of the wire. Run the new wire around the harness; do not try to thread the wire through the harness. Place the new wire in clips with the harness or attach to the harness with electrical tape.

The proper gauge or size of an electrical wire depends on:

1. Total length of the wire in circuit.

2. Total amperes that the wire will carry.

IMPORTANT: **When replacing a defective wire in a circuit, use the same or heavier gauge of wire for replacement. Never use an undersized wire because it will not carry the required load and will overheat.**

Wiring harnesses and connectors should be visually inspected for damage such as cracked or missing insulation, loose or pinched wires, damaged connectors, corroded connections, etc. Dielectric grease can be used between mating connectors. The dielectric grease will help provide a barrier against moisture and protect the terminals from corrosion.

Gauges

Multifunction gauges are used on modern machines to keep the operator informed on the various functions of the machine systems (Fig. 92).

JDPX5096

Fig. 92 — Multifunction Gauge

Examples of these gauges are: fuel gauge, water temperature gauge, and oil pressure gauge.

The fuel gauge is controlled by a sensing unit located in the fuel tank, and the water temperature gauge and oil pressure gauge are controlled by sensing units located in the engine radiator and cylinder block.

The sensing units are all variable resistance types and operate the gauges as follows:

The higher the water temperature, oil pressure, or level of fuel, the lower (or higher) the resistance in the sensing unit. This change in resistance causes more (or less) current to pass through the connecting wire to the gauge coil, which in turn causes a new reading on the gauge.

Diagnosis of Gauge Failures

Circuits for three common gauges are shown in (Fig. 93).

If a gauge does not register, the cause could be:

• Lack of current to the gauge.

• Poor ground connection.

• Connecting wire grounded to implement.

• A defective sensing unit or gauge.

Fuel Gauge

Oil Pressure Gauge

Coolant Temperature Gauge

JDPX5358

Fig. 93 — Three Mechanical Gauges and Their Circuits

If a gauge consistently registers too high, the cause could be:

• Poor connection between gauge and connecting wire.

• Broken connecting wire.

• Poor ground at sensing unit.

• Failure of gauge or sensor, usually the sensor.

If you cannot determine the cause of the failure, take the machine to a service shop for testing. If you find that a gauge or sensing unit is defective, replace it.

Indicator lamps often use small light bulbs which glow to tell of a failure.

If these lamps do not glow when the starter switch is turned on before starting the engine, first check for a defective bulb. Then, if necessary, check out the other causes given above. (Normally, the lamps should glow when the switch is turned on, then go out shortly after the engine starts, unless there is a problem.)

Meters

Ammeters

The ammeter is an instrument for measuring the strength of an electrical current in terms of amperes.

Normally the ammeter is connected directly to the regulator in series to measure the flow of current through the electrical system.

A typical ammeter consists of a moving magnet with attached needle placed close to a conductor between the ammeter terminals. Current flow through the conductor creates a magnetic field that deflects away from zero on the meter scale.

If an ammeter does not register correctly, replace it with a new ammeter. Do not attempt to repair a defective ammeter.

Voltmeters

Voltmeters are used to indicate the voltage of the electrical input in a circuit.

A typical voltmeter consists of a needle attached to a moving iron vane placed inside two stationary coils. The coil winding is parallel with the needle pivot and one winding tends to keep the needle at zero while the other tends to move the needle to the full scale deflection.

Voltmeters are connected in parallel with the voltage to be measured. Since the voltmeter has a high resistance, adding this component to the circuit will change the total circuit current very little, and the voltage reading obtained shows the true voltage present without the meter in the circuit.

If a voltmeter does not function properly, a new voltmeter must be installed. A defective voltmeter cannot be repaired.

Electric Hour Meter

Electric hour meters are used to show the operating time of a machine while the engine is operating at its rated speed.

The hour meter records the time in hours and only operates when the engine is running.

Do not attempt to repair a defective hour meter or its sending unit. When they fail, new components must be installed.

Switches

A switch is a device which opens, closes, or directs current in an electrical circuit.

All switches do basically the same job. The difference is in the way they are operated.

Servicing of Switches

If a switch is defective, always replace it with a new switch. Do not try to repair a defective switch. It is usually cheaper and safer to replace it.

IMPORTANT: **Always be sure to replace a defective switch with a switch of the same electrical rating. A switch with too high or too low a rating can burn out an electrical circuit.**

Electric Motors

Small DC electrical motors are used to perform auxiliary functions on some machines. For example, motors are used to operate air conditioner blowers (Fig. 94), ventilating and heating fans, and windshield wipers.

Take defective motors to a good electrical shop for servicing by trained technicians.

JDPX5789

Fig. 94 — Electric Motor Used to Operate Air Conditioner Blower Fan

Electronic Components

Accumulation of dust inside and outside of electrical components will deteriorate performance and shorten life.

Wipe clean the face plate of components with a dry cotton or microfiber cloth.

If the operator's cab is equipped with a CD player, clean the laser lens occasionally with a cleaning disk as instructed by the manufacturer.

IMPORTANT: Do not use any other solvents or cleaners unless they are specifically designed for cleaning laser lenses.

If the operator's cab is equipped with a stereo tape player, clean the tape head occasionally with a non-abrasive cleaning cartridge as instructed by the manufacturer.

IMPORTANT: Do not use any other solvents or cleaners unless they are specifically designed for cleaning tape heads. NEVER use anything that would scratch or mar the tape head.

Over an extended period of time, the tape head may become magnetized and a decrease in performance may result. When this happens, use a demagnetizer at the tape head as instructed by the manufacturer.

Cleaning the Machine

The operator's manual may not mention cleaning the machine. However, regular cleaning will pay off in pride, protection against dirt and chemicals, extra safety, and, in general, longer life for the equipment.

Paint can be damaged by long exposure to oil, grease, fertilizers, and sprays.

Grease and oil can accumulate and collect dirt which works its way into bearings and other precision parts. Grease on steps and handholds is also a safety hazard.

Cleaning also helps reveal leaks in the cooling system, engine blocks, hydraulic lines, and other parts.

IMPORTANT: Never pressure spray or hose a diesel engine while the engine is running as the injection pump can be damaged.

Directing pressurized water at electronic/electrical components or connectors, bearings and hydraulic seals, fuel injection pumps, or other sensitive parts and components may cause product malfunctions. Reduce pressure, and spray at a 45 to 90 degree angle.

Thoroughly clean the entire machine at least once each year or at the end of the working season. Also clean the machine when it gets very dirty or muddy or when it has been used around chemicals such as fertilizers or crop sprays.

Test Yourself

Questions

1. (T/F) Dry-type paper air filters may be cleaned in any good detergent.

2. (Fill in blank.) If _____ appear in the sight glass of an air conditioner, the refrigerant level is low.

3. Explain how a wheel bearing should be adjusted for tightness.

4. Match the following items covering tires with the correct corresponding item.

   A. Overinflation   1. Spinning wear

   B. Underinflation   2. Center tread wear

   C. Operator Abuse   3. Side tread wear

5. When rear tractor tires have the proper weight, what is the correct tire slippage rate in percent?

6. Name the three major items that must be considered in order to properly set up a tractor.

7. (T/F) The tire inflation pressure does not need to be the same in all tires on the same axle in order for optimum tractor performance to be achieved.

8. What should be done before attaching a grease gun to a grease fitting?

9. What are two effects of tightening a belt drive excessively?

10. Name three reasons for lubricating chains.

11. Which one of the reasons shown below may have caused a quick-blowing fuse to blow if the glass of the fuse is clear?
    A. Overload
    B. Short Circuit
    C. Open Circuit

12. (Fill in blanks.) The proper gauge or size of an electrical wire depends upon the _____ of the wire in circuit and the _____ that the wire will carry.

Tune-Up and Storage

10

Engine Tune-Up

Engine tune-up is probably the most important preventive maintenance that can be performed on a machine. However, most operators make the mistake of performing tune-up only when the engine is not running satisfactorily. This is often a costly error, because at this point the engine may be worn or damaged until it requires major repair or overhaul. Not only could these costly repairs be avoided by good maintenance, but operating costs could also be saved.

What Is Tune-Up?

Tune-up is the process of making checks and minor adjustments to improve the operation of the engine.

Tune-up is also preventive maintenance. Troubles can be caught early and prevented by checking out the engine before it actually fails.

When Should an Engine Be Tuned?

Regularly! The intervals for tune-up may vary from 500 to 1000 hours or each spring and fall, depending upon the operating conditions. But regularity is the key to tuning the engine so that major problems are prevented.

A badly worn engine cannot be tuned up. This is why the engine should first be checked to see if:

* A tune-up will restore it, or
* Major overhaul is needed.

Let's go through a visual inspection and dynamometer test first and then we'll see how tune-up follows it.

Visual Inspection

By inspecting the engine before tuning it, you can learn a lot about its general condition.

Oil and Water Leakage

Inspect the engine for any oil or water leaks. If the engine has been using too much oil, this often means an external oil leak. If the engine overheats, look for leaks in the cooling system.

Electrical System

Inspect the battery for corrosion, cracked case, or leaks at the cell covers.

Remove the cell caps and examine the tops of the battery plates ("Things which Affect the Life of a Battery" on page 6-9). If they are covered with a chalky deposit, this means one of three things:

* Electrolyte level has been too low.
* Battery charge has been too low, causing sulfation.
* Battery was charged at too high a rate, boiling out water.

Any of these conditions can reduce the life of the battery. If they have gone too far, the battery must be replaced.

Check the battery cables and connections for damage and looseness.

Be sure the cables are the right size. Many complaints of poor starting can be traced to battery cables that are too small.

To check for this, operate the starter with the engine cold. If the battery cable gets hot, the cable is probably too small.

Inspect the wiring harnesses. If they are too oil soaked, frayed, or corroded, replace them.

On spark-ignition engines, check the distributor for a cracked cap, excessive grease, or other damage.

Check the operation of the alternator or generator gauge or voltmeter. It should light or register when the starter switch is turned on.

Failure can be due to a burned-out bulb or an incomplete circuit, or the alternator or generator is not producing current. (Lack of current to the battery will show up as a discharged battery.)

If the oil pressure light does not go out, or the gauge doesn't register normal when the engine is running, stop the engine at once and find the cause. Check for low oil level in the crankcase or a short circuit in the line from sensor to gauge or light.

Stop the engine at once and find the cause.

Lack of engine oil pressure can result in failure of expensive parts inside the engine due to lack of lubrication.

Cooling System

Wait until the engine has been idle for several hours and the crankcase oil is cold, then loosen the crankcase drain plug and carefully turn it out to see if any water seeps out. If water is present, locate the cause of the cooling system leak.

Inspect the cooling system for leaks, deteriorated hoses, bent or clogged radiator fins, slipping fan belt, or any other condition which could result in improper cooling.

Air Intake System

Inspect the air intake system for possible leaks or restrictions. If the proper amount of clean air does not reach the engine, performance and durability will be affected.

VISUAL INSPECTION CHECKLIST

❏ OIL AND WATER LEAKAGE

❏ ELECTRICAL SYSTEM

   – Battery

   – Cables

   – Wiring

   – Indicator Lights

❏ COOLING SYSTEM

   – Water in Crankcase

   – External Leaks

   – Clogging

❏ AIR INTAKE SYSTEM

   – Air Leaks

   – Restrictions

❏ FUEL SYSTEM

   – Leaks

   – Restrictions

   – Clogged Filter

❏ STEAM CLEANING

Fuel System

Check the fuel system for leaks and for bent or dented lines which might cause a restriction.

Check the fuel transfer pump sediment bowl. On diesel engines, inspect the fuel filters for dirt, water, or other foreign matter.

Steam Cleaning

After checking for leaks, steam clean the engine. This not only helps to recondition the engine, it makes tune-up easier and troubles easier to spot.

Dynamometer Tests

If possible, test the engine on a dynamometer, both before and after it is tuned. Before tune-up, this test gives you the horsepower (kilowatt) output and fuel consumption of the engine as it is. This will help you to determine if a tune-up can restore the engine or whether an overhaul is needed. After tune-up, a dynamometer test will also let you measure the engine's improvement.

Fuel-Air Mixture — 1
Compression — 2
Ignition — 3
= Horsepower

JDPX5284

Fig. 1 — Three Basic Things Are Needed to Produce Engine Horsepower

Good performance by the engine depends on these basic things:

- Adequate supply of clean air and fuel
- Good compression
- Proper valve and ignition timing for good combustion

Failure or low performance on any of these factors (Fig. 1) makes it impossible to fully restore the engine.

Therefore, if the dynamometer test shows that any of these three factors is bad — as shown by low power — the engine will have to be reconditioned.

Make the dynamometer test as follows:

1. Connect the machine to the dynamometer (Fig. 2) using the manufacturer's instructions.

2. Operate the engine at about one-half load until the coolant and crankcase oil temperatures are up to normal. (This will take about 30 minutes — but is very important to a good test.)

3. Gradually increase the load on the engine until its speed is reduced to rated load speed as given in the engine technical manual.

4. Read the horsepower (kilowatts) on the dynamometer.

5. Compare the power with that given in the engine technical manual.

However, do not expect engines to always equal these specifications. But if the engine rates much lower than normal, this is a signal that service is needed.

NOTE: Shop dynamometers cannot be expected to give results on tractors which match the Nebraska tests, for these tests are run under only the most ideal conditions.

While the engine is operating under load, note the outlet of the crankcase ventilating system. If too much vapor appears, also remove the crankcase oil filler cap.

If an excessive amount of vapor or smoke appears here as well as at the vent, there is blow-by in the engine cylinders and they must be reconditioned before the engine will perform at its best.

NOTE: Instruments are available to measure the flow of air and gases through the crankcase ventilating system.

The normal rate of engine vapor flow is specified in the engine technical manual.

Any increase in flow over the specified amount indicates crankcase blow-by.

If the blow-by is excessive, have the engine reconditioned for good operation.

Even though the engine develops its rated power using a normal amount of fuel, a tune-up may still improve its efficiency. Consider both the hours of operation and the conditions under which the engine has been operated. It is far more economical in the long run to tune the engine before a lack of performance makes it mandatory.

Remember: Most manufacturers suggest a regular period of operation between tune-ups, such as spring and fall, or every 500 or 1000 hours of operation.

JDPX5285

Fig. 2 — Dynamometer Tests Before Engine Tune-Up

Engine Tune-Up Checklists

The following chart gives a capsule of the steps necessary to tune your engine at the recommended intervals. Where they apply, the chapter and page is given for the details of the procedure.

If, after performing these tune-up steps, the engine fails to respond properly, have a service shop make further tests. The engine may require adjustments or repairs that you are not able to perform because of the special tools and knowledge required.

AIR INTAKE AND EXHAUST SYSTEM CHECKLIST

❏ CLEAN OUT PRECLEANER (IF USED)

❏ REMOVE AND CLEAN AIR CLEANER

❏ CHECK COLD START AID, GLOW PLUGS, OR AIR HEATER FOR OPERATION

❏ CHECK EGR VALVE OPERATION

❏ INSPECT EXHAUST SYSTEM AND MUFFLER

❏ INSPECT TURBOCHARGER AND ITS CONNECTIONS

❏ INSPECT EXHAUST FILTER CERAMIC CORE

❏ INSPECT ALL CONNECTIONS TO AFTERTREATMENT DEVICE

❏ INSPECT DOSING INJECTOR SYSTEM

❏ CHECK CRANKCASE VENTILATING SYSTEM FOR RESTRICTIONS

❏ CHECK INTAKE MANIFOLD FOR LEAKS

❏ CHECK AIR INTAKE FOR LEAKS OR RESTRICTIONS

❏ CHECK RADIATOR FOR AIR BUBBLES OR OIL INDICATING COMPRESSION OR OIL LEAKAGE

❏ CHECK CYLINDER HEAD GASKET FOR LEAKS

❏ ADJUST VALVE TAPPET CLEARANCE

❏ CHECK ENGINE COMPRESSION

IGNITION SYSTEM
(SPARK-IGNITION ENGINES) CHECKLIST

❏ CLEAN SPARK PLUGS AND ADJUST GAP

❏ CHECK SPARK PLUG WIRES

❏ CHECK DISTRIBUTOR CAP AND ROTOR

❏ CHECK DISTRIBUTOR TIMING

FUEL SYSTEMS CHECKLIST

❏ CHECK FUEL LINES FOR LEAKS OR RESTRICTIONS

❏ CLEAN FUEL PUMP SEDIMENT BOWL

❏ LISTEN TO THE ELECTRONIC FUEL PUMP TO SEE IF IT OPERATES DURING PRIMING OF FUEL SYSTEM PRIOR TO STARTING

❏ CLEAN OR REPLACE FUEL STRAINER OR FILTER

❏ DRAIN SEDIMENT FROM GASOLINE OR DIESEL FUEL TANK

❏ BLEED DIESEL FUEL SYSTEM

LUBRICATING SYSTEMS CHECKLIST

❏ CHECK OPERATION OF PRESSURE GAUGE OR LIGHT

❏ DRAIN AND REFILL CRANKCASE

❏ REPLACE OIL FILTER

❏ INSPECT OIL COOLER

COOLING SYSTEMS CHECKLIST

❏ CHECK WATER PUMP FOR LEAKS AND EXCESSIVE SHAFT ENDPLAY

❏ INSPECT RADIATOR HOSES AND CLAMPS

❏ CLEAN AND FLUSH COOLING SYSTEM

JDPX5286

Fig. 3 — Dynamometer Tests After Engine Tune-Up

Dynamometer Tests After Tune-Up

The dynamometer test is the final check of overall engine performance after tune-up. It will tell you whether the tune-up has been adequate. Compare it with the dynamometer test made before tune-up.

Test for the following things:

1. Engine horsepower (kilowatts)

2. Exhaust analysis
   Smoke analysis (diesel)
   Carburetor adjustment (spark-ignition)

3. Fuel consumption

4. Crankcase blow-by

Most dynamometer manufacturers have instruments to be used with the dynamometer for checking the above items.

Use the engine technical manual for procedures and specifications.

NOTE: *If the engine fails to produce the desired power, and an air cleaner restriction test was not made at the beginning, make one now. It is possible that an air restriction is causing the loss of horsepower.*

A completely tuned engine should pass the dynamometer test with no problems.

However, the engine should not put out more power than it was designed for. Tampering with the engine to get extra power will shorten engine life and raise operating costs. It may also void the engine warranty.

Summary: Engine Tune-Up

Tune-up of an engine may seem like a long ordeal.

Actually, most of the items can be checked in a minute or two.

But why check out so many items if the engine has not actually failed?

The answer is that **tune-up is preventive maintenance**.

Before the engine fails, we keep it tuned up so that causes of future failures are corrected early and possible causes are prevented.

Tune-up catches the problems early — in the farm shop, not in the field.

Shop costs are much cheaper than field costs, and by scheduling the tune-up during a lull in operation, costly downtime at peak periods can be prevented.

Tune-up means that the engine is ready to go and the operator can depend on it for some long and productive hours on the job.

Fig. 4 — Why Regular Engine Tune-Up Pays

Storage Of Machines

When your machine is not going to be used for several months, it must be prepared for storage to prevent damage to components. Some manufacturers offer storage kits for these long periods of storage. The kits may include rust and corrosion preventives and plastic bags and tape to seal off openings.

A sample tractor storage procedure follows, indicating what steps to perform when preparing your machine for storage and when removing it from storage. Be sure to observe all safety precautions.

Placing in Long-Term Storage

IMPORTANT: **If the tractor will not be used for several months, the following recommendations for storage and removal from storage will minimize corrosion and deterioration.**

Perform the following steps for long-term storage:

1. Change engine oil and replace filter.
2. Add required amount of corrosion inhibitor to engine crankcase.
3. Service the air cleaner.
4. Add required amount corrosion inhibitor to the transmission-hydraulic system.
5. Drain fuel tank. Then refill 1.0 gal (4 L) of fuel with 12 oz (0.4 L) of corrosion inhibitor.
6. Pour required amount of corrosion inhibitor into intake system and crank engine a few revolutions.
7. Seal air inlets, exhaust, crankcase vent tube, crankcase fill cap, fuel tank cap, radiator overflow hose, and transmission-hydraulic system fill cap using plastic bags and tape.
8. Remove and store batteries in a cool dry location (keep batteries on trickle charger).
9. Coat all exposed surfaces with corrosion inhibitor.
10. Cover instrument panel, control levers, and seat.
11. Raise tires off the ground and protect tires from heat and sunlight.
12. Thoroughly clean the machine, touching up any scratched or chipped painted surfaces.
13. Lubricate all grease fittings.
14. Cover the machine with waterproof material if it is to be stored outside.
15. Remove tension on auxiliary drive belts. Remove belt from air conditioner pulley and fan pulley.
16. Rotate A/C compressor pulley several turns once a month to prevent seizure of compressor.

Removing From Storage

Perform the following steps to remove machine from storage:

1. Remove all coverings in cab.
2. Unseal all openings sealed during storage.
3. Open hood and check for accumulation of dirt or debris.
4. Check A/C compressor pulley for movement.
5. Install fan and A/C belts.
6. Check all fluid levels.
7. Fill the fuel tank.
8. Check tire inflation pressures.
9. Install batteries and connect cables.
10. Perform all 10-hour, 250-hour, 500-hour and 750-hour services as required.
11. Check all instruments and indicators by turning key to the ON position.

IMPORTANT: **DO NOT operate the starter for more than 30 seconds. Wait at least two minutes for starter to cool before trying again.**

12. Operate engine at slow idle for several minutes.

IMPORTANT: If air conditioning compressor is locked up, engine operation with compressor clutch engaged will damage belt or compressor.

13. Check air conditioning.

14. Check all other system functions.

15. Warm up before putting under load.

Test Yourself

Questions

1. (Fill in blanks.) Good preventive maintenance will reduce _____ costs and avoid costly _____.

2. List four systems of a machine engine that would be found on a tune-up chart.

3. (T/F) A badly worn engine can be restored by a complete tune-up.

4. Before tuning up an engine, what should be done?

5. When should dynamometer tests be made?

Troubleshooting

11

Operational Checks

Several machinery manufacturers provide a new approach to finding the cause of the most common malfunctions without the use of complicated diagnostic gauges and instruments. These operational checkout procedures are based on the maintenance person's ability to Look, Listen and Feel.

On the following pages you will find samples of operational checkouts. Of course, each machine will require it's very own specific procedure.

Use this procedure to check all systems and functions on the machine. It is designed so you can make a quick check of the operation of the machine while doing a walk-around inspection and performing specific checks from the operator's seat.

Should you experience a problem with your machine, you will find helpful diagnostic information in this checkout that will pinpoint the cause. This information may allow you to perform a simple adjustment that will reduce the downtime of your machine. Use the table of contents to help find adjustment procedures.

The information you provide after completing the operational checkout will allow you or your dealer to pinpoint the specific test or repair work needed to restore the machine to design specifications.

A location that is level and has adequate space to complete the checks will be required. No tools or equipment are needed to perform the checkout.

Complete the necessary visual checks (oil levels, oil condition, external leaks, loose hardware, linkage, wiring, etc.) prior to doing the checkout. The machine must be at operating temperature for many of the checks.

Start at the top of the left column and read completely down column before performing the check. Follow this sequence from left to right. In the far right column, if no problem is found (OK), you will be instructed to go to the next check. If a problem is indicated (NOT OK), you will be referred to either a section in this manual or to your dealer.

JDPX5275

Fig. 1 — Operation Check List

Turn Signal and Flasher Check

JDPX5277	Move turn signal lever to left turn position (A) and then right turn position (13). LOOK. Left front and rear amber lights and dash indicator (A), then right front and rear amber lights and dash indicator (B) must be flashing.	OK: Go to next check NOT OK: If turn signals do not work, check turn signal fuse. IF OK: Go to your dealer

Warning Flasher Check

JDPX5278	Pull out warning flasher switch knob. LOOK. Front (A) and rear (B) amber fights and both dash indicators (C) must be flashing.	OK: Go to next check NOT OK: Check turn signal fuse. IF OK: Go to your dealer.

Brake Light Check

JDPX5279	Depress brake pedal and observe brake lights (A). LOOK: Brake lights must come on.	OK: Go to next check NOT OK: Check brake light fuse. IF OK: Go to your dealer.

Horn Circuit Check

	Key ON. Push button. LISTEN: Horn (A) must sound	OK: Go to next check NOT OK: Check horn circuit fuse as specified in the machine operator's manual. IF OK: Go to your dealer.

JDPX5280

Mechanical Front Wheel Drive (MFWD) Driving Checks

MFWD Limited-Slip Differential and Control Linkage Check

Shift transaxle to 1st reverse. Engage MFWD and drive machine. Run engine at approximately 1200 rpm. Turn steering wheel for a full left or right turn and observe how the front tires attempt to slide sideways (side load), and the amount of tire scuffing. Disengage MFWD. LOOK. Tire side loading and scuffing must stop when MFWD Is disengaged. *NOTE: If tires attempt to slide sideways and tire scuffing is seen with MFWD engaged, limited-slip differential is working and power is being transmitted to MFWD.*	OK: Go to next check. NOT OK: Move MFWD control linkage to feel engagement detents. If no detents, inspect linkage to transfer case. IF OK: Go to your dealer.

MFWD Gear and Pinion Check

Drive machine at transport speed with MFWD engaged, then disengaged. LISTEN: MFWD must not whine.	OK: Go to next check. NOT OK: If MFWD whines, check oil levels and fill to correct levels. IF OK: Check backlash. Go to your dealer.

Troubleshooting

Troubleshooting is a form of preventive maintenance which can help you find and correct minor problems before they become major ones.

The basic procedures for maintaining the machine properly have been covered. However, all machines will fail from time to time. The following charts will help you to identify problems so that you can determine the possible causes and remedies.

These charts list causes of typical failures of the engine, power train, hydraulic system, electrical system, brakes and operator's cab.

JDPX5276

In most cases, these charts show only problems that you as an operator can remedy. Many problems require expert diagnosis and repair by a service shop. If you can't eliminate the problem, take the machine to a service shop for testing and repair. The charts are arranged in the following order:

- Engine
- Electrical systems
- Power train
- Hydraulic system
- Brakes
- Operator's cab

Engine Troubleshooting Chart

Problem	Cause	Remedy
Engine hard to start or will not start	No fuel or improper fuel.	Fill tank. If wrong fuel, drain and refill with proper fuel.
	Water or dirt in fuel or dirty filters.	Check out fuel supply. Replace or clean filters.
	Air in fuel system (diesel).	Bleed air from system.
	Low cranking speed.	Charge or replace battery, or service starter as necessary.
	Improper timing.	Check distributor (spark-ignition). Have service shop check injection pump (diesel).
	Defective coil (spark-ignition).	Replace coil.
	Cracked distributor cap or eroded rotor (spark-ignition).	Replace cap or rotor.
	Distributor wires loose or installed in wrong order (spark-ignition).	Push wire into sockets. Install wires in correct firing order.
	Fouled or defective spark plugs (spark-ignition).	Clean and regap plugs or replace them.
	Poor injection nozzle operation (diesel).	Have service shop clean or repair nozzles.
	Liquid fuel in lines (LP-gas).	Always turn on vapor valve when starting the engine.
	Engine flooded.	Wait several minutes before attempting to start engine. Do not choke engine again.
Engine starts but will not run properly	Fuel problem – dirt, air restrictions, or clogged filters.	Check fuel supply, bleed system (diesel), check for line restrictions, and clean or replace fuel and air filters and screens.
	Carburetor needs adjustment (spark-ignition).	Adjust idle and load fuel-air mixtures.
	Defective coil (spark-ignition).	Replace as necessary.
	Defective ignition resistor or key switch (spark-ignition).	Replace resistor or switch.
	Fouled or defective spark plugs (spark-ignition).	Clean and regap plugs or replace them.
	Cracked distributor cap or eroded rotor (spark-ignition).	Replace cap or rotor.
Engine detonates (gasoline)	Wrong type of fuel.	Use proper octane fuel.

Engine Troubleshooting Chart (Continued)

Problem	Cause	Remedy
Engine pre-ignites (gasoline)	Distributor timed too early.	Retime distributor.
	Distributor advance mechanism stuck.	Free mechanism.
	Faulty spark plugs or spark plug heat range too high.	Install new plugs that have proper heat range.
Engine backfires (spark-ignition)	Spark plug cables installed wrong.	Install in correct firing order.
	Carburetor mixture too lean.	Adjust carburetor.
Engine knocks	Improper distributor timing (spark-ignition).	Time distributor.
	Improper injection pump timing (diesel).	Have service shop check injection pump.
	Worn engine bearings or bushings.	Have service shop replace.
	Loose bearing caps.	Have service shop tighten to proper torque
	Foreign matter in the cylinder.	Have service shop remove material and repair engine.
Engine overheats	Defective radiator cap.	Replace cap.
	Radiator core plugged with dirt and debris.	Clean radiator core.
	Defective thermostat.	Replace thermostat.
	Loss of coolant.	Check for leaks and correct.
	Loose fan belt.	Adjust tension.
	Cooling system has scale deposit build-up.	Use cooling system cleaner to remove scale.
	Overloaded engine.	Reduce load or shift into a lower gear.
	Incorrect engine timing.	Time distributor (spark-ignition). Have service shop time injection pump (diesel).
	Engine low on oil.	Add oil to the proper level.
	Wrong type of fuel.	Use recommended fuel.

Engine Troubleshooting Chart (Continued)

Problem	Cause	Remedy
Lack of power	Air cleaner dirty or obstructed.	Clean or replace air cleaner. Remove obstruction.
	Restriction in fuel lines, filters, or carburetor.	Clean plugged parts.
	Wrong type of fuel.	Use recommended type.
	Frost at fuel-lock strainer (LP-gas).	Clean strainer.
	Governor not operating properly.	Have service shop adjust or repair.
	Valves in engine head leaking.	Have service shop recondition.
	Incorrect valve clearance.	Adjust clearance.
	Low engine compression.	Have service shop check and repair engine.
	Incorrect timing.	Time distributor (spark-ignition). Have service shop time injection pump (diesel).
	Carburetor improperly adjusted or dirty (spark-ignition).	Have service shop clean and adjust carburetor.
	Wrong spark plugs or plugs fouled (spark-ignition).	Clean, regap or replace spark plugs.
	High engine operating temperature.	See "Engine overheats" on page 6.
	Low engine operating temperature.	Check thermostat.
	Vent on fuel tank plugged (gasoline and diesel).	Check fuel tank cap.
Engine uses too much oil	Crankcase oil too light.	Use recommended weight of oil.
	Worn pistons and rings.	Have service shop recondition.
	Worn valve guides or stem oil seals.	Have service shop replace.
	External oil leaks.	Eliminate leaks.
	Oil pressure too high.	Have service shop adjust pressure.
	Restricted air intake system.	Check system and relieve restriction.
Oil Pressure too low	See "Engine uses too much oil."	

Engine Troubleshooting Chart (Continued)

Problem	Cause	Remedy
Engine uses too much fuel	Clogged or dirty air cleaner.	Clean or replace air cleaner.
	Improper type fuel used.	Drain fuel tank and fill with recommended fuel.
	Engine overloaded.	Reduce load or shift into lower gear.
	Improper valve clearance.	Adjust valve clearance.
	Engine out of time.	Time distributor (spark-ignition). Have service shop time injection pump (diesel).
	Incorrect carburetor adjustment.	Adjust carburetor.
	Engine not operating at proper temperature.	Check thermostat.
	Choke in closed position.	Open choke or adjust linkage if necessary.
Engine exhausts black or gray smoke	Improper type of fuel.	Drain fuel tank and fill with recommended fuel.
	Clogged or dirty air cleaner.	Clean or replace air cleaner.
	Defective muffler.	Replace muffler.
	Engine overloaded.	Reduce load or shift into a lower gear.
	Fuel injection system faulty.	Have service shop determine cause and repair.
	Engine out of time.	Time distributor (spark-ignition). Have service shop time injection pump (diesel).
	Incorrect carburetor adjustment.	Adjust carburetor.
	Improper type fuel.	Drain fuel tank and fill with recommended fuel.
	Low engine temperature.	Allow engine to warm up to normal temperatures before operating under load,
	Defective thermostat.	Replace thermostat.
	Engine out of time.	Time distributor (spark-ignition). Have service shop time injection pump (diesel).

Electrical Systems Troubleshooting Chart

Problem	Cause	Remedy
Low battery output	Low electrolyte level.	Add distilled water to proper level.
	Low specific gravity.	See "Low battery charge."
	Defective battery cell.	Replace battery.
	Cracked or broken case.	Replace battery.
	Low battery capacity.	Replace battery with one of recommended capacity.
Battery uses too much water	Cracked battery case.	Replace battery.
	Overcharged battery.	Apply load to battery and have voltage regulator checked.
Low battery charge	Excessive loads from added accessories.	Remove excessive loads or install larger alternator.
	Excessive engine idling.	Allow engine to idle only when necessary.
	Continuous drain on battery.	Clean battery top. Check for component grounded or shorted.
	High resistance in circuit.	Clean and tighten connections. Replace faulty wiring.
	Faulty charging operation.	See "Low charging circuit output."
Low charging circuit output	Slipping drive belts.	Inspect belt tensioner or adjust belt tension.
	Excessively worn or sticking brushes in alternator or generator.	Replace brushes.
	Defective alternator.	Replace unit or have service shop repair.
Noisy alternator	Defective or badly worn belt.	Replace belt.
	Worn or defective bearings.	Have service shop replace bearings.
	Loose mounting or loose pulley.	Tighten mounting and pulley.
	Misaligned drive belt and pulley.	Realign belt and pulley.
Sluggish starting motor operation	Low battery charge.	Charge battery.
	High resistance in circuit.	Clean and tighten wiring connections.
	Defective starting motor.	Have service shop repair.
	Starting motor bearings dry.	Lubricate bearings or replace sealed bearings.
	Engine oil viscosity too high.	Drain oil and replace with viscosity of oil recommended for cold temperatures.

Electrical Systems Troubleshooting Chart (Continued)

Problem	Cause	Remedy
Starting motor will not operate	Low battery charge.	Charge battery.
	High resistance in circuit.	Clean and tighten connections.
	Starter safety switch open.	Move shift lever to neutral or park position.
	Defective or improperly adjusted starter safety switch.	Have service shop adjust or replace switch.
	Defective starter switch.	Replace switch.
	Defective starter.	Have service shop check, repair, or replace starter.
Misfiring of engine	Improper spark plug heat range.	Replace plugs with hotter or colder range plugs as required.
	Bad plug wiring.	Replace plug wires.
	Worn spark plug electrodes or fouled plugs.	Clean plugs and regap. Replace plugs if necessary.
	Defective spark plugs.	Replace plugs.
	Incorrect distributor timing.	Retime distributor.
	Insufficient voltage available to spark plugs.	See "Low voltage at spark plug."
Low voltage at spark plug	Dirt or moisture in distributor cap.	Clean distributor cap.
	Cracked distributor cap.	Replace cap.
	Eroded distributor rotor.	Replace rotor.
	Defective spark plug cables.	Replace cables.
	Defective ignition coil.	Replace coil.
	Loose wire connections.	Tighten all connections.
Dim lights	High resistance in circuit or poor ground on lights.	Clean and tighten all connections. Replace faulty wiring.
	Low battery charge.	Charge battery.
	Defective light switch.	Replace switch.
Alternator indicator lamp glows intermittently	Excessive resistance in battery lead to unit or regulator.	Clean and tighten all connections. Replace faulty wiring.
	Excessive internal resistance in alternator.	Replace brushes or take to service department.
		Have unit repaired or replaced.

Electrical Systems Troubleshooting Chart (Continued)

Problem	Cause	Remedy
Oil pressure indicator lamp fails to light	Burned-out bulb.	Replace bulb.
	Open circuit or excessive resistance in wiring.	Clean and tighten all connections. Replace faulty wiring.
	Defective lamp body.	Replace lamp body.
	Faulty oil pressure switch.	Replace switch.
Oil pressure lamp remains on with starting switch off	Defective lamp body.	Replace lamp body.
	Grounded wire to oil pressure switch.	Repair or replace wiring.
	Faulty oil pressure switch.	Replace switch.

Power Train (Clutch) Troubleshooting Chart

Problem	Cause	Remedy
Clutch slips	Too little clutch pedal free travel.	Adjust clutch pedal free travel.
	Operator riding clutch pedal.	Do not ride clutch pedal.
	Worn clutch disks.	See dealer for repair.
Clutch grabs or chatters		Take the machine to a service shop for repair or adjustment.
Clutch squeaks	Clutch release bearing dry.	Lubricate bearing.
	Clutch actuating mechanism dry.	Lubricate linkage and shafts.
Clutch rattles and vibrates		Take the machine to a service shop for repair or adjustment.

Power Train (Mechanical Transmission) Troubleshooting Chart

Problem	Cause	Remedy
Transmission noisy	Transmission oil level low.	Fill transmission with proper lubricant.
	Worn or broken gears.	See dealer for repair.
Transmission hard to shift		Take machine to service shop for repair or adjustment.
Transmission sticks in gear	Clutch not releasing.	Adjust clutch pedal free travel.
	Shift linkage binding.	Free linkage.
	Worn shift linkage.	Have dealer repair.

Power Train (Mechanical Transmission) Troubleshooting Chart (Continued)

Problem	Cause	Remedy
Transmission slips out of gear		Take machine to service shop for repair or adjustment.
Transmission leaks oil	Oil level too high.	Drain to proper level.
	Gaskets damaged or missing.	Have dealer install new gaskets.
	Drain plug loose.	Tighten drain plug.
	Lubricant foaming excessively.	Use recommended lubricant.

Power Train (Hydraulic Assist Transmission) Troubleshooting Chart

Problem	Cause	Remedy
Machine will not move	Cold weather starting clutch disengaged.	Engage clutch.
	Park lock engaged.	Release lock.
	Control linkage binding or disconnected.	Free linkage or connect linkage.
	Oil filter plugged.	Replace oil filter.
Shifts erratically	Shift control disconnected or binding.	Free controls or connect disconnected parts.
Low system pressure	Plugged oil filter.	Replace filter.
	Low oil level.	Fill to proper level.
Transmission overheating	Reservoir oil level too low or too high.	Bring oil level to proper level.
	Plugged oil filter.	Replace filter.
	Plugged core in oil cooler.	Clean core.

Power Train (Torque Converter) Troubleshooting Chart

Problem	Cause	Remedy
Overheating	Oil level too low.	Fill to proper level.
	Machine overloaded.	Reduce load.
	Plugged oil cooler core.	Clean core.
Noisy	Major failure or maladjustment.	Take machine to service shop for repair or adjustment.
Oil leaks	Loose bolts or damaged gaskets.	Tighten bolts. Have service shop replace gaskets.
	Loose fittings or oil lines.	Tighten fittings and lines.
Machine lacks power or acceleration	Major failure or maladjustment.	Take machine to service shop for repair or adjustment.

Power Train (Hydrostatic transmission) Troubleshooting Chart

Problem	Cause	Remedy
Machine will not move	System low on oil.	Fill to proper level.
	Faulty control linkage.	Free linkage.
	Disconnected oil line.	Reconnect oil line,
	Mechanical failure.	See dealer for repair.
Neutral hard to find	Faulty speed control linkage.	Adjust control linkage.
System overheating	Oil level too low.	Fill to proper level.
	Oil cooler core plugged.	Clean core.
	Engine fan belt slipping or broken.	Tighten or replace belt.
System noisy	Air in system.	Check oil supply; fill if low. Check for loose fittings and tighten.
Sluggish acceleration and deceleration	Air in system.	Check oil supply; fill if low. Check for loose fittings and tighten.
Hard shifting	Speed control lever not in neutral.	Position lever in neutral.

Power Train (Differential) Troubleshooting Chart

Problem	Cause	Remedy
Noisy	Oil level too low.	Fill to proper level.
Difficult to turn	Differential lock will not release, brakes dragging, or differential lock stuck.	Take machine to service shop for repairs.
Mechanical lock does not hold	Linkage not in adjustment.	Take machine to service shop for repairs or adjustment.
Hydraulic lock does not hold	Valve malfunction or linkage not in adjustment.	Take machine to service shop for repairs or adjustment.

Hydraulic System Troubleshooting Chart

Problem	Cause	Remedy
System does not operate	Little or no oil in system.	Fill to proper level. Check system for leaks.
	Oil of wrong viscosity.	Drain and refill system with proper oil.
	Oil filter plugged.	Replace filter.
	Restriction in system.	Take machine to service shop for repairs.
	Oil leaks.	Tighten fittings and lines.
	Slipping or broken pump drive belt.	Tighten or replace belt.

Hydraulic System Troubleshooting Chart (Continued)

Problem	Cause	Remedy
System operates erratically	Air in system.	Check for leaks and tighten fittings and lines.
	Cold oil.	Allow system to warm up.
System operates slowly	Cold oil.	Allow system to warm up.
	Oil viscosity too heavy.	Drain and refill system with proper viscosity of oil.
	Engine speed too slow.	Operate engine at recommended speed.
	Low oil supply.	Fill to proper level.
	Air in system.	Check for leaks and tighten fittings and lines.
System operates too fast	Adjust cylinder ram speed.	See operator's manual.
	Adjust or repair.	Adjust per operator's manual. For repair, see dealer.
System overheating	Operator holding controls in power position too long.	Return controls to neutral when not in use.
	Incorrect oil viscosity.	Use recommended viscosity of oil.
	Low oil level.	Fill to proper level. Check for leaks.
	Dirty oil.	Drain and refill with clean oil.
	Oil cooler core plugged or dirty.	Clean core.
Foaming oil	Low oil level.	Fill to proper level.
	Water in oil.	Check for leaks.
	Wrong kind of oil.	Drain and replace oil.
	Air leak.	Drain and replace with recommended oil.
Noisy pump	Low oil level.	Tighten lines and fittings.
	Air in oil.	Fill to proper level. Check for leaks.
Components leaking	Failure of major parts.	Check for leaks. Tighten lines and fittings.
		Take machine to service shop for repairs.

Brakes Troubleshooting Chart

Problem	Cause	Remedy
Brakes not holding	Glazed, greasy, or worn linings.	Replace linings.
Brakes not releasing	Cables or linkage binding.	Adjust linkage and cables.
	Foreign material lodged in brake mechanism.	Remove material.
Pedal bounces or spongy	Hydraulic brakes: air in system.	Bleed brakes.
No brakes	Hydraulic brakes: air in system.	Bleed brakes.
	Manual brakes: linings worn or linkage out of adjustment.	Replace linings or adjust linkage.
	Power brakes: accumulator discharged.	Take machine to service shop for repairs.
Machine pulls to one side	Brakes adjusted unevenly.	Adjust brakes.
Hydraulic brakes operate erratically	Contaminated fluid.	Drain and clean system. Refill system with proper fluid. Bleed brakes.

Operator's Cab Troubleshooting Chart

Problem	Cause	Remedy
Blower not keeping dust out	Defective seal around filter.	Check seal condition. Check filter for proper installation.
	Defective or dirty filter.	Replace or clean filter.
	Air leaks into cab.	Check cab for leaks. Plug leaks.
	Blower air flow too low.	See "Blower air flow too low."
Blower air flow too low	Clogged filter or air intake screen.	Clean filter or intake screen.
Heater will not heat	Air trapped in heater core.	Bleed air from heater.
	Defective thermostat in engine.	Replace thermostat.
	Air conditioner turned on.	Turn off air conditioner.
Heater will not shut off	Heater hoses connected improperly.	Change hose connections.

Operator's Cab Troubleshooting Chart (Continued)

Problem	Cause	Remedy
Air conditioner will not cool	Blower air flow too low.	See "Blower air flow too low" on page 15.
	Compressor belt slipping.	Tighten belt or inspect belt tensioner.
	Lack of refrigerant in system.	Check sight glass and have system recharged.
	Evaporator core plugged.	Clean core.
	Condenser core clogged.	Clean core.
	Heater turned on.	Turn off heater.
	Compressor not running.	Check fuse.

Safety

12

Introduction

JDPX5231

Each year 350 people die in machinery related accidents in North America, many more around the world. Many thousands receive serious injuries that disable them for the rest of their lives.

Many factors can cause an accident: carelessness, haste, poor judgment, lack of experience, and even mechanical failure created by lack of maintenance.

Don't become a statistic; learn and practice safe operating and maintenance procedures.

Recognize Safety Information

JDPX5232

This is the safety-alert symbol. When you see, this symbol on your machine or in the machine's manuals, be alert to the potential for personal injury.

Follow recommended precautions and **safe** operating practices.

Understand Signal Words

⚠ DANGER

⚠ WARNING

⚠ CAUTION

JDPX5233

A signal word — DANGER, WARNING, or CAUTION — is used with the safety-alert symbol. DANGER identifies the most serious hazards.

DANGER or WARNING safety signs are located near specific hazards. General precautions are listed on CAUTION safety signs. CAUTION also calls attention to safety messages in the machine's manuals.

Follow Safety Instructions

JDPX5234

Carefully read all safety messages in this manual, in the machine's operator manual, and on your machine's safety signs. Keep safety signs in good condition. Replace missing or damaged safety signs. Be sure new equipment components and repair parts include the current safety signs. Replacement safety signs are available from your dealer.

Learn how to operate the machine and how to use controls properly. Do not let anyone operate without instruction.

Keep your machine in proper working condition. Unauthorized modifications to the machine may impair the function and/or safety and affect machine life.

If you do not understand any part of the machine's operator manual and need assistance, contact your dealer.

Stop And Think

JDPX5235

Stop and think about the maintenance procedures. What could happen? How could it happen? What is the safest way? Read all safety instructions and follow them every time.

Get Familiar With Each Machine

JDPX5236

Don't rush into a maintenance job. Get very familiar with the specific functions and potential safety hazards of each machine. Always refer to the operator's manual of each machine. Even similar machines do not always have identical systems. So be very careful. Follow all safety instructions — every time. Remember: You are protecting yourself and others by being careful.

Practice Safe Maintenance

JDPX5237

Understand service procedures before doing work. Keep the area clean and dry.

Never lubricate or service a machine while it is moving. Keep hands, feet, and clothing from power-driven parts. Disengage all power and operate the controls to relieve pressure. Lower equipment to the ground. Stop the engine. Remove the key. Allow machine to cool.

Securely support any machine elements that must be raised for service work.

Keep all parts in good condition and properly installed. Fix damage immediately. Replace worn or broken parts. Remove any build-up of grease, oil, or debris.

Disconnect battery ground cable(s) (–) before making adjustments on electrical system or welding on machine.

REMEMBER: Always turn off the engine before you work on a machine.

Wear Protective Clothing

JDPX5238

Wear close fitting clothing and safety equipment appropriate to the job.

Prolonged exposure to loud noise can cause impairment or loss of hearing.

Wear a suitable hearing protective device such as earmuffs or earplugs to protect against objectionable or uncomfortable loud noises.

Protect Your Eyes

Eye Protection

Wear Goggles under Helmet   **Use Clear Lens in Welding Helmet**

JDPX5239, 5240

Eyesight is one of the most precious abilities we have. So protect your eyes very carefully. Wear safety glasses or face shields when you are using a chisel or punch. Wear a welding shield or a helmet when you are welding. Keep shield in place when you are chipping slag.

Protect Your Hearing

JDPX5241

Machines that are running make a lot of noise. Prolonged exposure to noise will damage your ability to hear. Therefore, you should always wear hearing protection such as ear plugs or muffs.

Prepare for Emergencies

JDPX5242

Be prepared if a fire starts.

Keep a first aid kit and fire extinguisher handy.

Keep emergency numbers for doctors, ambulance service, hospital, and fire department near your telephone.

Work in Ventilated Area

JDPX5243

Engine exhaust fumes can cause sickness or death. If it is necessary to run an engine in an enclosed area, remove the exhaust fumes from the area with an exhaust pipe extension.

If you do not have an exhaust pipe extension, open the doors and get outside air into the area.

Work in Clean Area

JDPX5244

Before starting a job:

* Clean work area and machine.
* Make sure you have all necessary tools to do your job.
* Have the right parts on hand.
* Read all instructions thoroughly; do not attempt short-cuts.

Service Machine Safely

JDPX5245

Tie long hair behind your head. Do not wear a necktie, scarf, loose clothing, or necklace when you work near machine tools, or moving parts. If these items were to get caught, severe injury could result.

Remove rings and other jewelry to prevent electrical shorts and entanglement in moving parts.

Use Tools That Fit

Poor Fit   **Proper Fit**

Incorrect   **Correct**

JDPX5246, 5247

Many serious accidents happen when the wrong tools are used or when tools are used that don't fit. Make sure you use metric-dimensioned tools on metric products and inch-dimensioned tools on products of customary design. Also, don't use tools for purposes they are not designed for.

Illuminate Work Area Safely

JDPX5249

Illuminate your work area adequately but safely. Use a portable safety light for working inside or under the machine. Make sure the bulb is enclosed by a wire cage. The hot filament of an accidentally broken bulb can ignite spilled fuel or oil.

Store Attachments Safely

JDPX5262

Stored attachments such as dual wheels, cage wheels, and loaders can fall and cause serious injury or death.

Securely store attachments and implements to prevent falling. Keep playing children and bystanders away from storage area.

Park Machine Safely

JDPX5248

Before working on the machine:

* Lower all equipment to the ground.
* Stop the engine and remove the key.
* Disconnect the battery ground strap.
* Hang a "DO NOT OPERATE" tag in operator station.

Stay Clear of Rotating Drivelines

JDPX5259

Entanglement in rotating driveline can cause serious injury or death. When operating with the PTO, no one must be allowed to remain in the vicinity of the rotating PTO stub shaft or drive shaft. Always ensure that the guards for PTO drive shaft, PTO stub shaft, and drive shaft guards are in position and that rotating shields turn freely.

Wear close-fitting clothing. Stop the engine and be sure the PTO driveline is stopped before making adjustments or connections or cleaning out PTO-driven equipment.

As soon as the PTO drive shaft has been removed, reinstall the guard over the PTO stub shaft.

Be Aware of Stored Energy

Spring Under Compression

JDPX5260

Stored energy can work for you, or it can be carelessly released and cause injury.

In many farm machines, energy is stored so it can be released at the right time, in the right way for you. Here are some components that store energy. You should recognize them as you use and service equipment.

- Springs
- Hydraulic systems
- Compressed air
- Electricity
- Raised loads
- Loaded mechanisms

Always release or disconnect the stored energy before you begin maintenance work.

Keep Cab/ROPS Installed Properly

JDPX5270

Make certain all parts are reinstalled correctly if the cab or rollover protective structure (ROPS) is loosened or removed for any reason. Tighten mounting bolts to specified torque.

Protection offered by cab or ROPS will be impaired if subjected to structural damage, involved in an overturn incident, or altered in any way by welding, bending, drilling, or cutting. A damaged cab or ROPS should be replaced, not reused.

Prevent Machine Runaway

JDPX5271

Avoid possible injury or death from machine runaway.

Do not start the engine by starting across starter terminals. Machine will start in gear if normal circuitry is bypassed.

NEVER start engine while standing on ground. Start engine only from operator's seat, with the transmission in neutral or "Park."

Support Machine Properly

JDPX5250

Always lower the attachment or implement to the ground before you work on the machine. If you must work on a lifted machine or attachment, securely support the machine or attachment.

Do not support the machine on cinder blocks, hollow tiles or props that may crumble under continuous load. Do not work under a machine that is supported solely by a jack. Follow recommended procedures in this manual.

Service Front-Wheel-Drive Tractor Safely

JDPX5251

When servicing a front-wheel-drive tractor with the rear wheels supported off the ground and rotating wheels by engine power, always support front wheels in a similar manner. Loss of electrical power or transmission-hydraulic system pressure will engage the front driving wheels, pulling the rear wheels off the support if front wheels are not raised. Under these conditions, front drive wheels can engage even with switch in disengaged position.

Service Tires Safely

JDPX5261

Explosive separation of a tire and rim parts can cause serious injury or death.

Do not attempt to mount a tire unless you have the proper equipment and experience to perform the job.

Always maintain the correct tire pressure. Do not inflate the tires above the recommended pressure. Never weld or heat a wheel and tire assembly. The heat can cause an increase in air pressure resulting in a tire explosion. Welding can structurally weaken or deform the wheel.

When inflating tires, use a clip-on chuck and extension hose long enough to allow you to stand to one side and NOT in front of or over the tire assembly. Use a safety cage if available.

Check wheels for low pressure, cuts, bubbles, damaged rims, or missing lug bolts and nuts.

Retighten Wheel Nuts

JDPX5267

Retighten machine wheel nuts at the intervals specified in the machine operator's manual.

Avoid Being Crushed

Crush Point

JDPX5265

There are many crush points on a machine. A crushing injury or death is caused if you get between two parts that move toward each other, like the front and rear portions of a four-wheel-drive articulated tractor.

JDPX5266

You can also get crushed if you get between a stationary part and a moving part, like between the 3-point hitch and the tractor. Another way to get crushed is to be under a machine that is not well blocked and the machine falls on you.

Disconnect Electrical Circuit

JDPX5252

Disconnect battery ground strap(s) before carrying out any electrical repairs or welding on the machine.

Prevent Battery Explosions

JDPX5254

Keep sparks, lighted matches, and open flame away from the top of battery. Battery gas can explode.

Never check battery charge by placing a metal object across the posts. Use a voltmeter or hydrometer.

Do not charge a frozen battery; it may explode. Warm battery to 16°C (60°F).

Handle Batteries Safely

JDPX5253

Sulfuric acid in battery electrolyte is poisonous. It is strong enough to burn skin, eat holes in clothing, and cause blindness if splashed into eyes.

Avoid the hazard by:

1. Filling the batteries in a well-ventilated area.
2. Wearing eye protection and rubber gloves.
3. Avoiding breathing in the fumes when electrolyte is added.
4. Avoiding spilling or dripping electrolyte.
5. Using the proper jump start procedure.

If you spill acid on yourself:

1. Flush your skin with water.
2. Apply baking soda or lime to help neutralize the acid.
3. Flush your eyes with water for 10–15 minutes.

Get medical attention immediately.

If acid is swallowed:

1. Drink large amounts of water or milk.
2. Then drink milk of magnesia, beaten eggs, or vegetable oil.
3. Get medical attention immediately.

Avoid High-Pressure Fluids

JDPX5255

The hydraulic system and the fuel injection system contain fluids under very high pressure. Small leaks in these systems will allow oil or fuel to escape with high velocity.

Escaping fluid under pressure can penetrate the skin, causing serious injury.

Avoid the hazard by relieving pressure before disconnecting hydraulic or other lines. Tighten all connections before applying pressure.

Search for leaks with a piece of cardboard. Protect hands and body from high-pressure fluids.

If an accident occurs, see a doctor immediately. Any fluid injected into the skin must be surgically removed within a few hours or gangrene may result. Doctors unfamiliar with this type of injury should contact other knowledgeable medical sources.

Avoid Heating Near Pressurized Fluid Lines

JDPX5256

Flammable spray can be generated by heating near pressurized fluid lines, resulting in severe burns to yourself and bystanders. Do not heat by welding, soldering, or using a torch near pressurized fluid lines or other flammable materials. Pressurized lines can be accidentally cut when heat goes beyond the immediate flame area.

Handle Fuel Safely — Avoid Fires

JDPX5268

Handle fuel with care; it is highly flammable. Do not refuel the machine while smoking or when near open flame or sparks.

Always stop engine before refueling machine. Fill fuel tank outdoors.

Prevent fires by keeping machine clean of accumulated trash, grease, and debris. Always clean up spilled fuel.

Handle Starting Fluid Safely

JDPX5269

Starting fluid is highly flammable.

Keep all sparks and flames away when using it. Keep starting fluid away from batteries and cables.

To prevent accidental discharge when storing the pressurized can, always keep the cap on the container and store in a cool, protected location.

Do not incinerate or puncture starting fluid containers, even when empty.

Handle Compressed and Liquid Natural Gas (CNG/LNG) Safely

Work in Well Ventilated Area

JDPX5258

Handle Compressed Natural Gas (CNG) safely. CNG is methane (natural gas) stored at high pressure. It spreads into air quickly.

Natural gas fumes can cause sickness or death. Always work in a well ventilated area.

Do not smoke when refueling or working on or around natural gas vehicles or equipment.

Keep natural gas vehicles away from sparks, flames, and electrical devices in operation, especially if you suspect a natural gas leak.

Service Compressed Natural Gas (CNG) and Liquid Natural Gas (LNG) Systems Safely

Avoid Fires

JDPX5796

Service Compressed Natural Gas (CNG) and Liquid Natural Gas (LNG) systems safely. Improper installation, service, or operation of natural gas storage and delivery components can result in fire, explosion, and/or serious injury.

Relieve natural gas fuel system pressure before working on the system. Properly tighten connections and check for leaks before pressurizing the fuel system.

Protect Against High Pressures of CNG/LNG Systems

Protect Against High Pressure

JDPX5797

Protect against high pressure. Natural gas fuel systems operate at high pressures. DO NOT disassemble or remove any natural gas fuel system components under pressure. Explosive separation of components, and the escaping natural gas can cause serious injury.

Relieve natural gas fuel system pressure before disconnecting any fuel system component.

Protect Against Extremely Cold CNG/LNG Leakage

Extremely Cold CNG/LNG Leakage

JDPX5798

Protect against extremely cold CNG/LNG leakage. Gas escaping from the natural gas fuel system is very cold. Contact with cold escaping gas or surrounding components can cause frostbite or skin damage.

Inspect for leaks by spraying a soap and water solution on joints, fittings, and other areas. Look for bubbles that indicate leakage from the system.

Service Cooling System Safely

JDPX5257

Danger of scalding!

With the engine shut off, first loosen the radiator cap or expansion tank cap only to the first stop to relieve the pressure before removing the cap completely.

Top off cooling system with coolant only when engine is shut off.

Avoid Harmful Asbestos Dust

JDPX5258

Avoid breathing dust that may be generated when handling components containing asbestos fibers. Inhaled asbestos fibers may cause lung cancer.

Components that may contain asbestos fibers are brake pads, brake band and lining assemblies, clutch plates and some gaskets. The asbestos used in these components is usually found in a resin or sealed in some way. Normal handling is not hazardous as long as airborne dust containing asbestos is not generated.

Avoid creating dust. Never use compressed air for cleaning. Avoid brushing or grinding of asbestos-containing materials. When servicing, wear an approved respirator. A special vacuum cleaner is recommended to clean asbestos. If not available, wet the asbestos-containing materials with a mist of oil or water.

Keep bystanders away from the area.

Please note designations on spare parts.

Observe Environmental Protection Regulations

JDPX5263

Be mindful of the environment and ecology.

Before draining any fluids, find out the correct way of disposing of them.

Observe the relevant environmental protection regulations when disposing of oil, fuel, coolant, brake fluid, filters, and batteries.

Dispose of Waste Properly

JDPX5264

Improperly disposing of waste can threaten the environment and ecology. Potentially harmful waste used with equipment include such items as oil, fuel, coolant, brake fluid, filters, and batteries.

Use leakproof containers when draining fluids. Do not use food or beverage containers that may mislead someone into drinking from them.

Inquire on the proper way to recycle or dispose of waste from your local environmental or recycling center. Do not pour waste onto the ground, down a drain, or into any water source.

Observe Road Traffic Regulations

JDPX5272

Always observe local road traffic regulations when using public roads.

Replace the slow-moving-vehicle emblem (SMV) if it is missing.

Use Safety Lights and Devices

JDPX5273

Slow moving tractors, self-propelled equipment, and towed implements or attachments can create a hazard when driven on public roads. They are difficult to see, especially at night. Avoid personal injury or death resulting from collision with a vehicle.

Flashing warning lights and turn signals are recommended whenever driving on public roads. To increase visibility, use the lights and devices provided with your machine. For some equipment, install extra flashing warning lights.

Keep safety items in good condition. Replace missing or damaged items.

Live with Safety

JDPX5274

Follow safe maintenance procedures. Make sure the machine is functioning properly, especially the safety systems. Install all guards and shields and ensure they work properly. Replace damaged or missing safety signs on the machine. Live with safety.

Summary

Safety is the most important consideration when you perform maintenance on a machine. A very small careless act can result in a major injury — possibly death. Whatever you do — safety comes first.

Test Yourself

Questions

1. (Fill in blank.) Approximately _____ people die in machinery related accidents in North America per year.

2. Name the three signal words.

   _____

   _____

   _____

3. (T/F) Unless so instructed within a diagnostic procedure, the engine should always be stopped before performing service.

4. Name four of the six components that store energy.

   _____

   _____

   _____

   _____

5. (T/F) Loose fitting clothing is not a safety hazard.

6. (Fill in blank.) A frozen battery should be warmed up to _____°F prior to charging.

7. (T/F) The high-pressure fluids within a fuel injection system or hydraulic system can escape with enough velocity to penetrate the flesh.

8. (Fill in blank.) A(n) _____ should be worn when working around materials containing asbestos.

9. (T/F) A lot of noise for a prolonged period will increase your hearing ability.

10. (Fill in blank.) Applying heat to a wheel and tire assembly will cause the air pressure in the tire to _____.

DEFINITIONS OF TERMS AND SYMBOLS

A

ACCUMULATOR — A container that stores fluids under pressure as a source of hydraulic power. It may also be used as a shock absorber.

ACTUATOR — A device that converts hydraulic power into mechanical force and motion. (Examples: hydraulic cylinders and motors.)

ANALOG — Signal which has a continuous range of possible voltages, usually 0 V (low) to 24 V (high).

ARTICULATE — To rotate from side to side.

B

BAP — Barometric Air Pressure. Pressure of the atmosphere (atmospheric pressure).

BLEED — The process by which air is removed from a hydraulic system.

BOOST — Pressurized air in the intake manifold.

BOTTOM — To reach the maximum travel of a component, as in a fully retracted cylinder.

BYPASS — A secondary passage for fluid flow.

C

CAC — Charge Air Cooler. Cools the compressed air from the turbine before it enters the intake manifold.

CAM — A rotary member with a raised portion to provide motion to or be rotated by a roller, pin, cylinder, or valve.

CAM LOBE MOTOR — A hydraulic radial piston motor in which rotational force is created by the outward movement of pistons against the lobes of a stationary cam.

CAN — Controller Area Network. The network on applications that allows communication between the engine control unit and some components.

CAVITATION — A phenomenon in which vacuum bubbles occur in a hydraulic system. The violent collapse of these bubbles can cause erosion of metal parts, noise, and vibration.

CHARGE SYSTEM — A low-pressure hydraulic system for supplying oil to the main system hydraulic pump.

CLOSED-CENTER SYSTEM — A hydraulic system in which the control valves are closed during neutral, stopping the inlet oil flow.

CLOSED-LOOP SYSTEM — A hydraulic system in which the pump and actuator are connected directly, without the use of a directional valve, and on which the operating oil does not normally return to the reservoir.

COMPONENT — One assembly in a hydraulic system.

CONTROLLER — A microprocessor that controls electro-hydraulic valve functions.

COOLER (OIL) — A heat exchanger that removes heat from a fluid. See Heat Exchanger.

COUPLER — A device to connect two hoses or lines, or to connect hoses to valve receptacles.

CRANKSHAFT POSITION SENSOR — Used to determine the angular position and velocity of the crankshaft in the 360° field of rotation.

CUSHION — A device built into the end of a cylinder which restricts outlet flow and thereby slows down the piston at the end of its travel.

CYCLE — A single complete operation of a component, which begins and ends in a neutral position.

CYLINDER — An actuator. A device for converting fluid power into limited linear or circular motion.

> Double-Acting Cylinder — A cylinder in which fluid force can be applied to the movable element in either direction.

> Follow-up Cylinder — Non-powered cylinder that signals the position of components or powered pistons in the system.

> Piston-Type Cylinder — A cylinder that uses a sliding piston in a housing to produce straight movement.

> Rotary Cylinder — A cylinder in which fluid force is applied to a movable vane to produce rotary motion.

> Single-Acting Cylinder — A cylinder in which fluid force is applied to only one side of a piston to move the element in only one direction.

> Slave Cylinder — See Follow-up Cylinder.

> Vane-Type Cylinder — A cylinder that uses a turning vane in a circular housing to produce rotary movement. See Rotary Cylinder.

D

DISPLACEMENT — The volume of oil displaced by one complete stroke or revolution (of a pump, motor, or cylinder).

DOC — Diesel Oxidation Catalyst. Part of the exhaust filter or aftertreatment device. Used to help reduce emissions.

DPF — Diesel Particulate Filter. Part of the exhaust filter or aftertreatment device. Used to help reduce emissions.

DRAG LINK — A mechanical feedback linkage or a connection that backs up a hydraulically actuated function.

DRIFT — Movement of a cylinder or motor due to internal leakage past components in the hydraulic system.

DTC — Diagnostic Trouble Code. A code that is stored in ECU memory when it detects a problem in the electronic control system. There are two types of codes: Active and Stored. These codes are displayed on monitor panels and can be recalled by the service tool.

E

ECT — Engine Coolant Temperature. The temperature of the engine coolant.

ECU — Engine Control Unit. Computer that controls the fuel, air, and ignition systems on the engine.

EGR — Exhaust Gas Recirculation. Used to help reduce emissions.

EFFICIENCY — The percentage of actual performance of a hydraulic component compared to the theoretical performance.

ENERGY — The mechanical work put into generating flow, pressure, and speed in the hydraulic oil that can be converted back to a mechanical output.

  Heat Energy — The energy that is lost in a system when pressure drops without accomplishing work turns to heat. Example: internal leakage or line restriction.

  Hydraulic Energy — The result of mechanical work put into generating oil flow with pressure that can be converted back to a mechanical output.

  Kinetic Energy — The result of mechanical work put into generating velocity in hydraulic fluid as would be used in a torque converter.

  Potential Energy — The work put into storing pressurized oil as in loading an accumulator.

F

FILTER (OIL) — A device that removes contaminants from a fluid.

FMI — Failure Mode Identifier. The second part of a two-part code that identifies control system fault codes according to the J1939 standard. This two-digit code identifies the type of failure that has occurred. The first half of the code is the Suspect Parameter Number (SPN).

FLOWMETER — A testing device that measures flow rate.

FLOW RATE — The volume of fluid passing a point in a given time.

FLUID POWER — Energy transmitted and controlled through use of a pressurized fluid.

FORCE — A push or pull acting upon a body. In a hydraulic cylinder, it is the product of the fluid pressure multiplied by the piston area. It is measured in pounds (newtons).

FRICTION — The resistance to fluid flow in a hydraulic system. An energy loss in terms of power output.

G

GEROTOR — A form of internal gear pump that uses lobes instead of gear teeth.

H

HEAT EXCHANGER — A device that transfers heat through a conducting wall from one fluid to another. See Cooler (Oil).

HORSEPOWER — English measure of work produced per unit of time.

HOSE — A flexible line usually made of reinforced rubber used to route oil from one component to another.

HPCR — High-Pressure Common-Rail. A device that distributes high-pressure fuel to the injectors.

HYDRAULICS — The engineering science of liquid pressure and flow.

HYDRODYNAMICS — The engineering science of the energy of liquid momentum (as used in a torque converter).

HYDROSTATICS — The engineering science of the energy of liquid's pressurized flow. All systems discussed in this manual are hydrostatic.

I

INERT GAS — A non-explosive gas.

L

LINE — A tube, pipe, or hose for conducting a fluid.

LOAD — The resistance to flow in an actuator as it is moved.

M

MANIFOLD — A fluid conductor that provides many ports.

MAP — Manifold Air Pressure. The pressure of the air in the intake manifold, sometimes referred to as "boost" pressure.

MOTOR (HYDRAULIC) — A device for converting fluid energy into rotary mechanical force and motion.

O

OPEN-CENTER SYSTEM — A hydraulic system in which the control valves are open to continuous oil flow when in neutral.

ORIFICE — A restricted passage in a hydraulic circuit. Usually a small drilled hole to limit flow or to create a pressure differential in a circuit.

O-RING — A static and/or dynamic seal for curved or circular mating surf aces.

OUT-OF-STROKE — The condition of a variable-displacement pump when it is maintaining a pressure but not delivering oil to the system.

P

PACKING — Any material or device that seals by compression. Common types are U-packings, V-packings, cup-packings, and O-rings.

PIPE — A line whose outside diameter is standardized for threading.

PISTON — A cylindrical part that moves or reciprocates in a cylinder to transfer hydraulic energy back to mechanical movement.

PORT — An opening for a fluid passage in a component.

POUR POINT — The lowest temperature at which a fluid remains liquid enough to pour.

POWER BEYOND — An adapting sleeve that allows working oil to be sent to another component.

POWER LIFT — Any device for hydraulically and/or mechanically raising an implement. On modern machines, it is often used to refer to the three-point hitch.

PRESSURE — Force of a fluid per unit area, usually expressed in pounds per square inch (psi) or kilopascals (kPa).

> Back Pressure — A pressure on the return side of a function.

> Breakout Pressure — The minimum pressure that starts moving an actuator.

> Charge Pressure — The pressure of the oil pumped to a system hydraulic pump.

> Cracking Pressure — The pressure at which a relief valve, etc., begins to open and pass fluid.

Differential Pressure — The difference in pressure between any two points in a system or a component (also called a pressure drop).

Full-Flow Pressure — The pressure at which a valve will pass the full flow of the system.

Operating Pressure — The pressure at which a system is normally operated.

Pilot Pressure — Pressure in a circuit used to actuate or control a component.

Rated Pressure — The manufacturer's recommended operating pressure for a component or the pressure at which a component will provide specific results.

Static Pressure — The pressure in a fluid at rest (a form of potential energy).

Suction Pressure — The absolute pressure (vacuum) of the fluid at the inlet side of the pump.

Surge Pressure — A momentary pressure increase caused by a rapidly accelerated column of oil.

System Pressure — The pressure that overcomes the total resistances in a system. It includes all losses as well as useful work.

Working Pressure — The pressure that overcomes the resistance of the working device.

PULSATION — Repeated small fluctuations of pressure in a circuit.

PUMP — A device that converts mechanical force into hydraulic fluid power.

Fixed-Displacement Pump — A pump in which the output per cycle cannot be varied.

Variable-Displacement Pump — A pump in which the output per cycle can be varied.

R

RAM — Random Access Memory. The portion of the computer memory within the ECU that is used when the ECU is running. All data in this memory is lost when the ECU is "OFF".

REGENERATIVE CIRCUIT — A circuit in which oil returning from the cylinder rod end is returned to the piston end. It can be used to speed up the action of a cylinder when very little force is required.

REMOTE — A hydraulic function, such as a cylinder, which is separate from its supply source. Usually connected to the source by flexible hoses.

RESERVOIR — A container for keeping a supply of working fluid in a hydraulic system.

RESTRICTION — A reduced cross-sectional area in a line or passage, which causes a pressure drop.

ROCKSHAFT — A rotating shaft and arm device to transfer a mechanical force. Usually used when referring to the hydraulically operated three-point hitch.

S

SEAT — The sealing surface on which a valve rests.

SENSOR — Device used by the ECU to monitor various engine parameters.

SERVO — A low-pressure control mechanism.

SOLENOID — An electromagnetic device used to position a hydraulic valve.

STARVATION — A lack of oil in vital areas of a system, usually the pump inlet.

STRAINER — A coarse filter.

STROKE — The length of travel of a piston in a cylinder or the changing of the displacement of a variable delivery pump.

SURGE — A momentary rise of pressure in a hydraulic circuit.

SWASHPLATE — A tilted plane surface in an axial-piston pump used to create reciprocating movements to pistons.

SYMBOLS, SCHEMATIC — Used on drawings as a shorthand representation of hydraulic system components.

SYSTEM — A series of components or circuits connected to each other. Usually includes everything using the oil of a pump's output.

T

TDC — Top Dead Center. Point of uppermost piston travel.

THERMAL EXPANSION — The increase in fluid volume due to temperature increase.

TORQUE — Turning effort usually measured in pounds-inch (lb-in.), pounds-foot (lb-ft), or newton-meters (N•m).

TUBE — A metal line sized by its outside diameter.

V

VALVE — A device that controls the pressure, direction, or flow rate of fluid.

Bypass Regulator Valve — A valve that maintains a constant flow to a circuit by dumping the excess oil.

Check Valve — A valve that permits oil flow in only one direction.

Closed-Center Valve — A valve in which inlet ports are closed in the neutral position, stopping flow from the pump.

Directional Control Valve — A valve that directs oil through selected passages.

Electro-Hydraulic Valve — A valve that is opened and closed by a solenoid.

Flow Control Valve — A valve that controls the rate of flow (also called a volume control valve).

Flow Divider Valve — A valve that divides the flow from one source into two or more branches (includes priority and proportional types).

Needle Valve — A valve with a tapered point that moves in relation to a seat to regulate the flow rate.

Open-Center Valve — A valve in which the inlet and outlet ports are open in the neutral position, allowing continuous pump flow through the valve.

Pilot Valve — A valve that is used to operate another valve or control.

Pilot-Operated Valve — A valve that is actuated by oil from a pilot valve.

Poppet Valve — A valve that rests on a seat. It can be manually or hydraulically opened to pass oil in only one direction.

Pressure Control Valve — A valve whose function is to control pressure (includes relief, pressure-reducing, sequencing, and unloading valves).

Pressure-Reducing Valve — A pressure control valve that controls outlet pressure.

Pressure Sequence Valve — A pressure control valve that directs flow in a preset sequence.

Priority Valve — A valve that ensures a supply of oil to one function before allowing flow to other functions.

Priority Flow Divider Valve — A valve that directs a constant oil flow to one circuit and dumps excess flow into another circuit.

Proportional Flow Divider Valve — A valve that divides the oil proportionally and directs it to all circuits at all times.

Relief Valve — A valve that limits the pressure in a system.

Rotary Directional Valve — A cylindrical-shaped valve that is turned to open and close hydraulic passages.

Selector Valve — A valve that selects one of two or more circuits into which it directs oil flow.

Shuttle Valve — A free-floating spool valve that moves in its bore to control oil flow based on the pressures acting against it.

Shutoff Valve — A valve that is opened to allow full flow, or closed to block or restrict oil flow.

Spool Directional Valve — A valve designed as a spool, which slides in a bore, opening and closing passages.

Stroke Control Valve — A device to control the output of a variable-displacement pump.

Thermal Relief Valve — A valve that limits the pressure in a system caused by heat expansion of oil.

Two-, Three-, Four-, or Six-Way Valve — A valve spool section having two, three, four, or six connecting ports.

Unloading Valve — A valve that dumps excess pump flow at a low pressure when the system requirements are met.

Volume Control Valve — A valve that controls flow rate (includes flow control valves, flow divider valves, and bypass flow regulators).

VALVE STACK — A series of control valves in a stack with common end plates and a common oil inlet and outlet.

VELOCITY — The speed at which fluid travels. Usually given as feet or millimeters per second.

VENT — An opening for the escape of air in a fluid reservoir or cylinder.

VISCOSITY — The measure of resistance of a fluid to flow.

VOLUME — The measure of a container's capacity, or the amount of fluid flow per unit of time. Usually given as gallons per minute (gpm) or liters per minute (L/m).

Abbreviations

ANSI — American National Standards Institute

ASAE — American Society of Agricultural Engineers (sets standards for many hydraulic components for agricultural use)

bar — Metric unit of measure for pressure

C — Celsius (temperature)

F — Fahrenheit (temperature)

gpm — gallons per minute (fluid flow)

hp — horsepower

I.D. — inside diameter

ISO — International Organization for Standardization (establishes many standards for worldwide use)

kg/cm^2 — kilograms per square centimeter (metric unit for pressure)

kPa — kilopascal (metric unit of measure for pressure)

kW — kilowatt (metric unit of measure for power)

lb-ft. — pounds-foot (torque or turning effort)

lb-in. — pounds-inch (torque or turning effort)

L/m — liters per minute

N•m — newton-meter (metric unit of measure for torque)

O.D. — outside diameter

psi — pounds per square inch (pressure)

rpm — revolutions per minute

SAE — Society of Automotive Engineers (sets standards for many hydraulic components)

MEASUREMENT CONVERSION CHART

METRIC TO ENGLISH	ENGLISH TO METRIC
Length	**Length**
1 millimeter = 0.03937 inches (in)	1 inch = 25.4 millimeters (mm)
1 meter = 3.281 feet (ft)	1 foot = 0.3048 meters (m)
1 kilometer = 0.621 miles (mi)	1 mile = 1.608 kilometers (km)
Area	**Area**
1 meter^2 = 10.76 square feet (sq. ft)	1 square foot = 0.0929 meter^2 (m^2)
1 hectare = 2.471 acres (acre)	1 acre = 0.4047 hectare (ha)
(1 hectare = 10 000 m^2)	(1 hectare = 10 000 m^2)
Mass (Weight)	**Mass (Weight)**
1 kilogram = 2.205 pounds (lb)	1 pound = 0.4535 kilograms (kg)
1 tonne (1000 kg) = 1.102 ton (tn)	1 ton (2000 lb) = 0.9071 tonnes (t)
Volume	**Volume**
1 meter^3 = 35.31 cubic feet (cu ft)	1 cubic foot = 0.02832 meter^3 (m^3)
1 meter^3 = 1.308 cubic yards (cu yd)	1 cubic yard = 0.7646 meter^3 (m^3)
1 meter^3 = 28.38 bushel (bu)	1 bushel = 0.03524 meter^3 (m^3)
1 liter = 0.02838 bushel (bu)	1 bushel = 35.24 liter (L)
1 liter = 1.057 quart (qt)	1 quart = 0.9464 liter (L)
	1 gallon = 3.785 liters (L)
Pressure	**Pressure**
1 kilopascal = 0.145 pounds per square inch (psi)	1 psi = 6.895 kilopascals (kPa)
(1 bar = 101.325 kilopascals)	1 psi = 0.06895 bars (bar)
Stress	**Stress**
1 megapascal =145 pounds per square inch (psi)	1 psi = 0.006895 megapascal (MPa)
(1 megapascal = 1 newton/millimeter^2)	1 psi = 0.006895 newton/millimeter^2 (N/mm^2)
Power	**Power**
1 kilowatt = 1.341 horsepower (hp)	1 horsepower (550 ft-lb/sec) = 0.7457 kilowatt (kW)
(1 watt = 1 Nm/s)	(1 watt = 1 Nm/sec)
Energy (Work)	**Energy (Work)**
1 joule + 0.0009478 British thermal units (Btu)	1 British thermal unit = 1055 joules (J)
Force	**Force**
1 newton = 0.2248 pounds force (lb-force)	1 pound = 4.448 newtons (N)
Torque or Bending Moment	**Torque or Bending Moment**
1 newton-meter = 0.7376 pound-foot (lb-ft)	1 pound-foot = 1.356 newton-meters (Nm)
Temperature	**Temperature**
°F = °C x 1.8 + 32	°C = (°F – 32) / 1.8

Metric Fastener Torque Values

Property Class and Head Markings	4.8	8.8	9.8	10.9	12.9
Property Class and Nut Markings	5	10		10	12

TS1163

	Class 4.8				Class 8.8 or 9.8				Class 10.9				Class 12.9			
	Lubricated[a]		Dry[a]		Lubricated[a]		Dry[a]		Lubricated[a]		Dry[a]		Lubricated[a]		Dry[a]	
SIZE	N•m	lb-ft	N•m	lb-ft	N•m	lb-ft	N•m	lb-ft	N•m	lb-ft	N•m	lb-ft	N•m	lb-ft	N•m	lb-ft
M6	4.8	3.5	6	4.5	9	6.5	11	8.5	13	9.5	17	12	15	11.5	19	14.5
M8	12	8.5	15	11	22	16	28	20	32	24	40	30	37	28	47	35
M10	23	17	29	21	43	32	55	40	63	47	80	60	75	55	95	70
M12	40	29	50	37	75	55	95	70	110	80	140	105	130	95	165	120
M14	63	47	80	60	120	88	150	110	175	130	225	165	205	150	260	109
M16	100	73	125	92	190	140	240	175	275	200	350	225	320	240	400	300
M18	135	100	175	125	260	195	330	250	375	275	475	350	440	325	560	410
M20	190	140	240	180	375	275	475	350	530	400	675	500	625	460	800	580
M22	260	190	330	250	510	375	650	475	725	540	925	675	850	625	1075	800
M24	330	250	425	310	650	475	825	600	925	675	1150	850	1075	800	1350	1000
M27	490	360	625	450	950	700	1200	875	1350	1000	1700	1250	1600	1150	2000	1500
M30	675	490	850	625	1300	950	1650	1200	1850	1350	2300	1700	2150	1600	2700	2000
M33	900	675	1150	850	1750	1300	2200	1650	2500	1850	3150	2350	2900	2150	3700	2750
M36	1150	850	1450	1075	2250	1650	2850	2100	3200	2350	4050	3000	3750	2750	4750	3500

a. "Lubricated" means coated with a lubricant such as engine oil, or fasteners with phosphate and oil coatings. "Dry" means plain or zinc plated without any lubrication.

DO NOT use these hand torque values if a different torque value or tightening procedure is given for a specific application. Torque values listed are for general use only and include a ±10% variance factor. Check tightness of fasteners periodically. DO NOT use air powered wrenches.

Shear bolts are designed to fail under predetermined loads. Always replace shear bolts with identical grade.

Fasteners should be replaced with the same class. Make sure fastener threads are clean and that you properly start thread engagement. This will prevent them from failing when tightening.

When bolt and nut combination fasteners are used, torque values should be applied to the NUT instead of the bolt head.

Tighten plastic insert or crimped steel-type lock nuts to approximately 50% of the dry torque shown in the chart, applied to the nut, not to the bolt head. Tighten toothed or serrated-type lock nuts to the full torque value.

Inch Fastener Torque Values

SAE Grade and Head Markings	No Marks (1 or 2[b])	5 5.1 5.2	8 8.2
SAE Grade and Nut Markings	No Marks (2)	5	8

TS1162

	Grade 1				Grade 2[a]				Grade 5, 5.1 or 5.2				Grade 8 or 8.2			
	Lubricated[b]		Dry[b]		Lubricated[b]		Dry[b]		Lubricated[b]		Dry[b]		Lubricated[b]		Dry[b]	
SIZE	N•m	lb-ft	N•m	lb-ft	N•m	lb-ft	N•m	lb-ft	N•m	lb-ft	N•m	lb-ft	N•m	lb-ft	N•m	lb-ft
1/4	3.7	2.8	4.7	3.5	6	4.5	7.5	5.5	9.5	7	12	9	13.5	10	17	12.5
5/16	7.7	5.5	10	7	12	9	15	11	20	15	25	18	28	21	35	26
3/8	14	10	17	13	22	16	27	20	35	26	44	33	50	36	63	46
7/16	22	16	28	20	35	26	44	32	55	41	70	52	80	58	100	75
1/2	33	25	42	31	53	39	67	50	85	63	110	80	120	90	150	115
9/16	48	36	60	45	75	56	95	70	125	90	155	115	175	130	225	160
5/8	67	50	85	62	105	78	135	100	170	125	215	160	215	160	300	225
3/4	120	87	150	110	190	140	240	175	300	225	375	280	425	310	550	400
7/8	190	140	240	175	190	140	240	175	490	360	625	450	700	500	875	650
1	290	210	360	270	290	210	360	270	725	540	925	675	1050	750	1300	975
1-1/8	470	300	510	375	470	300	510	375	900	675	1150	850	1450	1075	1850	1350
1-1/4	570	425	725	530	570	425	725	530	1300	950	1650	1200	2050	1500	2600	1950
1-3/8	750	550	950	700	750	550	950	700	1700	1250	2150	1550	2700	2000	3400	2550
1-1/2	1000	725	1250	925	990	725	1250	930	2250	1650	2850	2100	3600	2650	4550	3350

a. "Grade 2" applies for hex cap screws (not hex bolts) up to 152 mm (6 in.) long. "Grade 1" applies for hex cap screws over 152 mm (6 in.) long, and for all other types of bolts and screws of any length.

b. "Lubricated" means coated with a lubricant such as engine oil, or fasteners with phosphate and oil coatings. "Dry" means plain or zinc plated without any lubrication.

DO NOT use these hand torque values if a different torque value or tightening procedure is given for a specific application. Torque values listed are for general use only and include a ±10% variance factor. Check tightness of fasteners periodically. DO NOT use air powered wrenches.

Shear bolts are designed to fail under predetermined loads. Always replace shear bolts with identical grade.

Fasteners should be replaced with the same grade. Make sure fastener threads are clean and that you properly start thread engagement. This will prevent them from failing when tightening.

When bolt and nut combination fasteners are used, torque values should be applied to the NUT instead of the bolt head.

Tighten plastic insert or crimped steel-type lock nuts to approximately 50% of the dry torque shown in the chart, applied to the nut not to the bolt head. Tighten toothed or serrated-type lock nuts to the full torque value.

O-Ring Seal Service Recommendations

FACE SEAL FITTINGS WITH INCH STUD ENDS TORQUE

Stud End — Tube Nut

Stud Straight and Tube Nut

Bulkhead Union and Bulkhead Lock Nut

Lock Nut — Stud End

90° Adjustable Stud Elbow

Swivel Nut — Tube Nut

90° Swivel Elbow and Tube Nut

Nominal Tube OD/Hose ID				Face Seal Tube/Hose End					O-Ring Stud Ends		
Metric Tube OD	Inch Tube OD			Thread Size	Tube Nut/Swivel Nut Torque		Bulkhead Lock Nut Torque		Thread Size	Straight Fitting or Lock Nut Torque	
mm	Dash Size	in.	mm	in.	N•m	lb-ft	N•m	lb-ft	in.	N•m	lb-ft
	-3	0.188	4.76						3/8-24	8	6
6	-4	0.250	6.35	9/16-18	16	12	12	9	7/16-20	12	9
8	-5	0.312	7.94						1/2-20	16	12
10	-6	0.375	9.52	11/16-16	24	18	24	18	9/16-18	24	18
12	-8	0.500	12.70	13/16-16	50	37	46	34	3/4-16	46	34
16	-10	0.625	15.88	1-14	69	51	62	46	7/8-14	62	46
	-12	0.750	19.05	1-3/16-12	102	75	102	75	1-1/16-12	102	75
22	-14	0.875	22.22	1-3/16-12	102	75	102	75	1-3/16-12	122	90
25	-16	1.000	25.40	1-7/16-12	142	105	142	105	1-5/16-12	142	105
32	-20	1.25	31.75	1-11/16-12	190	140	190	140	1-5/8-12	190	140
38	-24	1.50	38.10	2-12	217	160	217	160	1-7/8-12	217	160

NOTE: Torque tolerance is plus 15 minus 20%.

FACE SEAL FITTINGS WITH METRIC STUD ENDS TORQUE

Stud End — Tube Nut

Stud Straight and Tube

Bulkhead Union and Bulkhead Lock Nut

Lock Nut
Stud End
90° Adjustable Stud Elbow

Swivel Nut
Tube Nut
90° Swivel Elbow and Tube Nut

Nominal Tube OD/Hose ID				Face Seal Tube/Hose End							O-Ring Stud Ends, Straight Fitting or Lock Nut						
Metric Tube OD	Inch Tube OD			Thread Size	Hex Size	Tube Nut/Swivel Nut Torque		Bulkhead Lock Nut Torque			Thread Size	Hex Size	Steel or Gray Iron Torque		Aluminum Torque	
mm	Dash Size	in.	mm	in.	mm	N•m	lb-ft	N•m	lb-ft		mm	mm	N•m	lb-ft	N•m	lb-ft
6	-4	0.250	6.35	9/16-18	17	16	12	12	9		M12X1.5	17	21	15.5	9	6.6
8	-5	0.312	7.94													
											M14X1.5	19	33	24	15	11
10	-6	0.375	9.52	11/16-16	22	24	18	24	18		M16X1.5	22	41	30	18	13
12	-8	0.500	12.70	13/16-16	24	50	37	46	34		M18X1.5	24	50	37	21	15
16	-10	0.625	15.88	1-14	30	69	51	62	46		M22X1.5	27	69	51	28	21
	-12	0.750	19.05	1-3/16-12	36	102	75	102	75		M27X2	32	102	75	46	34
22	-14	0.875	22.22	1-3/16-12	36	102	75	102	75		M30X2	36				
25	-16	1.000	25.40	1-7/16-12	41	142	105	142	105		M33X2	41	158	116	71	52
28											M38X2	46	176	130	79	58
32	-20	1.25	31.75	1-11/16-12	50	190	140	190	140		M42X2	50	190	140	85	63
38	-24	1.50	38.10	2-12	60	217	160	217	160		M48X2	55	217	160	98	72

NOTE: Torque tolerance is plus 15 minus 20%.

ANSWERS TO TEST YOURSELF QUESTIONS

ANSWERS TO CHAPTER 1 QUESTIONS

1. Preventive Maintenance accomplishes:

    a. Reduces failures

    b. Saves on operating costs

    c. Keeps equipment safe to operate

2. Preventive maintenance pays for itself, it saves money by reducing repairs and fuel consumption, and it increases efficient performance.

3. Because it is written specifically for your machine.

4. Before starting your machine each day:

    a. Perform daily maintenance

    b. Check the machine for damage and potential failure

5. Always think about what you are going to do before you do it.

ANSWERS TO CHAPTER 2 QUESTIONS

1. Parts of intake system, exhaust system, neither system or both systems:

    a. E

    b. I

    c. B

    d. I

    e. B

    f. I

2. d. All of these

3. e. None of above.

4. A – 2; B – 1

5. Compression

6. True.

7. True.

8. 1–2–4–3 or 1–3–4–2

9. TDC or Top Dead Center

10. Straight through and Reverse flow

11. Diesel particulate filter

12. Diesel oxidation catalyst

13. A - Passive

14. B - Reducing agent

ANSWERS TO CHAPTER 3 QUESTIONS

1. Knock

2. A – 2; B – 1

3. A. Fuel igniting too slowly.

4. Basic parts of LP-gas fuel system:

    a. Fuel tank (pressurized)

    b. Fuel strainer

    c. Converter

    d. Carburetor

5. Butane and Propane

6. Dirt

7. Jobs of the engine governor:

    a. Maintains a selected speed

    b. Limits the slow and fast speeds

    c. Shuts down the engine when it overspeeds

8. Basic parts of diesel engine:

    a. Fuel tank

    b. Fuel filters

    c. Transfer pump

9. Fuel filters

ANSWERS TO CHAPTER 4 QUESTIONS

1. Functions of engine oil to keep engines running:

    a. Reduce friction and wear

    b. Cool moving parts

    c. Seal the cylinders

    d. Keep the parts clean

2. Viscosity

3. False. When the crankcase oil becomes black, it shows that the oil is doing its job of keeping contaminants suspended.

4. False. Oil additives do wear out. Follow operator's manual for specified oil change recommendations.

5. Contamination

6. Types of lubricating system:

    a. Circulating splash

    b. Internal force feed splash

    c. Full internal force feed

7. Bypass system and full-flow system

8. Daily

9. This permits the dirt or contaminants to be agitated in the oil so that the contaminants will drain out with the old oil.

10. False. Tighten oil filters until the seal just touches, then tighten no more than a one-half turn. If the filter is tightened too tightly, the seal may become distorted and leak.

ANSWERS TO CHAPTER 5 QUESTIONS

1. To prevent overheating and to regulate temperatures

2. Without inhibitors, it will rust, corrode, and leave deposits in the engine.

3. C (distilled water) and D (rain water)

4. Rust or scale

5. −34°F (−37°C)

6. 1/3

7. False. The thermostat maintains a minimum temperature.

8. False. You could be burned seriously. Wait until the engine coolant has cooled.

9. Hot; Cold

10. Blow-by (of engine gases)

ANSWERS TO CHAPTER 6 QUESTIONS

1. A (burned valves) and D (excessive fuel consumption)

2. False. The <u>distributor</u> affects the timing.

3. Basic circuits:

    a. Charging

    b. Starting

    c. Ignition

4. Corroded terminals and acid deposits on the top of the battery provide a circuit for current to flow out.

5. Hydrogen gas is released by the battery when it is charging. This gas if very explosive.

6. False. An engine operating under these conditions should use a <u>colder</u> plug.

7. A (damaged plug wires) and B (cracked distributor cap)

ANSWERS TO CHAPTER 7 QUESTIONS

1. True. For example, SAE 80 gear oil has about the same viscosity as SAE 20 engine oil. (Only the numbers are different.)

2. Oils or fluids used in transmissions:

    a. Gear oil

    b. Automatic transmission fluid

    c. Transmission-hydraulic fluid

3. The barrel should be tilted.

4. Because the clutch facings wear down as they operate.

5. False.

6. Major types of mechanical transmissions:

    a. Sliding gear

    b. Collar Shift

    c. Synchromesh

7. False. The MFWD will remain engaged until either pedal is depressed. When both pedals are depressed, the MFWD will remain engaged. At higher speeds, the MFWD will automatically engage to aid in braking.

8. True.

9. Excessively grease may be thrown onto the clutch facing and cause the clutch to "chatter" when engaged.

10. Drive the machine until the transmission fluid is well agitated and heated.

ANSWERS TO CHAPTER 8 QUESTIONS

1. Maintenance problems of hydraulic system:

    a. Not enough oil in the reservoir

    b. Clogged or dirty oil filters

    c. Leaking connections

    d. Incorrect oil in the system

2. A – 2; B – 3; C – 1

3. False. You may damage the connection. Tighten the connection only until the leak stops.

4. Dirt

5. Compare your answer to any of the rules listed under "Safety Rules for Hydraulic Systems."

ANSWERS TO CHAPTER 9 QUESTIONS

1. False. Clean only in a good non-sudsing detergent.

2. Bubbles

3. Tighten the adjusting nut and turn the wheel until the wheel drags slightly, then back off the nut to the next slot.

4. A – 2; B – 3; C – 1

5. 10 to 15%

6. To properly set up a tractor:

    a. Total weight and distribution

    b. Type of ballast used

    c. Tire inflation pressures

7. False. For optimum tractor performance, all tires on the same axle must be inflated to the same pressure.

8. Wipe dirt and grease from the fitting.

9. Effects of tightening belt drive excessively:

    a. Belt heating

    b. Excessive stretch

    c. Damage to drive components, such as sheaves and shafts. The extra tightness will also place heavier loads on the bearings.

10. Reasons for lubricating chains:

    a. Reduce wear

    b. Protect against rust, corrosion, and heat

    c. Prevent seizing of pins and bushings

    d. Cushion shock loads

11. A. Overload

12. Length; Amperes

ANSWERS TO CHAPTER 10 QUESTIONS

1. Operating; Repairs

2. Engine systems found on a tune-up chart:

    a. Intake system

    b. Exhaust system

    c. Fuel system

    d. Electrical system

    e. Lubrication system

    f. Cooling system

3. False. A badly worn engine cannot be tuned up.

4. Visually inspect the engine and perform dynamometer test (if possible).

5. Before and after a tune-up

ANSWERS TO CHAPTER 12 QUESTIONS

1. 500

2. Danger, Warning, and Caution

3. True.

4. Components that store energy:

    a. Springs

    b. Hydraulic systems

    c. Compressed air

    d. Electricity

    e. Raised loads

    f. Loaded mechanisms

5. False. Wear close-fitting clothing appropriate to the job.

6. 60°F (16°C)

7. True.

8. Approved respirator

9. False. Prolonged exposure will damage your ability to hear.

10. Increase, resulting in a tire explosion

INDEX